GRAMMAR

CONTINUED ON BACK COVER

Jim Fritz
1979
Iuka Ave.
Cols, Ohio
1-4-50

COMPOSITION
FOR
TECHNICAL
STUDENTS

BY

J. D. THOMAS
ASSISTANT PROFESSOR OF ENGLISH
THE RICE INSTITUTE

CHARLES SCRIBNER'S SONS

NEW YORK   CHICAGO   ATLANTA   SAN FRANCISCO

TO

MY FATHER

*Who had confidence in this book
and its author*

FOREWORD

This book has been designed for the use of technical students. Not only engineers of technical schools but college and university majors in every branch of natural science, pure or applied, will discover that it is adapted to their special interests in composition. Furthermore, since men and women of all ages and conditions of life may be stu-dents, the author would be disappointed if anyone in the industrial world—or elsewhere—did not find it helpful for developing better habits of expression in technical English.

During the past generation, partly through the enlightened efforts of the American Society for Engineering Education,* and with the hearty coöperation of scientific and engineering departments, an in-creased emphasis has been placed upon the linguistic side of tech-nological studies. New courses in English have been offered, and those previously given have been expanded or specialized to meet the particular needs of students working in the sciences. Though much varied in detail, the subject matter of these classes ordinarily embraces review of such basic skills as grammar, spelling, and punctuation; study of exposition, description, narration, and argumentation as ap-plied to technical discourse; and practice in writing letters and reports. Oral English very commonly is included, for educators now generally recognize that professional students need training in that form of communication. Good models of technical or semitechnical com-position often are assigned for collateral reading or for classroom discussion.

Composition for Technical Students is a comprehensive textbook that serves all those purposes. It treats style (Chapter I), fundamentals and mechanics (Chapters II–V), the four modes of discourse (Chap-ters VI–VII), and forms of the whole composition (the letter, Chap-ter VIII; the research article, Chapter IX; the report, Chapter X; the speech, Chapter XI). Usable exercises for each chapter are included (Appendix A), together with a full section of supplementary read-ings (Appendix B). All discussions and illustrations are directly related to the experiences and requirements of technical students.

* Formerly the Society for the Promotion of Engineering Education. A resolution authorizing the new name was passed at the annual meeting of the Society in 1946, and the change became legally effective on December 18 of that year.

The author has greatly benefited from Professor A. M. Fountain's *A Study of Courses in Technical Writing,* Raleigh, State College of Agriculture and Engineering of the University of North Carolina (Bulletin No. 15 of the Engineering Experiment Station), 1938. Other deep obligations are too numerous to be recounted here; grateful acknowledgments have been and are being made privately to those who, in different ways, have helped during several years of preparation of the book. The writer wishes to state publicly his indebtedness to Professor M. V. McEnany of the Department of Electrical Engineering at the Rice Institute, who read and criticized the technical passages inserted as examples of various aspects of composition. The index was compiled by the author's wife, Helen Kathleen Thomas, to whom many other thanks are due for hard work at every stage of the manuscript.

Sources of copyrighted material, quoted by kind permission of the proprietors, are given in detail on the page where each quotation begins.

CONTENTS

ix

CONTENTS   xiii

APPENDICES

COMPOSITION
FOR
TECHNICAL
STUDENTS

CHAPTER I

GOOD ENGLISH IN TECHNICAL STYLE

TECHNICAL ENGLISH: GOOD ENGLISH

To regard an engineering report, a paper or speech on a phase of science, or any other such professional communication as a substandard kind of expression is an unintelligent attitude. Careless habits of technical composition are not excusable by any sophistic argument that errors of language "make no difference" in certain specialized styles. *First and last, good technical English is good English.*

Graphs, sketches, formulae, and the like—apart from accompanying lettering—obviously are neither good nor bad English, though they have their own rules of correctness. In textual passages of scientific and technological discussion, on the other hand, the normal standards of grammar, punctuation, and general usage are obligatory. Technical style has its peculiarities, in vocabulary especially and in mechanics to some extent. Nevertheless, all styles practiced by the English-using world are adaptations of the same fundamental language to different uses. If properly executed, technical composition is a form of standard English.

BRITISH AND AMERICAN ENGLISH

Partial divergence. The language of educated Americans, strikingly unified despite the great size and racial variety of the nation, is noticeably different from the mother tongue, British English. Deviation of spelling is typified by the use of *or* in the United States for many words written elsewhere with *our* (e.g., *vapor* against *vapour*). More frequently the difference is in sound rather than spelling; for instance, the English pronounce *clerk* as "clark" and *schedule* as "shedule," and the cultivated British pronunciation of *laboratory* throws the accent on the second rather than the first syllable. Everyone is aware of certain outright differences of diction, such as *petrol*

1

against *gasoline*. *A Dictionary of American English,* a work in four large volumes edited at the University of Chicago by Sir William Craigie and Professor James Hulbert, exhibits the wealth of vocabulary developed or freshly applied in the United States to supplement, and often to replace, British expressions.

Because the English language is decidedly more conservative in Great Britain than in the United States, Englishmen find greater difficulty with contemporary American compositions than Americans do with English. This problem is illustrated for technical terms by the following excerpt from an article, entitled "Doodlebugs and Bulldozers," which appeared in the British journal *Engineering* for August 9, 1940: *

> Engineers nurtured in the Victorian tradition may well wonder whether the title, "Doodlebugs and Bulldozers," has been taken from some unremembered corner of the writings of Lewis Carroll, or whether it is merely a misplaced attempt at humour, but, either way, they would be wrong; both terms are current at the present day in the engineering nomenclature of the United States—indeed, the first-named seems to have an applicability almost as general as that of the invaluable British invention, "gadget." Rather curiously, the usually well-informed Partridge's *Dictionary of Slang and Unconventional English* appears to know it only as meaning "a small cheap car," and attributes to it a date somewhat before 1935. It is evidently in a broadly similar sense that the term is applied to what, in this country, we should be content to call a railcar; according to the brief reports of the recent serious collision at Cuyahoga Falls, near Cleveland, Ohio, the petrol-electric unit involved was "a one-carriage affair commonly known as a 'doodlebug.'" There is no very severe strain on the imagination in tracing a fanciful resemblance between the agitated progress of such small vehicles and that of the tiger beetle, genus *Cicindelidae,* to which Tom Sawyer addressed the incantation that ought to have led to the recovery of his lost marble, but which somehow failed to work; but it is a far cry from the insect that he invoked as a doodlebug, to an assembly consisting of a dragline excavator and a barge carrying the rest of the equipment used in gold dredging.
>
> The reasons underlying the use of the term "bulldozer" are even more obscure, and the obscurity is deepened by the fact that it is employed to designate . . . different devices. In civil engineering, a bulldozer is a machine for levelling spoil, the surplus being pushed out of the way by means of a tractor-propelled

* Vol. CL, page 112.

blade which operates in a manner somewhat similar to the action of a ploughshare. . . . In mechanical engineering, the bulldozer is a form of straightening or bending press for heavy steel sections, and is a stationary machine which may be actuated either hydraulically or mechanically. . . .

Basic unity. Differences separating British and American English, of the several kinds indicated, do not change the major fact that our general language is bound together by a single grammar and reflects a united intellectual tradition. Fortunately, also, the great bulk of both literary diction and scientific terminology is held in common. Comprehension of writer by reader, or mutual intelligibility among literate speakers, practically never is difficult. In all its branches, English is essentially one language.

CRITERIA OF GOOD ENGLISH

The universal standard. Correct formal English is determined by the current language of cultivated writers and speakers. Dictionaries, grammars, and textbooks (this one, for example) do not legislate; they record the educated practices of their time.

The national standard. Natives of the United States must accept as right for themselves the best linguistic customs of their own country, for nothing is gained in trying to import and artificially establish foreign habits of speech. If, for instance, an American college student should suddenly change his natural pronunciation of *been* to "bean," his classmates certainly would not be slow to detect and scorn the affectation. The same rule is valid for vocabulary, idiom, spelling, and pronunciation: wherever a difference has become established as national good usage, the native form should be preferred.*

TECHNICAL VOCABULARY AND STYLE

International element. The vocabulary of the natural and applied sciences is usually a recognizable mark of technical style. With due allowance for national peculiarities, scientific terminology has a strongly international character. Although the world today lacks a complete, universal medium of communication equivalent to the Latin of medieval and early modern learning, technical nomenclature† is similar in all languages. The relative identity of diction, together with

---

* On the problem of dialectal differences within American English, see the discussions in Chapter III of regional "accent" (D 9b) and provincialisms (D 18).

† This specialized vocabulary has been dubbed "Schenectady Greek" because much of it is composed from Greek roots. Most of the rest is from Latin; however, numerous other languages, ancient and modern, are represented as sources of words and elements.

unity of subject matter, makes for closer resemblance of scientific than of literary style, throughout not only English-speaking countries but the world at large.

Science and the expanding language. English, especially in the United States, has been vigorously expanding during the past hundred years or more. The importance of science and technology as sources of growth in vocabulary is shown in the following passage from a pamphlet written by Everett E. Thompson and distributed by the publishers of the Merriam-Webster dictionaries:

... [T]he rapid growth of our language has taken place since Webster's time, since the beginning of the industrial era. It is industry and commerce, and especially the development of the sciences, leading to improved intercourse between nations and to far-reaching contacts with other races—almost entirely in the nineteenth and twentieth centuries—that have been responsible for the marvelous growth of our vocabulary. In 1839 photography was in its infancy and since that date the major sciences— chemistry, physics, biology, medicine—have expanded enormously. Laboratories and scholars, research and travel, new inventions and discoveries, have made necessary a corresponding increase in our vocabulary of terms to name and describe all these new developments. Not only have the major sciences advanced but new ones have arisen—psychology, sociology—and the major sciences themselves have developed subdivisions—entomology, bacteriology, ecology, electronics, electrochemistry—that have grown to be almost as large as the parent.

... Entomology alone comprises more than 500,000 different species, each little insect with its specific name. . . . Chemistry also has an expanding vocabulary, although here the process of forming new names is usually by compounding, just as the substances themselves are formed. The total of scientific acquisitions is, of course, far beyond the scope of any ordinary dictionary.

From these brief notes it may be seen that the possible total number of words in the language, including all scientific nomenclature, is simply overwhelming. Yet this very statement shows with some clarity, I think, that the new scientific terms actually selected for inclusion in the dictionary [*Webster's New International Dictionary,* ed. 2]—terms that it is possible that you or I or someone will want to know the meaning of—must represent a very large part of the words that we have added, and are adding every day . . .

(By permission. From *Our Changing Language,* copyright, 1940, by G. & C. Merriam Co.)

Varieties of technical style. Style in language can never be reduced to exact rule, for verbal communication, like any other highly developed technique, is capable of minute specialization. A style may reflect the individuality of the writer or speaker, his specific purpose and his relation to the readers or audience, and the peculiar nature of his subject. Technical styles are those suited to the communication of various scientific topics by informed or skilled persons. There are three general classes of technical composition.

(1) PURELY TECHNICAL STYLE

Function and characteristics. A purely technical style is natural for reports prepared and read by specialists, lectures before professional audiences, engineering handbooks, articles in technical journals, etc. The style varies with the user and subject matter; nevertheless, it has certain basic characteristics. It is plain, impersonal, and factual. Usually simple in sentence structure, with a smaller number of words per sentence than most other kinds of formal communication, it closely packs what it has to say. Precision of statement being the most important consideration, the purely technical style makes full use of specialized diction. In consequence of the high proportion of words from Greek and Latin roots, it is the least Anglo-Saxon of all types of composition in English.

Nonverbal aids. Furthermore, the purely technical style is marked by extensive use of the formulae, equations, and other sign writing developed by every branch of science. It freely employs tables, curves, and all types of pictorial devices that may help to convey technical meaning.

(2) POPULAR TECHNICAL STYLE

Function. The expert in any technical field is a person whose special knowledge separates him from the general public. From the point of view of the average man, a purely technical article might as well be written in a foreign tongue; what he learns of the mysteries of science must come to him through popular writing and speaking. He wants to know: "What is a plutonium pile?" or "How does 'F.M.' work?" or "Where are the all-plastic automobile bodies that were predicted during the war?" Rightly, he expects clear, accurate answers on his own level of comprehension.

Characteristics. The popular style must, accordingly, be greatly different from the purely technical. As far as possible, it chooses fa-

miliar words; but when professional, or otherwise difficult, terms must
be employed, it carefully defines and illustrates their meaning. Ordinary men insist that an explanation "come down to cases." Instances, analogies, evidences, and applications related to familiar situations are helpful, and narratives of events are likely to prove more
interesting to the popular than to the technical reader. Simplicity,
without falsification, is necessary; so is fullness of statement. The
writer or, especially, the speaker on "popular science" must repeat and
emphasize, approaching his subject from several angles and not hesi-
tating to use a large number of words to express a little meaning. He
is seldom able to assume much previous information; he must painstakingly explain what to him may be utterly obvious. Curtness or
impatience would defeat his purpose.

(3) MIDDLE TECHNICAL STYLE

Function.   A large group of intelligent and well-educated laymen occupies a position midway between the specialist and the man
on the street. (Included in the group are many technical experts in
certain fields, who may be only "intelligent and well-educated laymen" in other departments of scientific knowledge.) A substantial
part of technical composition is directed to such persons. Reports, for
instance, often are prepared by experts for consideration and action
by industrial boards or public agencies having group authority, and
perhaps wide individual experience, but lacking specific skill in the
matter under consideration. A purely technical style might be a mistake in business correspondence concerning a specialized activity, such
as a phase of engineering, when the addressee is not a professional
colleague; neither may a "popular" manner of expression be warranted
unless the addressee is wholly outside the industry. Many books, articles, and public lectures bring the scientific knowledge of experts to
mature readers and audiences who have a good general education but
little, if any, training in the subject under discussion. Efficient communication then depends upon a "middle" range of technical style.

Characteristics.   On the whole, the structures of language in this
style are more normal than in the two other basic technical styles.
The extreme simplification and the sometimes awkward repetition required in popular treatments of science are not necessary.
Reliance is placed less on avoidance of the proper idiom and nomenclature of the subject than upon definition and explanation. Occasional reference to a dictionary may be expected of the reader, but of
course the writer does not display rare words by preference. Although

such purely technical devices as equations, drawings, and graphs may be indispensable, they are not allowed to push the text altogether aside. Nearly always, a point made symbolically is also expressed in ordinary sentences.

Advantage for the course in technical English. The middle style is particularly advantageous for a course in technical English. It meets the frequent complaint by students of the sciences that their language teachers, being mainly interested in aesthetic literature, slight the subjects of most vital concern to the class. On the other hand, it does not confront an instructor with the task of marking papers that sometimes consist chiefly of symbols rather than of ordinary language. The average student in a professional curriculum receives ample training in purely technical communication, such as the preparation of routine laboratory reports. The purpose of the class in technical English is to reinforce—not to duplicate—that work by concentrating effort upon general principles of logic, sound composition, and correct language in the service of scientific and technological subject matters.* Very often, too, sections are not composed exclusively of students enrolled in the same department of engineering or theoretical science. Through the medium of a middle technical style, members of a mixed group can improve their proficiency in English by writing and speaking, with full intelligibility to one another (and to the instructor), on topics within their respective fields of specialization. Many recommendations and illustrations given in the following chapters assume that the middle range of technical style is largely to be used in the course for which this book is the text.

* In an article on "New Objectives in Engineering Education," *Bulletin of the American Association of University Professors,* XXXII (1946), 265–275, Allen H. Blaisdell, Associate Professor of Mechanical Engineering at the Carnegie Institute of Technology, observes (pages 270–271):
"Possibly one of the most striking deficiencies of engineering graduates, and to some extent of engineers as a group, is the lack of ability to express themselves with ease and clarity in both oral and written language, even in matters of an engineering nature. Many of the duties of the practicing engineer are confined within the narrow boundaries of a well-defined procedure which is familiar to the members of his particular branch of the profession. Consequently, he is able to communicate his needs, ideas, and experiences to his associates with fair success. But once place him in the not uncommon position of dealing with situations of a more general nature, and his faltering use of language is quickly evidenced."

CHAPTER II

PROBLEMS OF GRAMMAR

What grammar is. Grammar is a science generalized from linguistic usage and formulated in rules. It is one among the social sciences, which, being grounded on the psychology of human behavior, are known as <u>inexact by contrast</u> with their physical counterparts such as chemistry or astronomy. Discrepancy and change in language must not, however, be mistaken for anarchy. In speech and writing —just as in musical composition or the etiquette of dress—principles of right and wrong, of better and worse, are determined by cultivated practice. Grammarians investigate and systematically report the best current usages.* Although discovery of the "best" users of English might appear difficult in theory, in practice the masters of a language are easily recognized by their manifest excellence.

The grammar of scientific communication. Certain peculiarities of technical vocabulary and style have been indicated in Chapter I; problems of the mechanics and organization of compositions in this style, or group of styles, will be discussed in later chapters. Students must not confuse the careless talk of shop and field, or the crude jottings of temporary memoranda, with the proprieties of formal presentation of technical facts and ideas. They owe to themselves frequent and conscious attention to good models of composition in their own branches of study. All writers and speakers on science and technology are not equally skilled, but by intention, at least, *the grammar of formal scientific expression is uncompromisingly standard.*

PROBLEMS OF NUMBER

The law of number is as follows:

1. A finite verb agrees in number with its subject; a pronominal word agrees in number with its antecedent.

* Besides studying these formal, current customs, grammarians explore many other phases of language, including historical developments and colloquial and dialectal practices.

EXPLANATIONS

(1) *Definitions:*

Number: Singular (one only) and plural (two or more).

Finite verb: Any form of any verb *except* (a) an infinitive, (b) a participle, or (c) a gerund.

Pronominal word: A pronoun or pronominal adjective. Pronouns function like nouns without actually naming persons and things. Pronominal adjectives, including the possessive adjectives (*my, our, your, his, her, its, their*), are derived from pronouns but used as adjectives.

(2) Not all pronouns have antecedents; in particular, the indefinite pronouns (e.g., *someone, others*) do not. A pronoun lacking a definite antecedent determines its own number, like a noun.

(3) Observe that an inflectional *s*, the regular sign of a plural noun, is the sign of the third person *singular* (never plural) of the present indicative of most verbs.

Note: A noun may be plural without having an inflectional *s*. Native words such as *feet, mice,* and *children* offer no difficulty. Among nouns that retain a foreign plural ending in *a* are *phenomena* (singular, *phenomenon*), *data* (singular, *datum,* seldom used except in expressions like *datum point*), *strata* (singular, *stratum*), and *genera* (singular, *genus*). Some nouns (most but not all of which end in *s*) have the same form in the plural as in the singular: e.g., *horsepower, apparatus* (or: *apparatuses,* but *not* "apparati"), and *series.* Other plurals terminating in an *s* that is not strictly an inflectional ending include such nouns as *analyses* (singular, *analysis*) and *hypotheses* (singular, *hypothesis*).

(4) In some constructions the subject follows the verb. Do not mistake the word *there,* introducing a sentence or clause, for the subject.

Caution: Do not allow a predicate noun to attract a verb into a different number from that of the subject.

RIGHT: Our greatest *need is* (not *are*) modernized plant designs.

Subject-Verb Agreement

See also G 11.

2. A compound subject coördinated by *and* requires a plural verb, regardless of the individual number of the member subjects.

9

RIGHT: A jack plane and a jointer *are* on the bench.

Or: On the bench *are* a jack plane and a jointer.

Or: There *are* a jack plane and a jointer on the bench.

Exception 1: When the compound subject refers to a unity, a singular verb is correct.

RIGHT: A brace and bit *is* on the bench.

             Orlock and Sons *is* a reliable supply house.

Exception 2: When *each* or *every* modifies coördinated singular nouns, the verb is singular. (Pronominal words referring to a compound subject modified by *each* or *every* also are singular.)

RIGHT: *Every* animal and plant *attempts* to perpetuate *its* kind.

3. With a compound subject coördinated by or or nor, the number of the verb is determined solely by the number of that individual subject nearer (or, of more than two, nearest) to the verb. (See also G 20.)

RIGHT: *Is* a *router,* a grooving plane, or a rabbet on the bench?

             No router, grooving plane, or *rabbet is* on the bench.

             Are any *gouges* or chisels on the bench?

             There *are* neither *gouges* nor chisels on the bench.

Note: When the individual subjects are of both numbers, good style dictates that the sentence or clause be so constructed that the operation of G 3 results in a plural verb.

CORRECT GRAMMAR BUT POOR STYLE: Neither nails nor a *hammer was* to be found.

CORRECT GRAMMAR AND IMPROVED STYLE: Neither a hammer nor *nails were* to be found.

Caution: Carefully distinguish between G 2 and G 3. The conjunction joining the members of a compound subject determines which rule operates: G 2 with *and,* G 3 with *or* or *nor.*

4. Nouns or pronouns intervening between a subject and a verb have no effect upon the number of that verb. The number of a verb is determined exclusively by the number of its subject.

RIGHT: *They* as well as he *are* interested in city planning.

        A *program director,* together with two announcers and a control-room engineer, *was* on duty.

Or (construction changed to compound subject) : A program director, two announcers, *and* a control-room engineer *were* on duty. (Cf. G 2. Notice, also, the difference of punctuation immediately before the verb in the two forms of the sentence.)

Note: Along with the grammatical number, the person of a verb is determined solely by the subject.

RIGHT: *He,* as well as I, *is* [third person singular] to be assigned to the project.

You, in addition to me, *are* [second person singular or plural, depending on reference] to be assigned to the project.

We, after long delay, *were* [first person plural] called.

5. The indefinite pronouns one, each, either, neither, **and** another, **together with all indefinite pronouns ending in** one, **or** body, **are singular in number and therefore require singular verbs.** Similarly, they are referred to by singular pronouns and possessive adjectives.

RIGHT: *Everyone* in favor will please raise *his* right hand.

Caution: Do not confuse the conjunction *neither,* used as a correlative of *nor,* with the pronoun *neither,* which as subject always takes a singular verb. (See examples of the correlative conjunction *neither . . . nor* under G 3.)

RIGHT: *Neither* of them *has* ever found work in which *he* could profit by *his* natural inventiveness.

Note 1: The negative phrase *no one* is always singular, but its shortened form, *none,* is now construed as plural when the reference is definitely to more than one.

RIGHT: None *are* so certain as those who "know" what they have not yet learned.

Note 2: Solid and divided forms based on *every* and *any* (e.g., *everyone, every one; everything, every thing; anyone, any one*) have a difference of meaning, which in pronunciation is indicated by shifted stress.

RIGHT: *Everybody* is invited.

Every **body** is under the control of its nervous system.

6. Collective nouns (e.g., committee, crowd, class [*i.e., of students*], number, majority) **may be construed as either singular or**

11

plural, depending on whether the whole or the individual membership is emphasized.

RIGHT: The committee *is* holding its first meeting.

But: The committee *are* in violent disagreement among themselves.

The number of wires between each two junction boxes *was* large.

But: A number of conflicting thoughts *were* passing through my mind.

Caution: When, as often happens, a collective noun is used as a subject, any pronominal words referring to it must not conflict with the verb in number.

RIGHT: A board of arbitration *has* been appointed, and *its* (not *their*) decision will be mandatory.

7. Expressions of aggregate quantity, even though plural in form, generally are construed as singular. This rule covers fractions and phrases stating arithmetic relations, as well as ordinary expressions of amount.

RIGHT: Two times two *is* four.

Two thirds of the income *has* been reinvested.

Forty kilowatt-hours *was* registered by the meter.

Note 1: G 7 is flexible, and usage varies. Some persons, for instance, insist that "two and two" or the like should be followed by a plural verb, in conformity with the basic G 2; however, common practice justifies the singular.

Note 2: When expressions of quantity do not merely specify an aggregate amount, but stress the units that compose the aggregate, they are construed as plural.

RIGHT: Half of the cylinders *were* badly ruined. (*Half . . . was* would be misleading, suggesting perhaps the upper half of each cylinder.)

Two hundred bags of Brazilian coffee *were* being piled on the dock. (*But:* Two million pounds of coffee *was* purchased in Brazil.)

Seventy per cent of the graduates *were* war veterans.

8. Technical nouns ending in ics normally are construed as singular.

12

RIGHT: Mathematics *underlies* almost all natural science.

Economics formerly *was* known as political economy.

Note: Some nouns ending in *ics* are both singular and plural, with a difference of meaning. In a plural sense they suggest practice rather than theory.

RIGHT: Acoustics *is* an important branch of physics.

But: The acoustics of the auditorium *are* excellent.

Pronominal Words

See also *Exception 2* under G 2, and the *Caution* under G 6.

9. *A pronoun or pronominal adjective referring jointly to a compound antecedent is plural if the individual antecedents are coördinated by and; it agrees with the nearer (or, of more than two, the nearest) of antecedents coördinated by or or nor.*

Note: The two parts of this rule are analogues, respectively, to G 2 and G 3, the rules that govern the agreement of verbs with compound subjects.

RIGHT: The thermometer, the watch, the platform scale, *and* the indicator served *their* purpose in the test.

The contractor defaulted, and neither the foreman *nor* the *laborers* ever received *their* wages.

An oilfield truck *or bulldozer* must be repaired at the place where *it* happens to break down.

Exception: Singular pronominal words are, of course, correct in reference to a compound antecedent that names only one person or thing. Cf. *Exception 1* under G 2.

RIGHT: A painter and paperhanger usually can find work in one or the other of *his* two trades.

10. *Singular words like* sort, kind, class, *and* type *must not be modified by plural demonstratives.*

RIGHT: *that class* of motors; *this type* of people.

ALSO RIGHT (with a difference of meaning): *those classes* of motors; *these types* of people.

11. *A relative pronoun (who, which, that) must not be construed as singular when its antecedent is a plural object of the preposition of following the word one.*

13

RIGHT: He is one of the ablest hydrographic engineers who *have* devoted *their* skill to the Coast and Geodetic Survey. (The logic of this type of sentence is more readily grasped by means of a simple transposition:

Of the ablest hydrographic engineers who *have* devoted *their* skill to the Coast and Geodetic Survey, he is one [but not the only one].)

Note: Rarely, the word *one* may actually be the antecedent of the relative pronoun. *One* is then either heavily stressed by the voice or else preceded by *the only* (sometimes merely by *the*).

RIGHT: Smith is *one* of my acquaintances who *is* wholly unqualified for his profession.

Or: Smith is *the only one* of my acquaintances that *is* wholly unqualified for *his* profession. (Observe that these sentences are entirely different in logic from the sentence marked RIGHT directly under G 11. They do not indicate that Smith is one *among* several wholly unqualified acquaintances of the writer. Rather, the first form strongly hints and the second positively asserts that the other acquaintances are professionally qualified, whereas Smith's incompetence is unique.)

PROBLEMS OF CASE

EXPLANATIONS

(1) *Definitions:*

Case: A property of substantives, indicating their relation to other words; the three cases are the nominative, the possessive, and the objective.

Substantive: A noun or the equivalent (e.g., a pronoun).

(2) Inflectional endings, apart from the possessive case, are used in modern English only for the objective case of some (not all) pronouns. As nouns and also gerunds have the same form in both the nominative and the objective, most errors and problems of case involve pronouns.

Distinctions of Nominative and Objective Cases

12. The linking verb, or copula, to be links substantives in the same case.

RIGHT: *It* [nominative] was *I* [nominative] with whom you corresponded.

Smith [nominative] was thought to be *I* [nominative].

But: They thought *him* [objective] to be *me* [objective].

Note 1: Many other linking verbs occur besides *to be,* but they are seldom followed by pronouns. No error is possible in the form of a noun; cf. Explanation (2), page 14.

Note 2: Neither *to be* nor any other linking verb "takes" the nominative case. The peculiarity of a copula is that it does not require any fixed case; instead, it connects substantives in the *same* case, which usually is the nominative but may be the objective. See the last of the three sentences marked RIGHT following G 12.

13. A pronoun and another substantive in apposition with each other are in the same case.

How to determine correct form. Normally the pronoun is in apposition with a noun. Temporarily omit the noun, reading the sentence without it. The right form of the pronoun will then be evident.

RIGHT: They have nominated *us* three seniors as their representatives. (They have nominated *us* . . . as their representatives.)
We three seniors are candidates. (*We* . . . are candidates.)

Note: The compounds *myself, yourself, himself, herself, ourselves, yourselves,* and *themselves* are never correctly used as independent nominatives, but must accompany, as intensives, the corresponding nominative forms of the personal pronouns (*I myself, you yourself, he himself,* etc.). These compounds and also *oneself* (or *one's self*) are, however, used independently as objects of prepositions (e.g., *by himself*) and of reflexive verbs (e.g., *to injure oneself*). They practically never accompany objective forms of the personal pronouns, because of the awkwardness of the resulting combinations (e.g., *them themselves*).

RIGHT: Any consulting engineer—*I myself,* for instance—could advise the School Board about the specifications.

14. A pronoun is in the same case as any other substantive or substantives coördinated with it.

How to determine correct form. Temporarily omit all coördinated terms except one pronoun. The right form of that pronoun will then be evident.

RIGHT: *They* and *we* formed a partnership. (*They* . . . formed a partnership; . . . *we* formed a partnership.)

The bureau employed my partner and *me*. (The bureau employed . . . *me*.)

15. A relative pronoun takes its case from its construction in the clause in which it stands. *Who* is the nominative form of the inflected relative pronoun; *whom*, the objective form. The same distinction applies to the corresponding compound pronoun *whoever* and *whomever*, or *whosoever* and *whomsoever*.

How to determine correct form. To discover whether *who*(*ever*) or *whom*(*ever*) is correct in any sentence, proceed as follows:

1. Locate all *finite* verbs (viz., all besides infinitives, participles, and gerunds); then find the subject of each finite verb. (A combined form, such as *had fused* or *should have been performed*, counts as only one verb.) If any finite verb has no other subject than the pronoun in question, then *who* or *whoever* in the correct form.

2. If all finite verbs have subjects other than the pronoun in question, observe whether the sentence contains any form (finite or otherwise) of the linking verb *to be*, with which *who* or *whoever* possibly may be required as a predicate nominative. (Cf. G 12.)

3. If *who*(*ever*) is not demanded by Step 1 or Step 2, then *whom* or *whomever* is the correct form.

Caution: The procedure outlined in these three steps is entirely reliable, but only if rigorously followed. The general plan is to eliminate *who*(*ever*) before accepting *whom*(*ever*) as correct. The procedure cannot be safely operated in reverse, for frequent mistakes will result from assuming that *whom*(*ever*) is the right form simply because the pronoun occurs in a position that makes it appear to be the object of a verb or preposition. Often the whole clause introduced by the pronoun functions as the grammatical object of that verb or preposition, while *within* the dependent clause *who* or *whoever* is the subject of a finite verb and therefore is nominative. *Look first of all for subjects.*

RIGHT: We learned *who* had been appointed. (*Who* is the subject of *had been appointed*.)

I know *whom* he means. (Both finite verbs have subjects, *I* and *he*, respectively; and the sentence does not contain *to be*.)

But: I know *who* he is. (Although, as before, both finite

16

verbs have subjects, *who* is a predicate nominative with the linking verb *is,* a form of *to be.*)

    Who was he supposed to be? (*Who* is a predicate nominative with the infinitive *to be.*)

    He gives instruction to *whoever* will pay the stipulated fee. (*Whoever* is the subject of *will pay.* The object of the preposition *to* is the whole clause in which *whoever* serves as subject.)

    That assertion cannot be made of anyone *whomsoever.* (*Anyone* is the object of the preposition *of*; therefore *whomsoever,* as the appositive of *anyone,* also is in the objective case. Cf. G 13.)

    Whomever he instructed, paid in advance. (The grammar of this sentence is somewhat difficult, yet clear on analysis. The subject of *paid* is the clause *Whomever he instructed.* Within this dependent clause, *instructed* has *he* for subject and *Whomever* as object.)

    The rings were installed by a mechanic *who* the manager said was the best in the shop. (*Who* is the subject of *was,* not the object of *said.* Keep in mind that every finite verb must have a subject.)

    But: The rings were installed by a mechanic *whom* the manager called the best in the shop. (Both finite verbs have subjects; *whom,* being neither the subject of a verb nor a predicate nominative, is correctly objective. Compare the last two examples until you clearly perceive their difference of grammatical structure. Observe, in particular, that the first version has three finite verbs, the second only two.)

Note 1: Step 2 is the only difficult one of the three. The mere fact that a sentence contains some form of the verb *to be* does not necessarily mean that *who* (*ever*) will be required as a predicate nominative. Some other noun or pronoun may be the predicate nominative; again, the construction may require the objective case (cf. *Note 2* under G 12); or *to be* may be completed by an adjective or a prepositional phrase instead of by a substantive. Understand, also, that forms of *to be* employed as auxiliaries with other verbs (e.g., WERE *operating,* IS *wound,* ARE BEING *assembled*) do not function as copulas.

RIGHT: The navigator gives headings to the pilot, with *whom* he is in constant communication.
Or: The navigator tried to give a heading to the pilot, *whom* he was frantically calling over the intercommunication system.
(Neither sentence contains a predicate substantive, despite the occurrence of *is* or *was.*)

RIGHT: *Whom* do you want *me* to be in the pageant? (The copula *to be* here links two objective pronouns, *me* and *whom*.)

16. Like, *being a preposition, introduces a substantive in the objective case.* Do not employ *like* to introduce either a pronoun in the nominative case or a clause.

RIGHT: It looks *like rain*.
But: He held the composing stick *as if* (or: *as though*) he was an inexperienced typesetter.

RIGHT: My brother writes very much *like me* (or: *as I do*).
But: Do *what* (or: *as*) you are told.

17. *Since* **as** *(signifying degree) and* **than** *are conjunctions, a pronoun following either of these words has the case it would have in a fully expressed clause.*

RIGHT: I have studied twice as hard *as he* [studied], but he seemed to learn more *than I* [learned].
      He taught them more *than us* [i.e., more than he taught us], but we like him better than *they* [i.e., better than they like him].

Note: Often the meaning of a sentence containing *as* or *than* would be entirely changed if a pronoun following the conjunction were to be written in the wrong case. For a similar reason, ambiguity may arise if a noun follows the conjunction, inasmuch as all nouns are invariable in the nominative and objective cases. When necessary, expand the construction sufficiently to reveal the intended sense.

AMBIGUOUS: Smith hires Jones oftener than Brown.

CLEAR (with one meaning): Smith hires Jones oftener than Brown does.

CLEAR (with another meaning): Smith hires Jones oftener than he does Brown.

Possessive Case

Formation of the possessive case is explained in Chapter IV: see Apostrophe (Principle II), P 26.

18. *Except as part of certain customary expressions,* **nouns that do not signify persons** *(including organizations)* **or animals should not**

18

be employed in the possessive form. Phrases formed with the preposition *of,* governing the objective case, should be substituted.

RIGHT: Bernoulli's theorem; a shepherd's crook; attorneys' fees; the home office's ruling; camel's hair.

POOR: the laboratory's interior; a flooring's joists.

IMPROVED: the interior of the laboratory; the joists of a flooring.

RIGHT (sanctioned by custom) : the sun's rays; a day's work; ten cents' (*or:* dollars') worth. (*Caution:* Most figurative expressions of this class—e.g., "a stone's throw" and "at wit's end"—are trite; in formal composition, therefore, they generally should be avoided.)

19. The following constructions must be carefully discriminated according to the intended meaning: (1) a gerund (or verbal noun) preceded and modified by the possessive form of a noun or pronominal word; (2) a noun or pronoun in the objective case followed and modified by a participle. Despite their close resemblance, these constructions are entirely different in logical meaning.

RIGHT (with a possessive as modifier): We did not know of the *builder's having tried* in vain to obtain a permit. (We knew of the builder, but we did not know of his futile efforts to obtain a permit.)

He insisted on *everyone's knowing* some practical mechanics. (To "insist on everyone" would be meaningless; what he insisted on was the knowledge of mechanics.)

I dislike him as a person, but I admire *his* constant *striving* for improvement.

RIGHT (with a participle as modifier): The watchman caught a *man trying* to enter the building.

A license is required of *anyone operating* a factory.

I can still remember *him, having attached* his line, carefully *maneuvering* the log into position.

Exception: In violation of logic and grammatical regularity, gerunds sometimes are preceded by substantives in the objective case when possessive forms would be unidiomatic or awkward. However, such abnormal constructions are preferably avoided.

LOGICAL BUT AWKWARD: The chairman, becoming confused, would not even permit any member's or guest's rising to a point of order.

ACCEPTABLE BUT ILLOGICAL: The chairman, becoming confused, would not even permit any member or guest rising to a point of order.

BETTER: The chairman, becoming confused, would not even permit anyone's rising to a point of order.
Or: The chairman, becoming confused, would not even permit any member or guest to rise to a point of order.

PROBLEMS OF PERSON
See also the *Note* under G 4.

EXPLANATIONS

(1) *Definition:*

Person: A property of substantives and finite verbs, indicating the relation of the former, as subjects, to the latter; the three persons are the first (with *I* or *we* as subject), the second (with *you* as subject), and the third (with any other subject besides *I, we,* and *you*).

(2) *You,* though originally only plural, has long served also for the singular of the second person.

(3) Verbs agree in person with their subjects; pronouns, with their antecedents. However, very few mistakes are possible except in discrimination of *shall* and *will* and *should* and *would.*

Minor Problems of the First Person Singular

20. *When* I, *occurring as a member of a compound subject coordinated by* or *or* nor, *is the individual subject nearer (or, of more than two, nearest) to the verb, the first person singular of the verb must be used.* (Cf. G 3.)

RIGHT: Either he or *I am* available.
He or *I* always *open* the building at 7:30 a.m.
Neither he nor *I do* that kind of heavy machining.

21. *When the subject of a verb is a relative pronoun having* I *or* me *as its antecedent, the first person singular of the verb must be used.*

RIGHT: *I,* who *want* . . . ; *I* that *am* . . . ; . . . to *me,* who *have* done . . .

Shall, Will and Should, Would

Although in casual speech and informal writing *shall* is seldom used and *would* is often substituted for *should,* the distinctions explained by the following rules are among the recognized tests of good English. They should, therefore, be carefully observed in all serious composition, including business correspondence, public speaking, and engineering and industrial reports.

22. For predicting or discussing the future in declarative statements, shall *is employed in the first person;* will, *in the second and third persons.*

RIGHT: *I* (or: *We*) *shall* be pleased to have your reply.

     You will find brass, cast iron, or steel about equally serviceable for the supporting plate.

     He (or: *She, Mr. Smith, They*) *will* do well to reconsider the offer.

23. For stating what the writer or speaker (not, necessarily, the person or persons addressed or discussed) **is determined to bring about,** will *is employed in the first person;* shall *in the second and third persons.*

RIGHT: *I* (or: *We*) *will* faithfully carry out your instructions.

     You (or: *He, She, Mr. Smith, They*) *shall* honor the note, or *I* (or: *we*) *will* force settlement by legal action.

Note 1: Observe that G 23 exactly reverses G 22. This reversal of the normally expected forms signifies that the writer or speaker is not predicting or discussing in an ordinary manner, but giving orders, threatening, or emphatically promising.

Note 2: G 23 has a special relevance to technical writing, in that *shall* with the third person of the passive voice constantly occurs in specifications (e.g., "Arresters shall be installed . . ."; "Daily tests shall be run . . ."; "The flash point should be determined by the . . . method.")

24. Ordinarily, should *is employed in the first person;* would, *in the second and third persons.*

RIGHT: I *should* think that *you* (or: *he, she, Mr. Smith, they*) *would* be competent to draw the plans.

     We *should* prefer to avoid delay.

Note: Observe that the basic rule (G 24) for *should* and *would* corresponds to the basic rule (G 22) for *shall* and *will*. Thus, both "sh" forms (*shall* and *should*) are used normally in the first person; both "w" forms (*will* and *would*), normally in the second and third persons.

25. In a dependent clause introduced by if, even if, or even though *(sometimes by* though *alone or* although), should *is employed in all three persons.** Choice between *should* and *would* in the main (independent) clause is determined by G 24 in the usual manner.

RIGHT: IF *I* (or: *we*) SHOULD finish early, *I* (or: *we*) *should* like to go to the library.

    THOUGH *you* (or: *he, she, Mr. Smith, they*) SHOULD finish early, *you* (or: *he,* etc.) *would* have insufficient time to prepare the report.

26. Would is employed in all three persons with the special meaning: "to be willing to." †

RIGHT: *I* (or: *we, you, he, she, Mr. Smith, they*) *would* gladly undertake the commission.

Caution: With expressions containing such verbs as "prefer," "like," and "be willing" or such adjectives as "[be] happy" and "[be] able," *G 26 cannot logically operate.* Therefore, *should* is used in the first person, according to G 24.

RIGHT: We *should* be willing, under certain conditions, to waive the restriction. ("We *would* be willing . . ." is redundant, equivalent to "We are willing to be willing.")

    I *should* be glad to undertake the commission. (The meaning is *not* that "I am willing to be glad." Contrast this sentence with the one marked RIGHT directly below G 26, where *would* with the adverb "gladly" signifies, logically, "to be willing [to undertake] in a glad spirit.")

But: You (or: *He, She, Mr. Smith, they*) *would* be glad to undertake the commission. (Although G 26 does not govern this sentence, *would* in the second or third person is normally required by G 24.)

---

    * *Should* serves also in all three persons, as an approximate but milder synonym of *ought*, to express obligation. Native users of English employ this form automatically, without possibility of error.

    † *Would* serves also in all three persons to express habitual occurrences of the past (i.e., what formerly *would* occur regularly or repeatedly). Native users of English employ this form automatically, without possibility of error.

Note: G 26 takes precedence whenever it conflicts with any other rule concerning *should* and *would*.

RIGHT: We *would* merge if you *would*.

Even though the power company *would* [i.e., is willing to] install a line, we prefer our own supply.

But: EVEN THOUGH the main power supply SHOULD be interrupted, operation would be continuous. (Here G 26 does not apply, and G 25 therefore operates.)

27. A question employs that form (shall, will, should, or would) which, according to the foregoing rules, is correct in the answer.

RIGHT: *Shall you* be of age before your graduation? (Answer: Yes, I shall [G 22].)

Will you give me your word? (Answer: Yes, I will [G 23].)

Will one three-cent *stamp* be sufficient? (Answer: No, it will not [G 22].)

Should you enjoy visiting the plant? (Answer: Yes, I should [G 24].)

Would you go even if *it should* rain? (Answer: Yes, I would [G 26] even if it should [G 25] rain.)

PROBLEMS OF TENSE

EXPLANATIONS

(1) *Definitions:*

Tense: A property of verbs, both finite and nonfinite, indicating time either absolutely or in relation to that of other verbs.

Finite verb: Any verb having person and number; i.e., any verb form other than a verbal.

Nonfinite verb, or **verbal:** An infinitive, a gerund, or a participle.

Principal parts: Present infinitive, past, and past participle. (Because certain verbs, e.g., *may,* are never actually used as infinitives, the first principal part is more accurately defined as the first person singular of the present indicative.)

(2) From the principal parts of any verb, the conjugation in all tenses, voices, and moods can be fully developed, except for the abnormalities in the present of *to be* and an irregularity in the third person singular of the present indicative of a few other verbs (e.g., the form *has,* the lack of an inflectional *s* in *shall* or *will,* and the *e* in *goes* or *does*). Many verbs, of course, are incapable of a passive voice, and

some are defective in other forms; for instance, a few lack the past participle, and with it the whole series of perfect tenses.

(3) Verbals, unlike finite verbs, have tense inflections for only the present (*coming; to come, to be coming*) and the perfect (*having come, having been coming; to have come, to have been coming*). Observe, however, the "progressive" as well as the "simple" present and perfect forms.

(4) The so-called "sign of the infinitive," *to,* may or may not occur. Compare the two infinitives in this sentence: "They tried *to make* him *agree.*"

Note: A "split infinitive" results from the interposition of some word or words between *to* and the verbal element, e.g., TO *completely* CLOSE or TO *at that instant* DISCONNECT. The split infinitive is avoided by careful stylists except when it is absolutely necessary to prevent ambiguity or awkwardness. (Splitting of combined verb forms, e.g., IS *completely* CLOSED or MUST *at that instant* BE DISCONNECTED, also should be avoided as much as possible. However, smoothness and preservation of sense very often demand separations of this kind. Note that TO HAVE *often* USED has a split verb form but is not a split infinitive.)

Principal Parts

28. Accurately distinguish between the three pairs of frequently confused verbs shown below in opposite columns. Their principal parts should be memorized, and then practiced in sentences until complete mastery is achieved.

Transitive Must *either* have an object *or* be in the passive voice			*Intransitive* Can *neither* have an object *nor* be in the passive voice (See *Exceptions,* below.)		
Pres. *Inf.*	*Past*	*Past* *Participle*	*Pres.* *Inf.*	*Past*	*Past* *Participle*
raise	raised	raised	rise	rose	risen
lay	laid	laid	lie	lay	lain
set	set	set	sit	sat	sat

RIGHT (with direct object): He *raised* the *roof* one foot.
He *has laid* the *linoleum.*
He *is setting* the *posts.*

24

RIGHT (in passive voice): The roof *was raised* one foot.
The linoleum *has been laid*.
The posts *are being set*.

RIGHT (intransitive): The tower *rises* to a great height.
Both ends *should lie* flat.
Next term he is expected *to sit* on the council. (Note that the passive voice of the main verb, *is expected,* does not prevent the infinitive, *to sit,* from functioning intransitively.

Exception 1: In certain meanings *set* is correctly employed intransitively.

RIGHT: The plaster *sets* hard. The sun *sets* in the west.

Exception 2: A kind of passive construction is possible with intransitive verbs when they are completed by certain particles that have the form (but not the normal function) of prepositions.

RIGHT: Chairs *are sat on,* and beds *are lain upon.* (Similarly, a joke is laughed *at*; friends can be conversed *with*.)

29. Learn the principal parts of every verb that is frequently employed; look up the principal parts of any other verb when it is employed occasionally. Consult a dictionary or grammar; do not guess.

30. List of Principal Parts.

Below are listed common verbs in which mistakes of conjugation often are made. When the historical development of the word has included more than one form of a principal part, that currently preferred is shown. An asterisk indicates the main dangers of error in form or spelling, or of choice of a less desirable form.

Pres. Inf.	Past	Past Part.	Pres. Inf.	Past	Past Part.
beat	beat	*beaten	drag	*dragged	*dragged
become	*became	*become	draw	*drew	*drawn
begin	*began	*begun	drink	*drank	*drunk
bite	bit	*bitten	eat	ate	*eaten
blow	*blew	*blown	fall	fell	*fallen
break	broke	*broken	fly	flew	*flown
bring	*brought	*brought	forget	forgot	*forgotten
burst	*burst	*burst	get	got	*got
choose	chose	*chosen	give	*gave	*given
come	*came	*come	go	went	*gone
deal	*dealt	*dealt	grow	*grew	*grown
dive	*dived	*dived	know	*knew	*known
do	*did	*done	lead	*led	*led

25

Pres. Inf.	Past	Past Part.	Pres. Inf.	Past	Past Part.
lend	lent	lent	sing	sang	*sung
loan	loaned	loaned	sink	sank	*sunk
pay	*paid	*paid	speak	spoke	*spoken
prove	proved	*proved	steal	stole	*stolen
ride	rode	*ridden	swear	swore	*sworn
ring	rang	*rung	swim	*swam	*swum
run	*run	*run	take	took	*taken
see	*saw	seen	throw	*threw	*thrown
shake	shook	*shaken	wear	wore	*worn
show	showed	*shown	write	wrote	*written

Note: In some verbs variant forms of certain parts of speech have specialized meanings (e.g., past and past participle *hanged*, for capital punishment by hanging, in place of *hung*). *Lie* meaning "to prevaricate," with past and past participle *lied*, is a different verb from *lie* (entered under G 28) meaning "to recline."

Sequence of Tenses

Most problems of the sequence of tenses are solved automatically by native speakers, without recourse to the rules that must be studied by a foreigner learning English in school. The most common errors involve the perfect infinitive or the present participle; therefore close attention should be paid to G 32 and G 33. G 31 explains a usage in which the normal sequence of tenses may be correctly set aside.

31. Phrase a general truth or continuing fact in the present tense, even in connection with a main clause in the past or past perfect tense.

RIGHT: I found that sanitary engineering *is* not offered as a separate curriculum in most technical colleges.

As early as 1616 William Harvey was convinced that the blood *circulates* (not *circulated*).

Before Galileo's birth Copernicus had shown that the sun *is* (not *was*) the center of our system.

But: In 1615 the Inquisition proclaimed that the earth *was* (not *is*) the physical center of the universe.

32. Do not use the present participle to represent a time earlier than that of the finite verb with which it is associated. Use the perfect participle or a different construction.

WRONG: *Completing* the wooden base, I next formed the metal frame.

RIGHT (perfect participle): *Having completed* the wooden base, I next formed the metal frame.

WRONG: *Beginning* at noon, he will be through by nightfall.

RIGHT (different construction): If he begins at noon he will be through by nightfall.
Or: He will begin at noon and be through by nightfall.

33. *Use the perfect infinitive to represent only a time earlier than that of the verb (finite or nonfinite) on which the infinitive directly depends.* For *all other* time relationships in the past, present, and future, use the present infinitive.

RIGHT (perfect infinitive): I should like [now] *to have entered* [before].
I should have liked [then] *to have entered* [still earlier].
I shall be glad [later] *to have entered* [now, or at some time before that indicated by "shall be glad"].

RIGHT (present infinitive): I should like [now] *to enter* [now].
I should like [now] *to enter* [later].
I should have liked [then] *to enter* [then].
I should have liked [then] *to enter* [afterwards].
I shall wish [later] *to enter* [then].
I shall wish [later] *to enter* [still later].

RIGHT: He is known *to have been trying* for years *to secure* a patent. (The perfect infinitive, "to have been trying," represents a period earlier than that of the finite verb, "is known," on which it depends; the present infinitive, "to secure," represents the same period as that of the perfect infinitive, "to have been trying," on which it depends. The fact that "to have been trying" is in the progressive form, as distinguished from the simple perfect [i.e., *to have tried*], does not affect the operation of G 33.)

PROBLEMS OF MOOD (THE SUBJUNCTIVE)

EXPLANATIONS

(1) *Definitions:*
Mood: A property of finite verbs indicating the manner in which the action or state of being is represented; the three moods are the indicative, the imperative, and the subjunctive.
Indicative: The normal mood of statements and questions.
Imperative: The mood of direct command.
Subjunctive: The mood of various kinds of unreal or emotional representation.

27

(2) Since no difficulty is encountered with the indicative and imperative moods, only the subjunctive will be discussed below.

(3) Constructions with modal auxiliaries—in particular, with *may, might, could,* and *would*—often express essentially subjunctive meanings. The true subjunctive is, therefore, employed less frequently in English than otherwise would be necessary.

(4) For another cause, the subjunctive mood appears to occur even less often than in actuality: namely, the fact that the English subjunctive usually is identical with the indicative. The only differences *of form* in subjunctive verbs are these three:

    (a) *be* throughout the present tense of the verb *to be* (used alone or as an auxiliary) in place of *am, is,* and *are;*

    (b) *were* (used alone or as an auxiliary) in place of *was;*

    (c) absence of inflectional *s* in the third person singular of the present tense: e.g., *come* in place of *comes, have* (used alone or as an auxiliary) in place of *has, cross* in place of *crosses.*

The subjunctive mood is employed for three purposes:

34. Were *rather than* **was** *must be used in a subordinate clause that is definitely contrary to fact.* (Except when *were* is substituted for *was,* subjunctives serving this function do not differ from the corresponding indicative forms. The correct tense is chosen automatically.)

RIGHT: He wishes that every well *were* a producer. (But not every well is a producer.)

If I *were* king! (But I am not king.)

Every man feels as if he *were* not destined to die. (But no man is immortal.)

A simplified equation was written as though the only sugar present *were* glucose. (But other sugars were present.)

Even if perpetual motion *were* possible, it could never be a source of energy for external work. (But it is not even possible.)

35. After *if, though, as if, even though, as though, and lest, the subjunctive mood is used to express what the speaker or writer regards either as probably contrary to fact or as emotionally unpleasant.* (This rule seldom operates in technical composition.)

RIGHT: If this *be* treason, make the most of it!

Though he *shake* your hand and *eat* your bread, beware lest his knife *slit* your throat in the night.

The road must be built even though (*or:* even if) it *bankrupt* three counties.

Caution: Do not use the subjunctive with *if* or *though* except when it is required by G 34 or permitted by G 35.

RIGHT (indicative mood): The reported yield looked as if a catalyst *was* needed.

No fire hazard will be incurred if only the rated current *is* used.

Even though he *has* unusual imitative talent, he wholly lacks the faculty of original design.

36. The subjunctive mood is used after expressions of necessity, urging, and command.

RIGHT:　Mr. Chairman, I move that the minutes *be* approved as read.
Our advice is that a public accountant *examine* the books.
The judge ordered that the court *be* cleared.
It is necessary that the solution then *stand* for several hours.

PROBLEMS OF DISCRIMINATION BETWEEN ADJECTIVES AND ADVERBS

EXPLANATIONS

(1) *Definitions:*

Adjective: A word that modifies a substantive (noun, gerund, or pronoun).

Adverb: A word that modifies a verb, adjective, or other adverb.

Modify: To describe or limit; to state a quality, condition, or relation of a word or group of words (the word or words modified).

Comparison: The inflection of adjectives and adverbs in the positive, comparative, and superlative degrees (e.g., *high, higher, highest; skillful[ly], more skillful[ly], most skillful[ly].*

(2) Remember that participles and gerunds, although derived from verbs, function as adjectives and substantives, respectively.

(3) Avoid common mistakes about adverbs. (A) Not all adverbs end in *ly*, and numerous words that end in *ly* are not adverbs. (B) *Both* adjectives and adverbs tell how, when, and where; they can be distinguished only by the classes of words they modify. (See *Definitions,* above.)

Attention to the following rules will prevent common mistakes in the discrimination of adjectives and adverbs:

37. Verbs describing impressions of the physical senses are followed by adjectives modifying the subject (i.e., by predicate adjectives), not by adverbs.

RIGHT: Fur feels *soft* to the fingers.

His letters usually sound *cheerful*.

It tasted very *good*.

A person who looks *bad* may feel *good* (or: *well*).

Note 1: The difference between "to feel (*or:* look) *well*" and "to feel (*or:* look) *good*" is that *well* more specifically refers to health as such, whereas *good* refers to a total feeling or appearance of well-being. In this construction both *good* and *well* are adjectives—although in many other constructions, of course, *well* functions as the adverb corresponding to the adjective *good* (e.g., "He did *well* [adverb modifying *did*] last year"). Do not be misled by the correctness, on one occasion, of "I feel *well*" [adjective, not adverb] into saying wrongly, "I feel *badly*" [adverb] on another.

Note 2: Adverbs can modify verbs such as *feel, taste,* and *look* used in the sense of *performing the act* of feeling, tasting, etc.

RIGHT: Look *closely*. The unknown gas was smelled very *cautiously*. (*But:* The unknown gas smelled *acrid* [not acridly].)

38. A verb may be followed either by an adjective modifying the subject or object of the verb, or by an adverb modifying the verb itself.

Caution: This rule does not mean that regardless of whether an adjective or an adverb is employed, the construction is always correct. Often only one type of modifier is logically possible. When a choice must be made, it furnishes the reader or listener with an important clue to the exact meaning intended by the composer of the sentence.

RIGHT: The *line* must be pulled TAUT [adjective].

The *airplane* landed SAFELY [adverb] on the broken gear.

Or: The *airplane* returned SAFELY [adverb] through heavy flak.

But: The airplane arrived SAFE [adjective] after the dangerous mission.

Press the button FIRMLY [adverb].

Make all *mountings* STEADY [adjective].

A soldier is taught to carry *himself* ERECT [adjective].
The car is guaranteed *to run* WELL [adverb].

39. The comparative and superlative degrees of adverbs ending in ly are formed with more and most.

Caution: Be sure to distinguish adverbs in *ly* from short adjectives (with or without *ly*), which have comparatives in (*i*)*er* and superlatives in (*i*)*est*.

RIGHT (adverbs): speedily, more speedily, most speedily; coolly, more coolly, most cooly; easily, more easily, most easily. *Exception:* early, earlier (*rarely:* more early), earliest (*rarely:* most early).

RIGHT (adjectives): speedy, speedier, speediest; cool, cooler, coolest; easy, easier, easiest; ugly, uglier, ugliest; costly, costlier, costliest.

Note 1: Some adverbs have two forms, one with and one without final *ly*. Commonly a difference of meaning (as between *late* [behind time] and *lately* [recently]) governs the choice; otherwise, the longer form generally is preferred in dignified style (e.g., *slowly* to *slow*).

Note 2: Adverbs not ending in *ly* are compared like corresponding adjectives. Thus, as examples, *good* (adjective) and *well* (adjective and adverb) have the same comparative and superlative forms, *better* and *best;* and the series *fast, faster, fastest* is employed, in each form, both adjectivally and adverbially.

Note 3: In all problems of constructing comparatives and superlatives *except* that covered by G 39, the ear of any native speaker of English is a safe guide to the choice between use of *more* or *most* and use of endings in *er* or *est;* in other words, whatever forms sound right are almost sure to be acceptable.

40. Because due is an adjective (not an adverb), the expression due to is incorrect unless due modifies a noun or the equivalent (viz., a pronoun or gerund). *Due to* at the beginning of a sentence or clause is practically certain to be faulty, and in any position the expression is wrong if *due* modifies an adjective or a verb.

RIGHT (*due* correctly used as adjective): The *reputation* of Swiss watches has been *due* to fine craftsmanship.

The *saving* of alloys *due* to the invention of tipped cutting tools became large.

Everyone on the force is *due* to receive separate notification.

Evidently, *spilling* was *due* to improper packing.

31

WRONG (*due* misused as adverb): *Due* to circumstances beyond our control, we *must delay* action.

Or: We *must delay* action, *due* to circumstances beyond our control.

Due to declining orders the future is *uncertain*.

Or: The future is *uncertain due* to declining orders.

RIGHT: Because of circumstances beyond our control, we must delay action.

The future is uncertain as a result (*or:* in consequence; on account; because) of declining orders.

Or: Declining orders make the future uncertain.

41. The words most **and** some **and such adjectives as** real, sure, **and** considerable **must not be mistaken for adverbs.**

WRONG: For finishing, *most all* types (or: *most any* type) of varnish can be used.

The situation has begun *to improve some.*

We have been *real busy* during the past season.

These instructions are *sure difficult* to follow.

Prices *have advanced considerable.*

RIGHT: For finishing, *almost* all types (or: *almost* any type) of varnish can be used.

The situation has begun to improve *somewhat.*

We have been *very* (or: *extremely; unusually*) busy during the past season.

Or: We *really* have been busy during the past season.

These instructions are *very* (or: *extremely*; etc.) difficult to follow.

Or: These instructions are *surely* difficult to follow.

Prices have advanced *considerably.*

Note on *"most" and "some"*: As correctly used in different constructions, *most* and *some* are either adjectives or pronouns. Their corresponding adverbs are *somewhat* and *almost*. (*Most* functions adverbially in forming the superlative degree of many adjectives and adverbs, but otherwise neither *most* nor *some* is an adverb.) The following rule of thumb is infallible: *If "almost" or "somewhat" makes sense, "most" or "some" is ungrammatical.* Observe that with *all*, even when employed substantively, and with pronouns constructed on *every* and *any*, the form *almost* (not *most*) is required.

RIGHT: *almost all* of us; *almost every*body; *almost any*body.

PROBLEMS OF LOGICAL CONSTRUCTION

42. A clause must not contain two or more negative terms to express a negative meaning. Besides obvious negatives beginning with *n, un,* or *in* (such as *no, not, n't* in contractions, *nobody, nor, never, unsatisfactory,* and *insoluble*), the following words —all meaning "not beyond a certain extent"—also are negative in significance: *hardly, scarcely, barely, only,* and (in the sense of "no more than" or "not otherwise than") *but.*

WRONG: I do *not* recall *hardly* a word of the lecture.

Nowhere in the crowd was *scarcely* anybody (or: *nobody*) we recognized.

It *won't* take *only* (or: *but*) a minute.

You *cannot* (or: *can't*) help *but* reach the same conclusion.

(*Note:* This familiar locution consisting of *not help but* followed by an infinitive, being grammatically unsound, should be avoided.)

RIGHT: I recall hardly a word of the lecture.

We recognized scarcely anybody in the crowd.

Or: We recognized almost nobody in the crowd.

It will take only (or: *but*) a minute.

You cannot (or: *can't*) help reaching the same conclusion.

Note 1: Two negative expressions in separate negative clauses do not constitute a violation of G 42.

RIGHT: The connecting rods were *not* the cause of vibration, *nor* were the bearings at fault.

Note 2: Two or more negative expressions in the same clause are correct if each has a separate function. Two may cancel each other to give a mildly or emphatically positive, rather than negative, force to a clause.

RIGHT (independent function): *Neither* the connecting rods *nor* the bearings were the cause of vibration.

But: The cause of vibration was *not* the connecting rods *or* the bearings. (Avoid using *nor* as a correlative of *not* within a single clause.)

I regard the proposal as *unwarranted, impractical,* and *irrational.*

RIGHT (cancellation): I *never* have regarded development of commercial gliders for heavy express as *unfeasible*. (The writer implies that at least he considers the development possible; he may even consider it probable.)

By *no* means is uranium the *only* source of atomic energy. (Potential sources exist in other elements.)

Note 3: The word *irregardless,* common in illiterate speech, is a barbarism for *regardless.* The prefix *ir* (equivalent to *in*) and the suffix *less* are both negative elements.

43. An introductory participle, gerund, infinitive, or elliptical (incompletely expressed) clause is said to "dangle" when the agent is not immediately identified by the subject of the following main clause.

WRONG: (Dangling participle) Neglecting to use the hood, chlorine may be inhaled.

(Dangling gerund phrase) By neglecting to use the hood, chlorine may be inhaled.

(Dangling infinitive) To avoid inhaling chlorine, the hood should be used.

(Dangling elliptical clause) When evolving chlorine, the hood should be used.

RIGHT: Neglecting (*or:* By neglecting) to use the hood, one (*or:* you; a chemist; the student; etc.) may inhale chlorine.

To avoid inhaling chlorine, use the hood. (The implied subject of the imperative is *you.*)

When evolving chlorine, one should use the hood.

Or (expansion of elliptical construction to a complete dependent clause): When chlorine is being evolved, the hood should be used.

Note: Other forms of the same general error, besides those mentioned in G 43 and illustrated in the examples, are possible but of less frequent occurrence. Any modifier "dangles" if it has nothing to modify or if what it modifies is not immediately clear. Some dangling constructions, however, are permissible. They include the nominative absolute (e.g., THE PATTERNS HAVING BEEN REMOVED, *the two halves of the mold are brought together*), a few special idioms (e.g., the locutions *according to* and *according as,* in which the participle has largely or completely lost its adjectival force; and the elliptical clause *if possible*), and certain transitional expressions (e.g., *as previously mentioned,* introductory to the whole following clause rather than merely to the grammatical subject). Prepositions (e.g., *concerning*) and conjunctions (e.g., *provided*) derived from participles are not, of course, considered to be dangling participles.

44. A "squinting" construction is a form of ambiguity in which a modifier might be understood as qualifying either a preceding or a following element, with a difference of meaning.

WRONG: Planting of the same land in cotton (←) frequently (→) is unscientific farming.

He told us (←) a year later (→) he would reconsider his decision.

RIGHT: Frequent planting of the same land in cotton is unscientific farming.

He told us *that* a year later he would reconsider his decision.

Or (with another meaning): He told us a year later *that* he would reconsider his decision.

45. A "false series" is a faulty "a, b, and c series" in which all the members are not both logically and grammatically parallel. This common error is a sign of inexpert writing and loose thinking. When logical or grammatical parallelism is violated, the characteristic dignity and neatness of a coördinate series is changed to crudity. (Improvement often demands radical revision, with abandonment of the "a, b, and c" structure.)

Note: The punctuation of a correctly constructed "a, b, and c series" is explained in Chapter IV; see P 1c, with the appended *Note* on punctuation between the last two members of the series. (See also P 5 and *Note 2* under P 1a, in the same chapter, concerning the use of semicolons instead of commas in certain forms of the series.)

WRONG: The four members performed, respectively, a d-c resistance test, an excitation test, a running-light test, a blocked-rotor test, and then the whole group assembled the data thus separately obtained. (The series has five parts: the first four consist of the repeated noun *test*, with its various qualifiers; the fifth, on the contrary, is an independent clause.)

Hydrofluoric acid is a liquid, volatile, highly corrosive, and cannot be kept in glass containers. (The sentence violates both logical and grammatical parallelism.)

A pier fifteen feet long would be sufficient during the coming summer, a ten-foot extension would be required for tying up the boat next winter at low river stage, or else we could reduce draft by removing the outboard motor. (The three independent clauses are not logically parallel.)

RIGHT: The four members performed, respectively, a d-c resistance test, an excitation test, a running-light test, and a blocked-rotor test; then the whole group assembled the data thus separately obtained.

Hydrofluoric acid is a volatile, highly corrosive liquid that cannot be kept in glass containers.

A pier fifteen feet long would be sufficient during the coming summer; however, unless we reduced draft by removing the outboard motor, a ten-foot extension would be required for tying up the boat next winter at low river stage.

46. A construction introduced by and, but, (n)or, or yet with a relative pronoun is incorrect unless parallel with a previous construction including the same relative pronoun.

WRONG: The greatest difficulty was moving the heavy rocks, *and which* was accomplished by use of a block and cable.

They are identical twins, *yet whose* aptitudes are markedly different.

The grid is an element *that* can repel the electrons flowing to the plate *or by which* the flow can be intensified.

RIGHT: Moving the heavy rocks, which was the greatest difficulty, was accomplished by use of a block and cable.

They are identical twins, yet they have markedly different aptitudes.

Or: Although identical twins, they have markedly different aptitudes.

The grid is an element *by which* the electrons flowing to the plate can be repelled or *by which* the flow can be intensified.

Or: The grid is an electrode that can either repel or intensify the flow of electrons to the plate.

47. The conjunction   that   must not be carelessly repeated to introduce a clause.

WRONG: The treasurer stated *that* unless past dues were collected immediately, *that* a special assessment must be levied.

RIGHT: The treasurer stated *that a special assessment must be levied* unless past dues were collected immediately.

Or: The treasurer stated *that* unless past dues were collected immediately, *a special assessment must be levied.* (Regardless of position, *that* introduces the italicized clause.)

48. A construction introduced by because may not be used either as a subject or as a predicate complement.

WRONG: *Because of* the steel structure *is* why the frame would be salvageable in case of fire.

The explanation of the garbled description *was because* many details still were restricted.

RIGHT: Because of the steel structure, the frame would be salvageable in case of fire.

The explanation of the garbled description was that many details still were restricted.

Note 1: The statement that a *reason* or *cause* is *because,* whether completed by a clause or by an *of* phrase, never is correct. Likewise, any other predicate complement of similar meaning is illogical when the subject is *reason* or *cause.*

WRONG: The reason for shielding the accelerating tube with lead *is because of* (or: *is on account of; is a result of;* etc.) the presence of X rays.

RIGHT: The reason for shielding the accelerating tube with lead is the presence of X rays. (A reason or cause is not *because* of something; it *is* something, expressed by a noun or the equivalent.)

Note 2: Many constructions in which *when* or *where* introduces a noun clause are faulty in the same manner explained, in relation to *because,* by G 48. In particular, the error of defining a term by means of a *when* or *where* clause should be avoided.

WRONG: A "sweat-out" *is when* (or: *is where*) dampness persists after plaster has set.

I *have heard where* safe manufacture of dynamite requires two widely separated plants.

RIGHT: A "sweat-out" is persistent dampness after plaster has set.

I have heard that safe manufacture of dynamite requires two widely separated plants.

49. A restrictive word expressing degree, such as hardly, almost, nearly, entirely, just, or only, should be placed next to the word or construction that directly receives its logical force.

WRONG: They barely offered [but did not pay?] us half the market price.

He only comes [but does not remain?] on Thursdays.

RIGHT: They offered us *barely half* the market price.

He comes on *Thursdays only*.

Or: He comes *only on Thursdays*.

50. Both members of the following pairs of correlative conjunctions should immediately precede parallel elements: both . . . and (also), either . . . or (else), neither . . . nor (yet), *and* not only . . . but (also).

WRONG: He *both* SECURED a professional degree from the university *and* HIS STATE REGISTRATION.

Modern signs are *not only* DESIGNED to convey information, *but also* FOR ATTRACTION by their beauty.

The transmission may form *either* A UNIT with the clutch *or* BE INDEPENDENTLY MOUNTED.

RIGHT: He secured *both* HIS PROFESSIONAL DEGREE from the university *and* HIS STATE REGISTRATION.

Modern signs are designed *not only* TO CONVEY information, *but also* TO ATTRACT by their beauty.

The transmission may *either* FORM a unit with the clutch *or* BE INDEPENDENTLY MOUNTED.

Note: In the final example of the group marked RIGHT, sufficient parallelism is established by the two verbal elements directly following the correlative conjunctions, despite the fact that the sense requires one to be active and the other passive. Such deviations from strict parallelism are permissible to the extent necessary for exact communication of meaning or avoidance of unnatural phrasing.

51. If part of an elliptical construction is to be mentally supplied from a complete construction parallel with it, the omitted and expressed words must be identical.

WRONG: The first three floors *are* for display and sales; the fourth floor, for offices; the loft, for storage. (The missing verb in the two elliptical clauses is the singular form *is,* which cannot be supplied by the plural form *are* of the first clause.)

RIGHT: The first three floors *are* for display and sales; the fourth floor *is* for offices; the loft *is* for storage.

Or (with *is* supplied to the third clause from the second):
The first three floors *are* for display and sales; the fourth floor *is* for offices; the loft, for storage.

Exceptions: In several types of double constructions involving elliptical elements, the *final* member (either coördinate or dependent) may omit forms imperfectly supplied by the first. Study the following examples carefully; observe that in the corrected versions the elliptical elements, whether grammatically parallel with the first clause or introduced by *if,* come *at the end of the whole construction.*

WRONG: Smith has as much seniority [omitted word: *as*], or perhaps more *than,* Brown.

Smith has one of the longest [omitted word: *records*], if not quite the longest *record,* of service in his company.

Or: Smith has one of the longest, if not quite the longest [omitted word: *record*], *records* of service in his company.

Smith never has [omitted word: *worked*] and never will *work* for any other employer.

RIGHT: Smith has as much seniority as Brown, perhaps more.

Smith has one of the longest records of service in his company, if not quite the longest.

Smith never has worked for any other employer and never will.

Note: With a series requiring use of the indefinite article, the form (whether *a* or *an*) that happens to occur first may serve for the entire series if no ambiguity results, or the article may be repeated with each member of the series.

RIGHT: a Gould ram, a storage reservoir, and an impulse turbine.

Or: a Gould ram, storage reservoir, and impulse turbine.

AMBIGUOUS (if separate units): a generator and oscillator.
CLEAR (two units): a generator and an oscillator.

52. Comparisons must be logically expressed. The following illustrations show various forms of illogical and logical comparison. See also G 17; G 39; and the examples, exclusive of the last, under *Exceptions* to G 51.

WRONG: A Diesel can operate at the *highest* thermal efficiency of *any other* internal-combustion engine (*or:* of *all other* internal-combustion engines).

Or: A Diesel can operate at *higher* thermal efficiency than *any* internal-combustion engine (*or:* than *all* internal-combustion engines).

RIGHT: A Diesel can operate at the *highest* thermal efficiency of *all* internal-combustion engines.

Or: A Diesel can operate at *higher* thermal efficiency than *any other* internal-combustion engine.

But (if true): A Diesel can operate at higher thermal efficiency than any external-combustion engine.

WRONG: Pavlov's *international reputation* was as great as any other *Russian scientist.*

RIGHT: *Pavlov's* international reputation was as great as any other *Russian scientist's.* (Repetition of "international reputation" is understood after "scientist's.")

Or: Pavlov's international reputation was as great as *that* of any other Russian scientist. (The pronoun "that" is understood to mean "[the] international reputation.")

WRONG: Because she thinks *fastest* but he has the *most retentive* memory, they prefer opposite kinds of tests.

RIGHT: Because she thinks *faster* but he has the *more retentive* memory, they prefer opposite kinds of tests. (The comparative degree of adjectives and adverbs, not the superlative, is employed in a comparison between only two persons or things.)

WRONG: more (*or:* most) unique(ly), perfect(ly), extinct, circular, etc. (Adjectives and adverbs that express absolute qualities or conditions have no comparative and superlative degrees. *Unique,* for instance, means "the only one of its kind"; since there are no degrees of oneness, nothing can properly be termed "more unique" or "uniquer" than something else, or the "most unique" or "uniquest" of a group. Similarly, the pterodactyl is not "more extinct" than the dodo, nor is one circle among several the "most circular.")

RIGHT (according to exact meaning): unique, more (*or:* most) nearly unique, more (*or:* most) unusual, remarkable, strange, etc.; perfect(ly), more (*or:* most) nearly perfect(ly), more (*or:* most) excellent(ly), skillful(ly), beautiful(ly), etc.; extinct, longer (*or:* longest) extinct, more (*or:* most) nearly extinct; circular, more (*or:* most) nearly circular. (See also Rule 2 under G 53.)

WRONG: more better; even more earlier; more (*or:* most) preferable; worser; fartherest (*or:* furtherest).

RIGHT: better (*or:* still better); even earlier; preferable, more (*or:* most) desirable; worse; farthest (*or:* furthest). (*Note:* The comparative and superlative *farther* and *farthest* normally pertain to physical distance; the corresponding *further* and *furthest,* to time or degree.)

53. Meaning limits the use of particular words in grammatical constructions. Note the following rules:

1. Because the intensives *so, such,* and *too* have a relative rather than self-expressed meaning, they should not be employed unless their sense is completed by a *clause or phrase of specification.* (Vague use of these words without completion, common in casual speech, should not be extended to any form of serious communication, written or oral.)

WRONG: A compass is *so important* to the camper.

What you say is *so convincing.*

Water supply becomes difficult because the region has *such extremely dry summers.*

We had *such luck.*

The problem was *too difficult.*

RIGHT: A compass is *very* (or: *extremely;* etc.) *important* to the camper.

What you say is *convincing.*

Or: What you say is *so convincing that I must grant your conclusions.*

Water supply becomes difficult because the region has *extremely dry summers.*

We had *extraordinary* luck.

Or: We had *such luck as we could never expect again.*

Or: We had *such luck that we were greatly encouraged.*

The problem was *too difficult for the time allowed* (or: *to be solved in the time allowed*).

Or: The problem was too difficult *for me* (or: *for me to solve without help*).

Exception: Sometimes a context, by clearly indicating the special bearing of *so, such,* or *too,* renders a completing clause or phrase unnecessary. For instance, immediately following mention or description

41

of the herringbone gear, the reference of the words "such gears" at the beginning of the next sentence would, of course, be self-evident.

Note: Avoid the exasperating *not too* locution. At best, while supposedly conveying information, it wastes the reader's or listener's time by stating the obvious; at worst, it is a mask to conceal ignorance or uncertainty.

UNCOMMUNICATIVE: The ground transportation system of Peru is *not too well developed.* (The sentence merely denies what no one would affirm, for transportation is never *too* well developed anywhere.)

INFORMATIVE (if true): The ground transportation system of Peru is poorly developed. (A better revision would either present specific data or make comparisons with other transportation systems.)

EVASIVE: I *don't* know *too much* about governmental regulation of business before the Industrial Revolution.

CANDID: I know almost nothing about governmental regulation of business before the Industrial Revolution.

INDEFINITE: To prevent sticking of the cubes in the freezing compartment, do *not* fill the trays *too full.*

EXPLICIT: To prevent sticking of the cubes in the freezing compartment, do not fill the trays over three quarters full.

2. As direct modifiers of adjectives and adverbs that express absolute qualities or conditions, the intensives *so, such,* and *too*—even though completed in the manner prescribed by Rule 1—and adverbs of the type of *very, unusually, extremely,* or *highly* are illogical.

WRONG: Their strength is *so equal* that either may be used.
The overtones were reproduced *very perfectly.*

RIGHT: Their strength is so *nearly* equal that either may be used.
The overtones were reproduced perfectly.
Or: The overtones were reproduced *almost* perfectly.
Or: The overtones were reproduced with high fidelity.

3. By a peculiarity of function, the adverbs *very* and *too* may qualify adjectives and other adverbs but not verbs; consequently, only participles that are wholly or predominantly adjectival in function may correctly take *very* or *too* as a direct modifier. Mistakes seldom are made except with past participles. (Present participles, especially

when standing before nouns, have much greater tendency to exercise a distinctly adjectival function.)

WRONG: very pleased; too destroyed; very (*or:* too) sprung.

RIGHT: very much (*or:* well) pleased; too thoroughly destroyed; very (*or:* too) badly sprung.

RIGHT (with distinctly adjectival participles): very pleasing; very drunk; too confusing; too crowded.

Caution: Review Rule 1 of G 53, on the necessary completion of *too.*

4. The adverb *quite* properly means "absolutely," "totally," or "positively"; therefore, it should not modify an adjective or adverb that expresses a relative quality or condition.

WRONG: quite fast, remote(ly), efficient(ly), brief(ly), often, hot, troublesome, etc.

RIGHT (according to exact meaning): extremely fast, unusually fast, over half an hour fast; remotely, very remotely; thirty per cent efficient, highly efficient; etc.

Note: Such expressions as *quite a large number* are literally meaningless, and *quite a few* ("positively a few") contradicts the intended sense. Avoid the *quite a* formula in all serious communication.

RIGHT: many; a large (*or:* considerable) number; an exceedingly (*or:* extremely; etc.) large number; more than a dozen; about twenty; 987; nearly a thousand.

5. Rightly used, the subordinating conjunction *because* introduces statements of actual cause; the coördinating conjunction *for,* on the other hand, introduces statements of evidence or explanation.

WRONG: The Acme Company has prospered greatly, because the firm is soon to take the lease of an entire block. (The projected lease shows the flourishing state of the firm, but obviously it has not *caused* that existing prosperity.)

RIGHT: The Acme Company has prospered greatly, for the firm is soon to take the lease of an entire block.

ALSO RIGHT (with logical assignment of cause): Because the Acme Company has prospered greatly, the firm is soon to take the lease of an entire block.

Caution: Review G 48, concerning misuse of *because* to introduce constructions that function as subjects or predicate complements.

6. The subordinating conjunction *while* is correct only when the time of the dependent clause is the same as that of the main clause and their simultaneous occurrence is an important point of the sentence. Substitution of *while* for a coördinating conjunction (*but* or *and*) is always improper.

RIGHT: The mixer is in continuous operation while concrete is being poured.

WRONG: While his formal schooling was brief, private study finally made him one of the notable scholars of his time.

RIGHT: Although his formal schooling was brief, private study finally made him one of the notable scholars of his time.
  But: While (*or:* Although) his formal schooling was brief, it laid a solid foundation for later private study.

ABSURD: Lamarck was born in 1744, Darwin was born in 1809, while Huxley was born in 1825.

RIGHT: Lamarck was born in 1744, Darwin in 1809, and Huxley in 1825.
  But: Lamarck, who died in 1829, finished his long life while Darwin was but a youth and Huxley was a mere child.

POOR: To most Americans the only possible terms are *truck* and *gasoline,* while *lorry* and *petrol* would be natural to an Englishman.

RIGHT: To most Americans the only possible terms are *truck* and *gasoline,* but (*or:* whereas) *lorry* and *petrol* would be natural to an Englishman.
But: The United States Navy mainly guarded the Pacific Ocean, while (*or:* whereas) the British fleet was concentrated in Mediterranean and Atlantic waters.

7. Arbitrary or blundering use of one part of speech for another is a menace to good English. The grammatical flexibility of our language tolerates a limited shifting of words from one function to another. (Nouns, especially, often come to be employed as other parts of speech; conversely, many nouns originally were verbs.) Hence, the line between impropriety and acceptable usage is sometimes hard to draw, but crudities of the kind illustrated in the following examples are indefensible. See also G 16 and G 17 and, on discrimination of adjectives and adverbs, G 37–41.

WRONG: to *suspicion* [noun for verb]; an *invite* [verb for noun]; try *and* do it [conjunction for preposition, introducing an infinitive]; *except* (or: *without*) they did it [preposition for conjunction]; report *immediately* you arrive [adverb for conjunction]; should (*or:* would) *of* done it [preposition for verb]; I *use* [i.e., formerly] to go [noun for verb]; to be *judge* severely [noun for participle].

RIGHT: to *suspect;* an *invitation;* try *to* do it; *unless* they did it (or: *except that* they did it; *without their having done* it) ; report *as soon as* you arrive (*or:* report *immediately upon* your arrival) ; should (*or:* would) *have* done it; I *used* to go; to be *judged* severely.

CHAPTER III

PROBLEMS OF DICTION

The building blocks of a language are the spoken or written words assembled to form its patterns of communication. Chapter II has treated of grammar, or the correct inflection and ordering of these elements in the English language. The present chapter is concerned with words as such, or diction: with spelling, with pronunciation, and with meaning and choice.

Diction and the dictionary. A dictionary, as its name implies, is a handbook of diction. It is as indispensable to efficient use of language as a table of logarithms is to mathematical·calculations, or the telephone book to the dialing of connections. The dictionary is not just a tool for student days, to be discarded after English has been, supposedly, mastered. No one obtains such mastery even in a lifetime; no one, even by the most concentrated study, could learn all that is to be known about English diction. Every engineer commits himself to unceasing use of the slide rule so long as he practices his profession. The dictionary is a similarly enduring tool that should be employed with the same diligence and for the same purpose, the obtaining of reliable information. A mistake in language is as reprehensible as a blunder in mathematics, and guessing is equally stupid in both.

Choice among dictionaries. Nothing can take the place of a good dictionary; almost nothing is so unsatisfactory as a poor one. When you purchase a dictionary, seek the advice of someone who fully understands the difference. Do not expect the cost of the recommended book to be less than several dollars, for production of a first-class dictionary at cut prices is impossible.

Desk dictionaries. The following compact or abridged dictionaries are all good. Since revisions are made from time to time, a copy bearing a recent date should be obtained.

(1) *Webster's New Collegiate Dictionary*, G. & C. Merriam Company. (A recently revised abridgment of *Webster's New International Dictionary*.) Only the G. & C. Merriam Company of Springfield, Massachusetts, publishes the genuine Webster's dictionaries: i.e., those in direct and continuous line of succession to the work of Noah Webster (1758–1843).

(2) *New College Standard Dictionary* (EM·PHA·TYPE Edition), Funk & Wagnalls Company. (The name of this latest revision is from a new system used for indicating pronunciation.)

(3) *The Winston Dictionary* (College Edition), The John C. Winston Company. (Formerly called *The Winston Simplified Dictionary*.)

(4) *The New Century Dictionary*, D. Appleton-Century Company. (Two vols.; larger than other desk dictionaries.)

(5) *The American College Dictionary* (Text Edition), Harper & Brothers. (A new publication; especially useful for recent technical words.)

(6) *The Concise Oxford Dictionary*, Oxford University (Clarendon) Press. (Shows British usages.)

Unabridged dictionaries. Larger dictionaries than those listed above are available for reference in libraries. They include:

(1) *Webster's New International Dictionary*.

(2) *New Standard Dictionary*.

(3) *A New English Dictionary*, generally known as *The Oxford English Dictionary*. (Ten vols., in twenty parts, plus supplement; the greatest of all dictionaries of English; shows British usages.) *The Shorter Oxford English Dictionary* (two vols.) is a very much larger abridgment of this work than *The Concise Oxford Dictionary*, entered as (6) in the preceding list.

Note: *A Dictionary of American English* (four vols.) is not an ordinary general dictionary, as by intention it disregards the major element of international English in the American vocabulary and investigates only those expressions originated or principally used in this country, or otherwise peculiarly related to the national life and history. It is a valuable reference work to supplement the British *Oxford*, mentioned just above.

THE PROBLEM OF SPELLING

"I never could spell." The first thing observed and judged by readers of any written composition is the spelling. Many students

seem to imagine that the familiar refrain, "I never could spell," is somehow a charm against the perils of orthography; they delude nobody except themselves. Good spellers are not endowed with a special faculty. They have simply done a job which, sooner or later, everyone who uses English must do: they have *learned* to spell.

Importance of a spelling list. The total vocabulary of the English language includes several hundred thousand separate words, of which any one person uses only a tiny fraction. Obviously, a prime step toward the mastery of spelling is the discovery by the learner of his own *active* diction, consisting of those several hundred or few thousand words, selected from the enormous resources of English, which he himself employs. (The number passively understood when written or spoken by others—including, of course, all those of the active vocabulary—always is very much larger.) A list such as that given at the end of this chapter (D 24) can be helpful to users of this book, but only as a basic group of words to which each student must make a great many additions, especially as relating to his own particular field of science or technology. No list, however large and carefully compiled, may ever be regarded as complete and final, for an individual vocabulary should never cease to grow.

Three classes of words. If you will analyze your own active vocabulary, you will find that the words fall into three groups with respect to spelling: (1) Probably the great majority will be expressions you are able to spell with complete assurance of accuracy, because you have previously learned them and have perfected the knowledge of their form by frequent repetition. (2) At the opposite extreme will be a small class of terms that you require only on rare occasions, perhaps only once or twice a year. In all likelihood you are uncertain of their exact spelling; possibly you would spell most of them right, but you would be conscious of guessing or relying on vague memory. (3) In between will lie a third group, smaller than the first but much larger than the second, of words habitually employed but not yet perfectly learned. Expressions of this class, which may number two or three hundred or even more, are the cause of most of your difficulty with spelling. What is the relative position of the *i* and *e* in *seize, believe, either,* and *receive?* How many medial *e's* are there in *precede, proceed,* and *procedure?* Do *inexhaustible* and *indispensable,* or *feasible* and *utilizable,* end in *ible* or *able?* Unanswered questions of these kinds are mainly at the root of your problem of spelling.

What to do. Various words must be treated differently according to the groups, as just outlined, into which they fall.

Classes (1) and (2): A word that really belongs to Class (1) can give no difficulty. However, suspicion of habitual spellings is a healthy state of mind, since a strong danger exists that mistakes confidently repeated may become ingrained and, in consequence, extremely difficult to correct. (As an instance, a student, having written a long paper on what he called military "court-martials," flatly rejected the plural form "courts-martial" when it was called to his attention, on the ground that he was right and the dictionary wrong.) On the rare occasions when words of Class (2) must be written, a dictionary *invariably* should be consulted. Guesswork is unintelligent, and saves almost no time if a desk dictionary is kept at hand during all written composition.

Class (3): Since this class consists of words needed frequently but not yet mastered, each word must either be individually learned or be verified from a dictionary every time it is set down on paper. The latter process will, perhaps, eventually bring about mastery, but it is uneconomical. On the other hand, no one can memorize the spelling of several hundred difficult words simultaneously. If you try to do so, you certainly will fail, and thus confirm the feeling that learning to spell is at best mysterious and at worst hopeless. What you should do is to learn *a* word, *one* word, *any* word from Class (3) of your own list; afterwards, another; and so on over as long a time as may be required. Study each word separately in a deliberate act of memory, with special attention to the combination of letters involving the chief difficulty.* Do not neglect *repetition* and *review* as important, related factors of the memorizing process. Adopt a regular schedule and follow it. If you will learn just one word every night for a year, well over three hundred words will have shifted from Class (3) to Class (1). Meanwhile, of course, and for the rest of your life, too, you must look up unlearned words whenever you have occasion to write them, but this need for the dictionary will grow markedly less burdensome as you continue to commit to memory your habitual vocabulary. By building on what you already know and memorizing single words at *regular* intervals, in a few months you can be an excellent speller. If you wait for the art to come to you spontaneously, you will remain a poor speller to the end of your days.

1. Spelling rules. Thus far, the rules of spelling have been passed over as if nonexistent. They are, indeed, of very limited value: col-

* You may even find that gross mispronunciation (in privacy) of certain words according to their spelling, e.g., "resist-*ance*" and "exist-*ence*," can be of help in fixing the orthography. (Avoid using this trick if you find that your public pronunciation shows the slightest tendency to suffer as a consequence.)

lectively, they cover but a small part of the English vocabulary, and many are so qualified by exceptions as to be practically worthless. The familiar rule about "*i* before *e* except after *c* or when the sound is 'ay' as in *weigh*," for example, has been faithfully learned by generations of students, all of whom eventually have discovered that it is unreliable because of the large proportion of exceptions among common words. No matter how this rule is refined or qualified, it cannot be made serviceable as a substitute for the dictionary; and the same admission would have to be made concerning most other spelling rules for English. Experience shows that only a few are of genuine value, either because they have no exceptions at all, or else because those that occur (cf. the *Exceptions* under D 4 and 5) are relatively few or self-evident.

Caution: These rules are helpful only if mastered. A half-understood rule is *worse* than useless—worse because it may lend spurious authority to an incorrect spelling, resulting from misapplication of the rule. Each rule governs a definite spelling situation, and under no circumstances are the different situations or rules interchangeable. In learning a rule, concentrate first on the precise total situation (shown in CAPITALS) to which it is applicable; then study its action within that situation (shown in ordinary print). Think the rules through, and keep applying them to various words that pass through your mind or occur in the course of your actual writing.

2. WHEN A SUFFIX BEGINNING WITH e, i, OR y IS ADDED TO A WORD ENDING IN c, PROVIDED THE c RETAINS ITS "k" SOUND, a *k* is inserted between the final *c* of the original word and the suffix of the derivative.

EXAMPLES: *shellac* plus *ed* gives *shellacked; traffic* plus *ing* gives *trafficking; picnic* plus *er* gives *picnicker; panic* plus *y* gives *panicky.*

3. WHEN A SUFFIX BEGINNING WITH A CONSONANT IS ADDED TO A WORD ENDING IN A CONSONANT, PROVIDED A TRIPLE LETTER WOULD NOT RESULT, all letters of the original word and of the suffix are retained without change.

EXAMPLES: *govern* plus *ment* gives *government; even* plus *ness* gives *evenness; final* plus *ly* gives *finally.*

But: full plus *ly* gives *fully* (not "fullly"); *shrill* plus *ly* gives *shrilly*; *will* plus *less* gives *will-less* or (rarely) *willess.* (English spelling does not admit a triple letter: i.e., the same letter written three times in succession without a space, a hyphen, or an apostrophe. The sole consonant that ever happens to fall under this ban, so far as D 3 is concerned, is *l*. If the suffix is *ly*, only two *l*'s are retained in the derivative; if the suffix is *less*, the preferred spelling is that illustrated by *will-less*, but an unhyphenated form with only two *l*'s also is permissible.)

Note 1: For the application of D 3, it is important to be sure of the spelling of the suffix, which is not necessarily the same as that of a similar independent word. In particular, the suffix *ful* should not be erroneously written with double *l*.

EXAMPLES: *faithful* (not "faithfull"); *spoonful* or *spoonfuls* (not "spoonfull" or "spoonfulls").

Note 2: Some derivatives of words ending in double *l* have two accepted forms, one regular and the other irregular: e.g., *skillful, skilful; dullness, dulness; installment, instalment*. However, the regular form retaining the double *l* is uniformly preferred in American usage.

Note 3: The verb *fulfill* (also spelled *fulfil*) may appear to be an exception, since the spelling "fullfill" (or "fullfil") with two medial *l*'s does not occur. In point of fact, *fill* (or *fil*) is not a suffix; therefore D 3 is inapplicable. *Fulfill* (from Anglo-Saxon *fulfyllan*) has been an independent word throughout the history of English.

4. WHEN A SUFFIX BEGINNING WITH A VOWEL IS ADDED TO A WORD ENDING IN SILENT e, the originally final *e* is retained only if the *e* is preceded by *c* or *g* and *at the same time* the suffix begins with *a* or *o;* otherwise the *e* is dropped in the new word.

EXAMPLES (*e* retained between *c* or *g* and *a* or *o*): *notice* plus *ably* gives *noticeably; manage* plus *able* gives *manageable; outrage* plus *ous* gives *outrageous.*

EXAMPLES (*e* dropped): *notice* plus *ing* gives *noticing; manage* plus *er* gives *manager; outrage* plus *ed* gives *outraged; receive* plus *able* gives *receivable; membrane* plus *ous* gives *membranous; stone* plus *y* gives *stony.*

Exceptions: A few derivative words ending in *ing* or *y* are exceptions to this rule. In each the retention of the originally final *e* (contrary to the rule) is for an obvious purpose of showing the pronunciation or of preventing confusion with another, more common word. These exceptions, therefore, cause little or no trouble.

51

EXAMPLES: *hoeing* (not "hoing"); *singeing* (cf. *singing*); *dyeing* (cf. *dying*); *gluey* (not "gluy").

Note: Some words falling under D 4, mostly ending in *able*, have two accepted forms, one regular and the other irregular: e.g., *sizable, sizeable; likable, likeable; usable, useable.* The regular spelling of such words (e.g., *sizable, likable, usable*) is always correct and almost always preferred, but in an insignificant number the irregular form is the more usual. Thus *mileage* is preferred to *milage* (which, however, is also an acceptable spelling); and of the alternative forms *mortgagor* and *mortgager,* the former (irregular) is more common than the latter (regular).

5. WHEN A SUFFIX BEGINNING WITH A VOWEL IS ADDED TO A WORD ENDING IN ANY CONSONANT EXCEPT c OR x, PROVIDED THE HEAVY ACCENT (main syllabic stress) OF THE ORIGINAL WORD DOES NOT SHIFT TO A DIFFERENT SYLLABLE IN THE DERIVATIVE, the originally final consonant is doubled if the following two conditions are met, *but unless both are fulfilled it is not doubled:*

(1) if the originally final consonant is *immediately* preceded by a *single vowel;* and

(2) if the heavy accent is on the originally final syllable. (*Note:* The only syllable of a monosyllabic word is, of course, "final.")

EXAMPLES (consonant doubled): *occúr* plus *ence* gives *occúrrence; refér* plus *ing* gives *reférring; sít* plus *er* gives *sítter; dróp* plus *ed* gives *drópped; flát* plus *en* gives *flátten; wét* plus *est* gives *wéttest; annúl* plus *able* gives *annúllable; tín* plus *y* gives *tínny.*

EXAMPLES (consonant not doubled because immediately preceded by another consonant instead of by a vowel): *talk* plus *ing* gives *talking; sing* plus *er* gives *singer; afford* plus *ed* gives *afforded; inform* plus *ant* gives *informant.*

EXAMPLES (consonant not doubled because preceded by two vowels instead of by a single vowel): *join* plus *ing* gives *joining; reveal* plus *er* gives *revealer; defraud* plus *ed* gives *defrauded; weak* plus *en* gives *weaken; ruin* plus *ous* gives *ruinous; appear* plus *ance* gives *appearance; room* plus *y* gives *roomy.*

EXAMPLES (consonant not doubled because stress is not on originally final syllable): *differ* plus *ence* gives *difference; óffer* plus *ing* gives *óffering; príson* plus *er* gives *prísoner; póison* plus *ed* gives *póisoned; équal* plus *ize* gives *équalize; solícit* plus *ous* gives *solícitous; prófit* plus *able* gives *prófitable.*

Exceptions: Among the many thousands of words falling under D 5, a small number of exceptions occurs. Examples are *gáseous* (not "gasseous"), *húmbugged* and *húmbugging* (not "humbuged" and "humbuging," because a single *g*, although expected from the accent on the first syllable, would falsely suggest a "j" sound), *inférable, transférable, crýstallize,* and *crýstalline.* (The last two mentioned are not, in actuality, exceptions to the rule, for they are not directly derived from the word *crystal.* Nevertheless, for practical purposes they must be learned as exceptions.)

Note 1: As can be seen from the EXAMPLES, D 5 is fully as important for words in which an originally final consonant is not doubled as for those in which doubling occurs. Some words, mostly with accent on the first syllable and stem ending in *l*, have two correct spellings (e.g., *tráveling, trávelling; tráveler, tráveller; tráveled, trávelled; équaling, équalling; équaled, équalled; márvelous, márvellous*). However, in American usage the regular form of such words (*tráveling, tráveler, équaled, márvelous,* etc.; also *cárburetor, kídnaper,* etc.) is always correct and generally preferred.

Note 2: Be sure to observe that D 5 *does not apply when the position of the principal accent shifts.* If the heaviest stress of the voice falls on different syllables in the original word and derivative, a dictionary must be consulted for the spelling of the latter. This problem of shifting accent (which, luckily, does not occur very often) is illustrated in the following words: *équal* plus *ity* gives *equálity; métal* plus *ic* gives *metállic; súlphur* plus *ic* gives *sulphúric; cáncel* plus *ation* gives *cancellátion; dáctyl* plus *ology* gives *dactylólogy; refér, prefér,* or *confér* plus *ence* gives *réference, préference,* or *cónference.* Note, however, that in *reférring* and *reférred* (from *refér*), *prefér-ring* and *preférred* (from *prefér*), *conférring* and *conférred* (from *confér*), *occúrring, occúrred,* and *occúrrence* (from *occúr*), and *óffering* and *óffered* (from *óffer*) the accent does not shift; therefore, the *r* is doubled or not doubled in accordance with the rule.

Note 3: The letters *y* and *w* never are doubled. Following a vowel they do not function as consonants, but as vowels (called semi-vowels), in that they blend to form a simple or diphthongal sound with the preceding vowel: e.g., *gray(ing), throw(er), gnaw(ed), annoy(ance).*

Note 4: Observe that D 5 does not cover words ending in *x* or *c*. Final *x*, which always represents two consonant sounds ("ks"), never is doubled when a suffix is added. Final *c*, also, never is doubled before a suffix; rather, a *k* is inserted if D 2 applies. (Thus, *shellac* plus *er* gives *shellacker*, not "shellaccer.")

Note 5: If the original word ends in a double consonant, the suffix is simply attached as one or more added syllables, since no further doubling can take place. When an originally single consonant is doubled before a suffix, the syllabic division is between the duplicate letters. Thus, whereas *misspelling* (from *misspell*) would be divided after the second *l* if split at the end of a line, *propelling* (from *propel*) or *expelling* (from *expel*) would be divided between *l's*. (The three words cited also could be broken, respectively, between the *s's*, after the *o*, and after the *x*: viz., *mis·spell·ing, pro·pel·ling, ex·pel·ling*.) For separation (between lines of writing) of inflectional *ed* and *es* from the stem of a word, see P 22b in Chapter IV.

6. WHEN s IS ADDED TO A WORD ENDING IN y, the combination of *y* plus *s* becomes *ies* if the *y* is preceded by a consonant, but remains *ys* if the *y* is preceded by a vowel.

EXAMPLES (*y* preceded by a consonant) : *cry* plus *s* gives *cries; apply* plus *s* gives *applies; deny* plus *s* gives *denies; ally* plus *s* gives *allies*.

EXAMPLES (*y* preceded by a vowel) : *relay* plus *s* gives *relays; deploy* plus *s* gives *deploys; alley* plus *s* gives *alleys*.

Note 1: Because the letter *u* following *q* is pronounced as a consonant (equivalent to *w*), *quy* plus *s* becomes *quies;* otherwise, however, *uy* plus *s* becomes *uys*. Thus *colloquy* plus *s* gives *colloquies*, but *buy* plus *s* gives *buys*.

Note 2: Be sure to understand that D 6 applies to verbs inflected with *s* in the third person singular of the present indicative (e.g., *he flies*), as well as to plural nouns (e.g., *houseflies*).

Note 3: A limited but minor rule concerning words terminating in *y* is as follows: WHEN A SUFFIX BEGINNING WITH A VOWEL IS ADDED TO A WORD ENDING IN *y* PRECEDED BY A CONSONANT, the *y* is changed to *i* in the derivative, except that before *i* it is retained as *y*.*

EXAMPLES (*y* changed to *i*) : *rectify* plus *er* gives *rectifier; deny* plus *ed* gives *denied; apply* plus *ance* gives *appliance*.

* For words in which the *y* is preceded by a vowel or in which the suffix begins with a consonant, no definite rule can be given.

54

(When alternative forms are correct—as *drier, dryer; driest, dryest*—the regular spelling with *i* in place of *y* is preferred.)

EXAMPLES (*y* retained before *i*): *applying; rectifying; denying; babyish; Toryism.*

7. Other aids to correct spelling. Three means to improvement of spelling have been recommended in the foregoing discussion: using the dictionary, memorizing individual words (from a personal list of expressions commonly employed), and learning the rules governing certain methods of forming derivatives from stems of known spelling. In addition, several kinds of attentiveness—to the writings of others, and to the form and sound of difficult or frequently confused words—also can be beneficial.

Attention to written texts. Hasty, careless skimming of written matter has little or no value for the mastery of spelling, but *observant* reading does much good. Remember, however, that bad spelling often gets into print, especially in newspapers and other forms of journalism. Be critical of what you read, with respect to superficial form, typified by spelling and punctuation, as well as to deeper considerations of content and logic. Use of the dictionary and wide reading are mutually helpful toward command of vocabulary (including spelling); neither is a substitute for the other.

Attention to pronunciation. The spelling of English is very far from being perfectly phonetic, as it would be if every sound were uniformly written and every spelling were uniformly pronounced. Nevertheless, despite serious inconsistencies between speech and spelling, including a general tendency of completely unstressed syllables to become reduced to a neutral blur while retaining a spelling indicative of their former sounds, accurate pronunciation is a real aid to correct writing. Many common errors of spelling result from the confusion, insertion, omission, or transposition of consonants, and many others from the dropping or adding of a whole syllable. Gross blunders of these kinds almost invariably can be prevented by careful sounding. Anyone is sure to have trouble with spelling if he says "incidently" or "evidentally" for *incidentally* or *evidently,* "excape" for *escape,* "mathmatics" for *mathematics,* or "heighth" for *height.*

8. Attention to similar words. The more nearly alike two or several different words are, the more liable they are to be misspelled through confusion of one with another. Expressions such as the following (especially those groups in which the sound is identical or closely similar) must be consciously distinguished, with persistent reference to the dictionary:

accept (receive), *except* (omit)

adopt, adapt (verb: [to] adjust), *adept* (adjective: skillful)

advice, device, and *prophecy* (nouns), *advise, devise,* and *prophesy* (verbs)

affect (verb: [to] modify or influence; [to] cultivate for display), *effect* (verb: [to] bring about), *effect* (noun)

already, all ready

altogether, all together

amateur, armature

antidote (remedy), *anecdote* (story)

bear, bare

benzene (C_6H_6), *benzine* (mixture of hydrocarbons)

break, brake

calorimeter, colorimeter

canvas (noun: cloth), *canvass* (noun and verb: solicitation or [to] solicit; detailed examination or [to] examine in detail)

capitol (noun: government building), *capital* (noun: chief city; property or funds; top of a column), *capital* (adjective)

compliment, complement

congenial (harmonious), *congenital* (from birth)

conscious, conscience, consciousness, conscientious

counsel (noun and verb: advice or [to] advise), *council* (noun: deliberative group), *consul* (noun: governmental agent)

course, coarse

credible (believable), *creditable* (worthy), *credulous* (gullible)

dextrose (sugar), *dextrorse* (twining to the right)

duly, dully

eight, eighth

entomology (science of insects), *etymology* (derivation of words)

formerly, formally

gorilla (ape), *guerrilla* (fighter in occupied territory) *grate, great*

hoard (noun and verb: [to] store), *horde* (noun: clan or crowd)

illusion, allusion, allude, elude, illusory, allusive, elusive

imminent (impending), *eminent* (distinguished), *immanent* (inherent), *emanate* (verb: [to] issue)

ingenious (clever or inventive), *ingenuous* (frank, naïve), *ingenuity, ingenuousness*

lead (noun: metal), *lead* (verb: present tense; noun), *led* (verb: past tense and past participle)

martial (of war), *marital* (of marriage)

oral (of the mouth), *aural* (of the ear)

perform, preform

plain, plane

practical (well adapted to the end in view), *practicable* (workable)

precedence (singular noun: right to precede), *precedents* (plural noun: prior instances), *precede* (verb: [to] go ahead of), *proceed* (verb: [to] go forward or continue)

principle (noun: general rule), *principal* (noun: invested funds; headmaster of a school), *principal* (adjective)

quite, quiet

raise, raze (demolish)

resin, rosin (resin from turpentine)

respectful(ly), respective(ly), respectable, respectably

sewage (content of sewers), *sewerage* (system of sewers)

stationary (adjective: fixed), *stationery* (noun: writing materials)

statue (image), *statute* (law), *stature* (height)

than, then

there, their

threw, through, thorough, though, thought

tinny (like tin), *tiny*

to, two, too

veneer, vernier

voltmeter, voltameter, voltammeter

THE PROBLEM OF PRONUNCIATION

Spelling and pronunciation are twin problems. Just as the first and most obvious test of a writer's literacy is his spelling, so a speaker is instantly judged by his pronunciation. If he says "cain't," "gittin," "genuwine," "ketch," or "ex-spearmint" (*experiment*), nobody will expect wisdom to accompany the bad diction. Although snap judgments of this kind are in a measure unfair, they contain a real element of justice. Intelligence is a general quality, and a person wise enough to know a subject ought to be wise enough to communicate it in correct language.

9. *Mutual relation of pronunciation and spelling.* As has been pointed out, careful pronunciation is an important means to mastery of spelling. Attention to spelling is equally helpful to pronunciation. Both problems are complicated by our badly unphonetic spelling; nevertheless, a fairly close correlation of spoken and written forms does exist with respect to consonants, stressed vowels, and number of syllables in a word. Perhaps more important is the fact that any deliberate effort to perfect either spelling or pronunciation promotes the habit of attending also to the other.

Dangers. Despite the relationship just noted, habitually faulty pronunciation is even more widespread than generally bad spelling. An incorrectly written word is visible and semipermanent, inviting examination and criticism, but a word wrongly spoken is gone with the breath by which it is uttered. Errors of pronunciation, much more easily than those of spelling, can become chronic without ever being recognized as problems; the poor speller usually knows that he is having trouble, but the poor speaker may honestly believe that his pronunciation is flawless. Because of the danger of complacency, self-criticism is of utmost importance. You must be willing to face the unpleasant fact that probably some, perhaps many, of your most inveterate pronunciations are violations of good English. If you take the attitude that whatever you say must be right (because you say it), you are throwing away almost all chance of developing your sense of pronunciation beyond its present stage.

What to do. Just as in all problems of diction, in pronunciation the key to the door of accuracy is the dictionary. Listening to the speech of others is seriously limited in value—much more so than reading of texts for the perfection of spelling. Practically all errors of pronunciation are acquired by conscious or unconscious imitation of associates. You can, of course, find speakers who are worthy of emulation, but you will soon discover that even they are not infallible. To acquire a sound pronunciation without constant recourse to a good dictionary is impossible. Look up several words every day: words from your reading, words you hear spoken (to verify the pronunciation given them by the speakers), words for which you know you will have need in your own formal or informal speech. The beneficial effect on your pronunciation will be immediate and will increase with great rapidity.

9a. *Diacritical symbols.* As has been mentioned in connection with the problem of spelling, the number of words that any one person uses, out of the hundreds of thousands available from the total vocabulary of English, is relatively small; and, on the whole, a pronunciation can be more quickly learned than a written form. The secret lies in understanding the diacritical and related marks employed by the dictionary consulted. Every general dictionary of modern English indicates sounds and stress by its own method, fully explained somewhere in the book (usually in the preliminary pages) and commonly synopsized on the top or bottom of each page of the actual vocabulary. *Learn to use your own dictionary by studying and repeatedly consulting it.* If at first you find the symbols for pronunciation confusing, ask someone familiar with the same dictionary to give you a little help. In a very few minutes you will be able to make effective use of the phonetic signs and transcriptions, and after some practice you will read them almost as rapidly as letters of conventional print. Observe, also, the position of accents as well as the consonantal sounds and the quality of vowels, for mistakes of pronunciation in English often result from throwing stress on syllables that should not be accented (e.g., "cément" for *cemént* or "compárable" for *cómparable*).

Note: Especially helpful, as dealing exclusively with pronunciation, is *A Pronouncing Dictionary of American English* (G. & C. Merriam). Unlike the Merriam-Webster *New International* and *Collegiate,* this dictionary employs for its transcriptions the alphabet of the International Phonetic Association, by means of which the component sounds of words are recorded with scientific accuracy. Many proper names and foreign expressions are entered.

9b. *Regional "accent."* The recognized spelling of American English is almost perfectly homogeneous throughout the country, but regional distinctions of the kind collectively termed "accent," together with some differences in choice and meaning of words, are very evident. In any section, moreover, a wide range of variation divides cultivated from uneducated speech. Grotesque peculiarities of low dialect make national differences appear much greater than they actually are among educated people of various localities. The whole problem of provincial American accents and vocabulary is somewhat delicate; however, the following generalities perhaps will not be questioned:

1. When all members of a group are of the same region, the cultivated speech of that region is appropriate to the whole group.

2. A speaker living in a region to which he is not native should use the cultivated speech either of his native region or of the region in which he lives, or a compromise that avoids the more extreme characteristics of either.

3. The best provincial speech is likely to be employed by professional people, especially those whose work necessitates public or semipublic speaking.

4. Persons whose work touches many sections or the country as a whole often develop a neutral American style of speech, avoiding any definitely provincial intonations and expressions. Everything considered, this tendency is desirable. However, except under extraordinary circumstances, no one should be expected or required to give up the cultivated speech habits of his native region if he prefers to retain them.

Note: See also D 18, *Provincialisms.*

THE PROBLEM OF CHOICE AND MEANING

In the sections beginning on pages 47 and 58, the written and spoken *forms* of words have been considered, each in isolation. Important as these externals are for a respectable command of the language, the deeper question of selecting diction for the precise expression of meaning is of much greater significance.

10. *Accuracy of scientific discourse.*   Science differs from everyday reasoning, not in kind, but in a rigid discipline having strict accuracy as its end. T. H. Huxley put the distinction thus:

> The method of scientific investigation is nothing but the expression of the necessary mode of working of the human mind. It is simply the mode at which all phenomena are reasoned about, rendered precise and exact. There is no more dif-

ference, but there is just the same kind of difference, between the mental operations of a man of science and those of an ordinary person, as there is between the operations and methods of a baker or of a butcher weighing out his goods in common scales, and the operations of a chemist in performing a difficult and complex analysis by means of his balance and finely graduated weights. It is not that the action of the scales in the one case, and the balance in the other, differ in the principles of their construction or manner of working; but the beam of one is set on an infinitely finer axis than the other, and of course turns by the addition of a much smaller weight.*

Similarly, the language of scientific expression, while basically that of ordinary discourse, aims at perfectly exact statement of meaning. Vagueness, emotional coloring, and indirectness are foreign to its purposes; the writer or speaker on pure or technological science fails unless his words, singly and in combination, are appropriate, economical, and unequivocal.

11. *Vocabulary building.* Reading of good texts in any field of interest, listening to informed speakers, and constant use of dictionaries (both general and specialized) are means of developing a vocabulary. The first two mentioned are so obvious as to require no emphasis, but many students overlook the great importance of the last.

The "dictionary habit." Some excellent general dictionaries of English were listed at the beginning of this chapter, and a selected list of dictionaries pertaining to several technical fields of knowledge will be found on pages 239–241 of Chapter IX, under the heading LIMITED ENCYCLOPEDIAS AND DICTIONARIES. When previously unknown expressions are read or heard, they usually are pinned down to their precise application only if a dictionary or similar reference work is consulted. Acquire the dictionary *habit.* A serviceable plan is always to keep ready to hand a piece of paper on which to jot down words to be looked up, with tags such as "sp." (spelling), "pron." (pronunciation), and "def." (definition) as reminders of what information is especially wanted. Later the entire list can be investigated as a group, together with other terms that are certain to suggest themselves by association. Time thus spent pays dividends in increased size and precision of vocabulary.

11a. *Significant parts of words.* The process of learning words

* From "The Method of Scientific Investigation." (See also page 169.)

is greatly speeded by attention to the fundamental meaning of the elements of which they are constructed. The four principal sources of modern English are Anglo-Saxon (Old English), French, Latin, and Greek, of which the latter two are particularly important for scientific nomenclature. However, without formal study of any language other than his own, an intelligent person can discover much about etymology (the derivation of words from earlier elements or sources), by cultivating the faculty of generalization while industriously making use of a good dictionary. Attention should be given to roots (the basic elements of words), to inflectional endings, and to affixes (including so-called combining forms, such as *pseudo, tetra,* and *graph,* as well as prefixes and suffixes in the strict sense, such as *pre, per, ante, in, un, sub, able, ible, ness, ate, ite,* and the like).

11b. *Value of studying etymologies.* Attention should be paid to the way in which words and elements combine to build longer words. To learn, for instance, that *recalcitrant* means "kicking back" evokes a vivid image of the Roman mules to which the Latin original of the word was first applied, and at the same time fixes the meaning (stubborn, ungovernable) permanently in the mind. *Penicillin* is vivified by the knowledge that this late pharmaceutical term is a linguistic cousin of the word *pencil* (in its primary sense of an artist's brush), conveying a suggestion of the shape of certain threadlike, tufted bodies characteristic of molds. Technical nomenclature is often figuratively sesquipedalian ("a foot and a half long")—e.g., *spectrophotometer* or *electrometallurgy*—and occasionally almost literally so —e.g., *tetramethyldiaminodiphenylmethane* or *alkyldioxynaphthalenecarboxylic.* By resolving polysyllables into meaningful parts, generally recognizable in recombination, students of any science find that rote memory need carry only a portion of the burden.

11c. *Synonyms.* The common belief that English has no perfect synonyms (words of identical meaning) can seemingly be refuted by such pairs as *yearly—annual, lousy—pediculous, invaluable—priceless,* and *innumerable (countless)* others. Still, synonyms are more often approximate than exact; generally, the more closely they are studied, the less they are found to overlap in discriminating application. Even true synonyms have a certain difference of suggestive or associative force, technically known as *connotation*—a term opposed to *denotation,* which signifies the literal or strictly intellectual content of words. The distinction is sometimes slight (e.g., *yearly—annual*), sometimes enormous (e.g., *lousy—pediculous*), with all possible gradations between (cf. *final, last, ultimate*). Always, however, it causes one word to be more suitable than another for a given context. In this sense, indeed, no perfect synonyms exist.

11d. *Collections of synonyms and antonyms.* All dictionaries employ the synonym as a definitional device. In addition, some give lists of approximate synonyms, often with brief explanations of their distinctions; and also of antonyms (i.e., words opposed in sense to the one defined at the point of entry). For more thorough investigation of related and contrasted meanings, several special reference works are available, including (in suggested order of utility to university students):

(1) *Webster's Dictionary of Synonyms.* (Carefully discriminates between words of similar meaning; includes antonyms.)

(2) *Roget's Thesaurus of English Words and Phrases.* (Long the standard collection; well indexed and extremely comprehensive; lists synonyms and antonyms in parallel columns; does not give definitions, and so must be used in conjunction with a conventional dictionary.)

(3) *Standard Handbook of Synonyms, Antonyms, and Prepositions.*

(4) *Crabb's English Synonyms.*

(5) *Allen's Synonyms and Antonyms.*

12. Objectionable diction. All diction is not on the same plane of dignity and propriety. The fact that an expression can be found in the dictionary does not necessarily certify it for serious use, since lexicographers record obsolete, illiterate, slangy, and provincial as well as standard forms of the language. (When consulting dictionaries, watch closely for the labels, usually abbreviated, by which substandard status is indicated.) Students of the sciences should recognize that technical discourse is less free than imaginative literature to employ abnormalities of language. The following categories, while only in part mutually exclusive and therefore imperfect as a classification, will serve as warnings against common mistakes that result from either poor choice of the individual word or faulty combination of words (apart from errors of grammar, already treated in Chapter II).

Note: The specialized terminology of any subject, unless it intrinsically lacks dignity,* is not to be regarded as abnormal English when used among practitioners and students of that field. It does become objectionable when addressed to persons who could not understand it without extensive study. For comments on this class of diction in different styles of technical composition review Chapter I from page 5 to the end.

13. *Improprieties.*   Any blunder of language could, of course, be called an impropriety, but in discussions of diction the term indicates misapplication of a word. (Improprieties are thus contrasted to barbarisms, treated in D 14.) The word *job,* for instance, when properly used, always denotes special, occasional, or contract work. In the sense of a regular, continuing employment of permanent or "steady" tenure, *job* is an impropriety; *steady job,* obviously, is a flat contradiction in terms. Still more offensive is the impropriety of using *job* to mean the *result* of completed work, such as an airplane or a coat of paint, rather than work as such. The noun *factor,* as another example, ought not to be vaguely employed to mean an event, experience, or fact; instead, it should be reserved to specify one of a complex of causes operating to produce a certain effect. Similarly, *proposition* ought not to be wrenched out of its normal significance of something formally proposed or asserted, nor should the verb *to contact* be misapplied to persons. Anyone who speaks of *contacting a prospect about a live-wire proposition* is guilty of matricide upon the mother tongue.

Examples of the grammatical error, a form of impropriety, in which one part of speech is wrongly employed for another, are shown at the end of Chapter II (G 53, 7).

14. *Barbarisms.*   Barbarisms are illegitimate coinages from legitimate words, typified by *enthuse* (from *enthusiasm* or *enthusiastic*), *muchly* (from the adverb *much*), and *alright* (from *all right*). Many slangy and vulgar expressions (see D 16) are barbarisms. On the other hand, some barbarisms rise to the status of colloquialisms (see D 15), and may even, in time, become correct English. Nevertheless, habitual use of words crudely coined from others is one

---

* Technical vocabulary, like every segment of English speech, exhibits all levels of dignity, from the literary down to the vulgar. The term *jargon* (which properly means the special diction of any occupational, fraternal, religious, educational, recreational, or other group whose membership is not primarily determined by geography) sometimes is applied as if it referred only to the levels of colloquialisms, slang, and vulgarisms—or the last two alone—instead of to technical vocabulary in general. Since, therefore, the expression might seem to imply condemnation, it is avoided in this book.

of the surest signs of illiteracy. It is also, unfortunately, a deliberate mannerism of many journalists and writers of advertising copy.

15. *Colloquialisms.* A colloquialism (the term is derived from a Latin word meaning "to converse") is an expression regarded as correct only for conversational style: that is, only for informal and semiformal speech and for informal writing, not for formal public speaking or for either semiformal or formal written composition. Thus, whether a word of this class violates good usage is determined by its suitability to the situation in which it occurs. For instance, a personal letter or a round-table discussion might make free use of colloquialisms that would be objectionable in a business letter or a platform address. Most contractions (*can't, shouldn't, I'm,* etc.) and many other shortened forms of words (*math, exam, ad, phone,* etc.) are colloquial. English abounds in colloquialisms of all sorts: separate words, as *date* (in the sense of an appointment or social engagement) and *flunk;* compounds, as *know-how;* and phrases, usually involving a verb, a preposition, or both, as *to put over, lots of* (or *a lot of*), and many expressions based on *get* (e.g., *to get going*). As has been mentioned, barbarisms sometimes acquire colloquial standing. Improprieties are even more likely to be colloquial; as random examples *smart* and *fix* may be cited. Both words are irreproachable when used accurately (see any dictionary for their several respective meanings); however, they are only colloquially acceptable when the former is equated with *wise* or *intelligent,* and the latter (as a noun) with *predicament* or (as a verb) with *mend, arrange,* or *overcome* (as by cunning).

16. *Slang and vulgarisms.* Although slang is difficult to define, anyone can recognize it without the help of a definition. Vulgarisms are an allied category of offensive diction. Both terms signify expressions, usually not specifically ungrammatical or unidiomatic, that are incorrect in any form of written or oral discourse (except, of course, for special effects in fiction, dialect recitation, and the like). A vulgarism (from Latin *vulgus,* the common people or rabble) joins with incorrectness a quality of marked crudeness or coarseness, often but not necessarily amounting to indecency. Words like *go-getter, lambaste, swell,* (*the*) *bunk,* and *roughneck* are classified as slang; others like *bust, bull* (*session*), and *gent,* as vulgarisms. As a group, slang and vulgarisms occupy the bottom level of verbal dignity, and except in extremes of type they are very nearly indistinguishable.

Note: One difference is that slang usually is less stable. Three objectionable properties of most slang are its tendencies to be transitory, trite (cf. **D** 21), and vague. A few ill-defined words are constantly repeated to cover broad segments of meaning; presently they are heard no more, and others equally indefinite are speedily worn threadbare in their turn. Both colloquial and vulgar locutions frequently share the triteness—sometimes, too, the vagueness; and, rather less often, the impermanence—of slang. On the other hand, a great many slangy expressions have much of the characteristic inelegance of vulgarisms.

17. *Pretentious "literary" diction.* At an opposite extreme from slang and vulgarisms are certain rare or showy expressions sometimes hopefully employed by students for a supposed effect of "fine writing." Words of the character of *albeit, horrendous, plethora, nonce, adjure, dulcet, beholden, excogitable, peradventure, opine, umbrage,* and *eschew* are appropriate only within limited ranges of literary style and under judicious control. Used as an adornment they are pompous; occurring side by side with commonplace vocabulary, they are tasteless and even ludicrous. In practical composition on technical subjects, decorative language of this kind is certain to be disagreeable.

Foreign expressions.   Another form of the same mannerism consists in preferring "literary" foreign words and phrases to native or naturalized expressions of identical meaning. With a measure of humorous justice, English has been called a foreign language, for the custom of taking vocabulary from other tongues is part of its tradition. Nevertheless, borrowing is warranted only by need. No reader of this book will have to be told that coining of scientific nomenclature from Greek, Latin, and other roots, with due regard to sound principles of etymology, is an indispensable practice. (Terms so derived usually come instantly into approved usage, at least for technical discourse, seldom being required to serve the ordinary period of probation in italics before receiving naturalization.) Other foreign locutions, as well, often must be employed where native speech lacks equivalents. Still, the writer who deliberately concocts a hodgepodge of no-man's-English, thinking to display an international culture, loses unity of tone and may defeat the purpose of communication.

18. *Provincialisms.*   The question of provincial English heard in different parts of the United States has arisen before (review D 9b), in relation to the problem of correct pronunciation. Regional

66

"accents" are accompanied by provincial or local vocabulary unknown or uncommon elsewhere. *Allow* or *reckon* (think), *stoop* (porch), *you-all,* and *nineteen and forty-eight* (nineteen forty-eight) are examples. Household expressions mingled with English by partially assimilated racial groups (not to be confused with the class of sophisticated borrowings mentioned under *Foreign Expressions*) are among the sources of dialectal speech in the United States, and commonly are sectional in distribution. Typical of regional dialects are the "Cajun" (Acadian French of Louisiana), the Pennsylvania "Dutch" (German), and the Gullah (Negro). Provincial words and phrases, of both native and foreign origin, eventually may pass into literary usage; however, for the most part they attain no more than colloquial dignity. Thus, provincialisms of diction (apart from systematic differences in the pronunciation of standard words, called "accent") ordinarily are not fully established for serious discourse even within a limited region; and, so long as they *remain* regional, they obviously have no standing whatever in the national language. For purposes of written composition and formal speech on scientific topics, they must be regarded as almost wholly unacceptable.

19. *Redundancy.*   Redundancy—repetition or roundabout expression of thought—sometimes is justifiable to give deliberate emphasis or to clarify a point that might be obscure if stated tersely. Usually, however, it results from vagueness of thought, from laziness (rambling is much easier than rigorously economical phrasing), or from both. In the nineteen-word sentence, "With respect to corrosion, the determining causes that are the driving forces of that condition are six in number" (meaning: "Six causes produce corrosion"), fifteen superfluous words tire the reader's patience without increasing the information that four would convey.

20. *Tautology.*   The special form of redundancy called tautology, consisting in unconscious repetition of meaning through words having identical or overlapping import, is a considerable danger in English because of our large resources of vocabulary. It occurs in such useless duplications as *combine together, infinitesimally small, the autobiography of his life, and etc.,* and *the advance of progress.* Some of the faulty idioms entered under D 23 exhibit tautology (e.g., *seldom ever*) or general wordiness (e.g., *meet up with*). Occasionally, a double expression (e.g., *first and foremost*) may serve a legitimate rhetorical function, but phrases of this kind are mostly to be avoided.

21. *Triteness*. Expressions once striking, and usually dependent for their effect on figures of speech, are said to be trite (or hackneyed) when through overuse they have lost their original luster. They are like coins that have had their faces worn smooth by constant handling. (The word *trite* literally means "rubbed.") The greater the effect once given by a phrase, the more unsatisfactory that phrase probably will become if it is employed as a stereotype, for often the whole stylistic value of ingenious expressions turns on keen perception of boldly applied imagery. The man who excitedly telephoned the fire department that his house was "burning like a house afire" might well be excused, in the circumstance, for failure to deliberate upon wording; but hardly the student who wrote, "The surface has just been scratched on the subject of dental caries." Triteness is not always amusing; most of the time it is simply dull. Do not let your own writing and speech become a patchwork of worn-out scraps such as "the last straw," "an agony of suspense," "thus we see" (as a standardized formula for concluding all papers and talks), "thanking you in advance" (and similar tags of the old-fashioned style of letter writing), "the crack of doom," "each and every" (redundant as well as trite), and "as solid as the Rock of Gibraltar."

Note 1: As can be seen from some of the quoted examples, not all trite expressions are figures of speech. (Cf. the *Note* under D 16.)

Note 2: Inconsistency in figures of speech, which is even worse than triteness, also may result from vague attention to the imagery. (In fact, trite figures are especially likely to be confused.) Three errors should be avoided: (1) a mixed figure (e.g., "a *deluge* of *dry* remarks); (2) a figure incongruous with the literal context (e.g., "attention *rooted* in the *sky*"); and (3) discordant figures side by side (e.g., "*elbowed out* by a successor able to *blow his own horn*"). A sequence of fundamentally different figures of speech is not objectionable, however, if each is felt to be separate, yet not to clash glaringly or absurdly with any of the others, and if triteness is avoided.

22. Faulty idiom.

Individuality of idioms. The idioms of any language are its most individual elements. They are customary forms of expression, unaccountable to general principles of grammar and logic, developed by fixed arrangement of certain words.* Prepositions and adverbs (espe-

---

* Their origin in phrases may be obscured, however, by solidification: e.g., *somewhere*—from *some* plus *where*—is a correct idiom, whereas *someplace*—from *some* plus *place*—is incorrect. Also, a single word may be the proper replacement for a faulty idiom of two or more words: e.g., *meet* or *encounter* for *run up against*.

cially certain familiar monosyllables, such as *in, out,* and *up,* that are capable of functioning as either part of speech) very often are involved. The essentially arbitrary character of idioms is illustrated by the almost endless variety of meanings that can be derived—not all with equal dignity and propriety—from the verbs *take* and *put: viz.,* *take (put) in, take (put) out, take (put) off, take (put) up, take (put) down, take (put) on,* etc. The rightness of an idiom is determined exclusively by its acceptance in educated usage. By way of illustration, *cut in half* or *if and when,* although illogical, and *to make good,* although abnormal in grammar, are idiomatically correct.

Problems. Because every idiom is its own law, complete mastery of idiomatic English is difficult not only for foreign learners, to whom the problem may be almost insurmountable, but also for native users of the language. Incorrect idioms, like errors of spelling, of pronunciation, and of diction in general, tend to become ingrained through uncritical repetition. As in other problems of language, reading well-written books and articles, listening to careful speakers, and frequently consulting dictionaries for information on specific usages are all valuable means to improvement. Those who surrender to the habit of faulty idiom are not completely literate; moreover, they often blunt or confuse a meaning that could be expressed exactly by discriminating phrasing.

Examples. As random instances, *compare with* and *in comparison with* have different meanings from *compare to* and *in comparison to,* and *consist(ing) in* has a different meaning from *consisting of.* Study these idioms. The preposition *with* signifies a literal sense of *compare* or *comparison;* the preposition *to,* on the other hand, a figurative sense. Thus, one automobile might be compared *with* another to bring about points of likeness and differences, whereas a warship might be compared *to* a greyhound by way of simile. The expression *to consist of* properly introduces an analysis of composition; *to consist in,* a statement of fundamental or abstract quality. Thus, a diode consists *of* a filament and plate, with their wiring, enclosing envelope, and other fittings; rectification consists *in* the conversion of alternating to direct current. Careless writers and speakers generally obscure these distinctions by always using *to* with *compare* or *comparison,* and *of* with *consist.* Several other common mistakes in idiom, together with corresponding correct forms, are shown in the following table:

23. Glossary of Faulty Idioms.

FAULTY IDIOM	CORRECTION
agree with (a proposal)	agree to
aim at (with gerund)	aim to (with infinitive)
all of (with plural noun)	all
all the longer (*or:* farther; fewer; etc.) . .	still (*or:* even) longer (*or:* farther; fewer; etc.)
among the two	between the two
angry } mad } at (someone)	angry with
as } in } with } regards to	as } in } with } regard to; as regards
between the three (or more)	among the three (or more)
blame (something) on (someone)	blame (someone) for (something)
center (a) round	center in; center (up)on
could } would } had } of	could } have; had would } (*not* "had have")
doubt (*or:* question) but what	doubt (*or:* question) that (*or:* but that)
equally as bad (*or:* good; important; etc.)	equally bad (*or:* good; important; etc.)
has } have } had } got to	has } have } to; must had }
how come	why; how does it happen that
identical to	identical with
inside } outside } out } off } of	inside outside out off
a large (*or:* small; certain; etc.) percent of	a large (*or:* small; certain; etc.) percentage of; 85 per cent of
a long ways	a long way
a lot of, lots of	[*Colloquial for:*] very much; (a great) many
meet up with, run up against	meet; encounter

nowhere near	not nearly
plan on (with gerund or noun)	plan (with noun); plan to (with infinitive)
put across (*or:* over)	[*Colloquial for:*] communicate; convey
rarely ⎱ ever . . . . seldom ⎰	rarely; seldom; seldom if ever
refer back to	refer to
someplace, everyplace, anyplace, noplace, nohow, noway(s)	[*Vulgarisms for:*] somewhere, everywhere, anywhere, nowhere, not at all, in no way, by no means, etc.
speed ⎱ up . . . . slow ⎰	speed; accelerate slow; retard
sympathy for	sympathy with; pity for
tend to (except in sense of "have a tendency to")	attend to; tend
type ⎫ class ⎬ of . . . . sort ⎪ kind ⎭	(See *Note* following this glossary.)
wait on (in sense of "await")	wait for; await
where . . . at, where . . . to	where

Note: Such forms as *type of, class of, sort of,* and *kind of* should be directly followed by a noun. Avoid committing any of three errors: (1) interposing an indefinite article (*a* or *an*) between *of* and the noun; (2) omitting *of* after *type* or *class;* (3) using *sort of* or *kind of* adverbially, with the meaning of "somewhat," before an adjective or adverb.

WRONG: that kind (*or:* sort; type; etc.) of *a* generator; this *type* program (or: *class* program); *sort of* (or: *kind of*) inefficient(ly).

24. *Study List of Words for Technical Students.* The following list, instead of being limited to scientific terminology, brings together several hundred words that meet two criteria: (1) common use in technical discourse, regardless of whether the individual word is specifically technical; (2) known difficulty for university students, shown by frequent occurrence of mistakes in written or spoken form, or both. Detachable prefixes, suffixes, inflectional endings, and the like, are given in parentheses, without displacing the word to which they are added from its normal alphabetical position; for example, *indefinitely* is written "(in)definite(ly)" and alphabetized as *definite*. Since for the most part only spellings are recorded, a dictionary should be consulted to verify pronunciations and, whenever necessary, meanings.

abscissa
absence
absent
absolute(ly)
absorb(ent)
absorption
accelerate
accelerator
(in)accessible
accessory
accidental(ly)
accommodate
accumulate
acetylene
achieve(ment)
adherent
(in)admissible
adsorb(ent)
adsorption
advertise(ment)
advice (*noun*)
advise (*verb*)
adviser
aerate
aerodynamics
affiliation
aggravate
aggregate
agitate
agitator
alcohol
algebra(ic)
alkali
all right
amateur
amount
analysis
(*pl.,* analyses)

analyze
annular
(equi)angular
apart
apparatus
apparent(ly)
appearance
appendix
appraise(r)
appreciate
aqueous(ness)
argument
arithmetic
around
arrange(ment)
article
asbestos
ascend
ascent
assimilate(d)
association
athlete
athletics
attack(ed)
attendance
audible
authority
authorize
auxiliary
avoidance
avoirdupois
awkward
azimuth
balance(d)
barbarous
basic(ally)
Baumé
belief

believe
benefit
beneficial
binocular
brilliant
(Great) Britain
British
bulletin
business
buoyancy
buoyant
calendar
calibrate
capillary
carburetor
cast iron
(*noun*)
cast-iron
(*adjective*)
catalyst
ceiling
centimeter
centrifugal
changeable
chassis
circuit
column
combustible
commission
commit
committed
committee
committing
comparative(ly)
compass
compel
compelled
compelling

competent
competitive
complement (ary)
complete (ly)
compliment (ary)
compulsion
compulsory
concede
conceivable
conceive
condense
condenser
conductor
conduit
confidence
confident (ly)
confidential (ly)
conscience
conscientious (ly)
(un) conscious (ly)
consciousness
(in) consistent (ly)
constituent
contemptible
contingent
continual (ly)
continuous (ly)
control
controlled
controlling
convenience
(in) convenient (ly)
corollary
correlate
correspondence
correspondent
council
counsel
courteous
courtesy
(in) credible
criticism
criticize
crystalline
crystallize

curiosity
curious
cylinder
deceive
decision
(in) definite (ly)
democracy
(un) dependable
(in) dependence
(in) dependent
describe
description
desiccate
desperate (ly)
destroy
destruction
develop (ment)
device (*noun*)
devise (*verb*)
dictionary
dielectric
differ
differed
difference
differential
different (iate)
differing
diffuse
diffusion
digit
dilate
diligence
diligent
dilute
dilution
disappear
disappoint
disaster
disastrous (ly)
disintegrate
(in) dispensable
discipline
dissipate
distribute
divide

ductile
duly
durable
eccentric (ity)
(in) efficiency
(in) efficient
eighth
(in) eligible
eliminate
either
electrolysis
electrolyte
embarrass (ment)
emission
emit
emitted
emitter
emitting
emphasis
emphasize
entomology
environment
equation
equidistant
equip (ment)
equipped
equipping
equivalent
essential (ly)
etc. (*not* "ect.")
evidence
evident (ly)
exaggerate
exceed
excel
excelled
excellence
excellent
excelling
except (ion)
exhaust
existence
existent
expel
expelled

expelling
expense
experience
experiment
experimental (ly)
explain
explanation
extension
extraordinary
extreme (ly)
facilitate
facilities
Fahrenheit
familiar
feasible
February
fictitious
filament
(in) filtrate
flexible
fluorescent
foreign
forceful
forcible
forest
forfeit
formal (ly)
former (ly)
forty
fortieth
fourteen (th)
fourth
gel
gelatin
genius
geometry
geophysics
government
gradient
grammar
grateful
grievous
guarantee
guard
height

hesitancy
hindrance
homogeneous
horizontal
humorous
hundredth (s)
hypocrisy
hypothesis
imaginary
immediate (ly)
impedance
incidence
incidental (ly)
infinite (ly)
influential
ingenious
inherent
innocuous
inoculate
instantaneous
integer
integral
(dis) integrate
intelligence
intelligent
intention
intentional (ly)
interchangeable
interfere
interference
involve (ment)
isotope
its (possessive =
  belonging to it)
it's (contrac-
  tion = *it is*)
itself
judgment
kilowatt
label
laboratory
(equi) lateral
led
(il) legible
liable

liaison
license (d)
(recti) linear
liquefaction
liquefy
(il) literate
logarithm
loose (= *release*)
lose (= *suffer
  loss of*)
lubricate
lying
(de) magnetize
maintain
maintenance
malleable
manufacture (r)
mathematics
meant
medicine
millimeter
mineralogy
miniature
miscellaneous
model
moderate (ly)
molecule
molecular
momentous
modern (ize)
motor
murmur
mysterious
naphtha
(un) necessary
(un) necessarily
necessity
negligible
neither
nickel
nineteen (th)
ninetieth
ninety
ninth
noticeable

nuclear
nucleus
occasion
occasional (ly)
o'clock
occur
occurred
occurrence
occurring
ocular
omission
omit
omitted
omitting
operate
operation
opinion
opportunity
optimistic
organization
orifice
origin
original (ly)
oscillator
oxygen
pamphlet
panel
paraffin
parallel (ing)
parasite
particle
particular (ly)
peculiar (ly)
penetrate
perceive
(im) perceptible
perforate (d)
perform
(im) permanent (ly)
permeable
(un) permissible
perpendicular
perseverance
persistent (ly)
personnel

persuade
pertain
pertinent
pessimistic
petrify
phase
phenomenon
   (*pl.*, phenomena)
phosphorous
   (*adjective*)
phosphorus
   (*noun*)
physical (ly)
physics
physiological (ly)
planet (ary)
(im) plausible
pneumatic
(de) polarize
polymerize
polyphase
poison (ous)
possess (ion)
(im) possible
potential (ly)
(im) practical (ly)
(im) practicable
practice
precede
precedence
precedent
preceding
prefer
preferable
preference
preferred
preferring
prejudice (d)
prepare
preparation
prevail
prevalence
prevalent
primitive
principal

principle
priority
privilege (d)
probably
proceed
procedure
profession
professor
pronunciation
propeller
protein
prove
psychological (ly)
psychology
public (ly)
pursue
pursuing
pursuit
quality
quantity
questionnaire
rarefaction
rarefy
realize
recede
receipt
receivable
receive (r)
recognize
recommend (ation)
refer
reference
referred
referring
regard (ing)
relative (ly)
(ir) relevant
remembrance
repair
repeat
repetition
replaceable
resemble
resemblance
reservoir

resilient
resistance
resistant
resonance
(ir) resistible
rheostat
rhythm
ridiculous
safety
Saturday
scarce (ly)
schedule
seismograph
seize
sentence
separate
(un) serviceable
several (ly)
severe (ly)
significance
significant (ly)
silhouette
similar (ly)
simultaneous (ly)
sincere (ly)
(in) soluble
(in) solubility
spatial
species
specific (ally)
specimen
spectrum
(pl., spectra)
statistical
statistician
statistics

stratum
(pl., strata)
strength
strenuous (ly)
strict
substantial (ly)
substantiate
succeed
success (ful)
superintend (ent)
supersede
supplement (ary)
suppress
surely
surprise
suspense
suspension
symmetrical
symmetry
synchronize
synchronous
systematic (ally)
tarpaulin
technical (ly)
temperature
tendency
tensile
theoretical (ly)
theory
thousandth (s)
tolerance
transmitter
trigonometry
truly
Tuesday

typical (ly)
unanimous (ly)
undoubted (ly)
uniform (ly)
usage
vacuum
valuable
valence
vehicle
ventilate
vernier
versatile
vertical
violent
viscosity
viscous
visible
volatile
volume
volunteer
Wednesday
weir
wrought iron
(noun)
wrought-iron
(adjective)
yield
writer
writing
written
X ray (noun)
X-ray (adjective; verb)
yours
zoology

CHAPTER IV

PROBLEMS OF PUNCTUATION

A functional system. Punctuation is a functional art: its purpose is to help written words express meaning. A composition stripped of all marks of punctuation—with the phrases, clauses, and sentences run together as they flow from the pen—would be almost unreadable; at most, the intended thought would be conveyed obscurely. Punctuation operates systematically, being understood as a set of signals between writer and reader. To be sure, the method is not identical in every language, and in English it has changed with time and shows minor national variations. Like any art, moreover, punctuation cannot be absolutely formalized, for some allowance must be left for subtle shading of thought or feeling, and even for the personality of individual writers. Nevertheless, the general system is well established by educated current usage, which is essentially the same in technical composition as in literary prose. Every student should learn the accepted standards and apply them to his own writing. To the extent that custom admits a variety of practices, he should strive for self-consistency and conformity to what appear to be the best and most rational models.

Punctuation "by ear" fails. Although the rhythms and intonations of spoken language in part serve the same functions as punctuation, they can not be directly correlated with the individual marks. Writers who try to punctuate "by ear" always fail to achieve even approximate conformity to the established system. Such distinctions as those between the comma and the semicolon, the semicolon and the colon, and parentheses and brackets are typical of the difficulties confronting persons who ignore theory. No shortcut method can be substituted for the study of punctuation as a definite technique peculiar to written composition.

Emphasis on principles. Some of the difficulty in mastering punctuation arises from the disconnected rules by which the subject often is presented. More fundamental than the rules, however, are the principles on which they are grounded. Actually, the use of each mark of punctuation is governed by a few basic principles, of which most of the rules are instances. *Concentrate upon principles.* The general procedure in most of this chapter is to treat principles as main entries under each mark of punctuation (P 1, P 2, etc.), and to give rules a subordinate position (P 1a, P 1b, etc.) under the principle from which they follow. Except when a single principle is stated for a given mark (cf. Colon: P 6), the principles are further identified by Roman numerals (cf. Comma, Principle I: P 1).

COMMA (,)

1. Commas are regularly used to separate from each other any pair or series of coördinate expressions   except: (1) independent clauses not connected by a coördinating conjunction; (2) two members of a compound subject, predicate, complement, object, or dependent construction. (Principle I)

> We received regular, progressive instruction and exercises in orthographic projection of points, lines, planes, and warped surfaces.

Observe that commas are used to separate *from each other* the elements involved. Accordingly, one less comma is needed than there are elements to be separated.

EXPLANATIONS

(1) *Definitions:*

   Coördinate: Standing side by side and having a logical and grammatical relation of approximate equality or close similarity. A series of adjectives modifying the same noun are coördinate with each other.

   Coördinating conjunction: *And, but, for, or, nor,* or *yet.* (Some authorities do not include *yet.*)

   Compound: A special coördinate relationship in which elements are joined by a coördinating conjunction.

(2) Concerning independent clauses not connected by a coördinating conjunction, see P 4 (Semicolon). Concerning compound dependent constructions and compound subjects, complements, and objects, see Class (9) under P 2a, and also P 3c.

(3) Although two compounded predicates (e.g., "He lifted the cover

and inserted a match") normally are not separated by a comma, the mark may be used if either or both are long or internally punctuated, if they are distinctly separate in topic (e.g., in the nature or time of their respective actions), or if the second is somewhat less important than the first.

RIGHT: The bimetallic strips are held open by the heat of the small electrical discharge through the vacuum, but return to the closed position, ready for the next operation, on disconnection of the lamp.

1a. Two independent clauses compounded by a coördinating conjunction normally are separated by a comma.

The unshaken mixture is a clear liquid, but stirring produces a cloudy suspension.

All lines shall be kept straight, and all surfaces shall be brought to a true level.

Note 1: Use of the comma as stated in P 1a is normal. Sometimes the semicolon is substituted (see P 5; cf. also *Note 2, immediately below*). No mark at all may be needed if the clauses are rather short and very closely connected in thought. Some mark of punctuation, however, must stand between independent clauses that are joined by *for* preceding a noun or *uninflected* pronoun (e.g., *that* as opposed to *he, him*); otherwise, *for* could momentarily be mistaken for a preposition governing the objective case.

WRONG: That night I was driving the family car for my father was out of town.

RIGHT: That night I was driving the family car, for my father was out of town.

Note 2: When the last two of three or more independent clauses are connected by a coördinating conjunction, the construction is a type of "a, b, and c series." (See P 1c; cf. G 45.) Consistent use, throughout the series, either of commas or of semicolons is correct. Do *not,* however, place semicolons between all the clauses except the last two and then precede the coördinating conjunction with a comma.

WRONG: Henry read off the data from his slide rule; I plotted a graph, and together we were able to solve the problem quickly.

RIGHT: Henry read off the data from his slide rule; I plotted a graph; and together we were able to solve the problem quickly.

Or: Henry read off the data from his slide rule, I plotted a graph, and together we were able to solve the problem quickly.

1b. Adjectives modifying the same noun are separated from each other by commas.

Broad, light-colored, overhung roofs are an adaptation to the hot, rainy climate.

Exception 1: Two adjectives joined by a coördinating conjunction omit the comma. (This situation is a type of compound dependent construction. Review the last part of Principle I: P 1.) Occasionally, however, the coördinating conjunction and the second adjective are, as a phrase, set off by commas. Cf. Class (9) under P 2a, and also P 3c.

RIGHT: Gross, or unadjusted, income is not applicable to Schedule 8.

Exception 2: Unless adjectives are genuinely coördinate—that is, unless they separately and equally modify the noun—no commas are inserted. In the phrase *a long, deep gash,* two qualities are attributed to the gash: it is long and it is also deep. A good test to prove the coördinate relationship of the adjectives is to transpose them (*a deep, long gash*); the meaning remains substantially the same. In the phrase *slovenly mechanical drawing,* the adjectives are not coördinate; rather, *mechanical* modifies *drawing* and the whole expression *mechanical drawing* is qualified by *slovenly.* Transposing the order (*mechanical slovenly drawing*) would destroy the intended meaning. See also P 24 (Hyphen: Principle III).

Caution: Do not put a comma after the *last* adjective of a series.

WRONG: A dry, hot, dusty, windy, day.

1c. Commas are used to divide from each other the members of an "a, b, and c series."

In the drawer were some old pamphlets, magazines, and newspapers, a treatise on outbreeding of domestic stock, and a manual of documentation.

Definition: The so-called "a, b, and c series" consists of three or more logically related elements of the same grammatical rank (i.e., three or more nouns, adjectives, adjectival clauses, prepositional phrases, etc.), the last two of which are joined by *and, or,* or (infrequently) some other coördinating conjunction.

Note: Many good writers omit the comma between the last two members of the series, i.e., between those joined by the conjunction, but if this practice is consistently followed (and punctuation should be consistent) it sometimes confuses the nature of the structure. The alternative practice of using the comma, strongly recommended by most American textbooks of grammar and style, is generally followed in technical writing.

AMBIGUOUS: In the drawer are two small pamphlets, a treatise on outbreeding of domestic stock and a manual of documentation. (How many volumes are in the drawer: two unspecified pamphlets and two specified books besides, or merely two pamphlets identified by their respective subjects? Only if the writer *always* includes commas throughout an "a, b, and c series" can the reader be sure that the latter part of the sentence is a compound appositive.)

2. Commas are regularly used to set off from the rest of the sentence semiparenthetical and nonrestrictive elements. (Principle II)

To be sure, the industry has abandoned the former sources, which have been made unprofitable by the new synthetic process.

Note: Observe that commas are used to set off *from the rest of the sentence* the elements involved. Because semiparenthetical and nonrestrictive elements, however, often occur at the beginning or end of a sentence, or internally at a point where some other mark of punctuation must be written, one of the two commas theoretically necessary to set off such an element is frequently absent. See also the *Caution* at the top of page 84.

2a. Classes of semiparenthetical elements. The expression "semiparenthetical" is rather indefinite, but no clearer synonym is available. Constructions of this kind are often (not always) sentence modifiers or sentence adverbs: i.e., words, phrases, or clauses not firmly integrated in the basic grammatical pattern of the sentence, but used to indicate transitions or other special relationships. They are more easily exemplified by classes than defined as a unified type, although they are usually easy to recognize in practice. Elements of Classes (1), (2), and (3) are not always semiparenthetical. When they are intended to be taken as essential and emphatic in force, rather than as secondary or incidental, no commas surround them. Sometimes the position of the element helps to show whether it is semiparenthetical.

RIGHT: The starch must first be hydrolyzed to maltose; it is next acted upon by the yeast.

But: First, a thermometer is suspended in the cup; next, oil is added.

(1) Explanatory and transitional words: *however, nevertheless, namely, conversely,* etc.

(2) Explanatory and transitional phrases: *for instance, for example, etc.* (et cetera), *to be sure, on the other hand,* etc.

(3) Explanatory and transitional clauses: *that is, we may say, as everyone knows,* etc.

(4) Abbreviations serving an introductory function: *i.e., e.g., viz.,* etc.

(5) Expressions used in direct address (of exceedingly rare occurrence in technical writing except, occasionally, in correspondence): e.g., "I must admit, *Mr. Jones,* that your reasoning is difficult to refute."

(6) Appositive constructions: An appositive construction consists of a word (ordinarily a noun) standing after another word, of the same grammatical rank, with which it has a common basic meaning. (If a noun or pronoun, it is in the same case as the principal word.) When a modifying word, phrase, or clause accompanies the appositive, the entire combination consisting of the appositive with its modifiers is enclosed in commas.

Appositives usually are set off by commas, but the commas are omitted if an appositive is definitely restrictive, i.e., absolutely necessary to the principal word. However, a long appositive (in particular, one in quotation marks) may be set off by commas even though it is restrictive.

The word *repair* is misspelled through confusion with the word *prepare.* ("The word" would be meaningless without its restrictive appositive in each part of the sentence.)

But:

The thought, "Without continual salvage of high-speed cutting tools, the war might have been lost on the home front," occurred to me as the theme for an article. (Although a restrictive appositive, the long quotation is set off by commas.)

(7) Absolute constructions: An absolute expression has a logical but not a grammatical connection with the rest of the sentence. The typical form is the so-called nominative absolute, containing a noun or

pronoun modified by a participle, *the noun or pronoun functioning neither as the subject of a verb nor as any kind of object.* (The italicized part of the foregoing sentence is itself an example of the nominative absolute.)

(8) Geographical expressions that complete other geographical expressions, and dates that complete other dates: for example, a state following a city; a country following a city or state, or both; and a year following a month, with or without the numerical date of the month.

Caution: Do not forget the second comma required to set off such expressions within a sentence.

WRONG: Charleston, West Virginia is his home.
January 3, 1903 was the date of his birth.

RIGHT: Charleston, West Virginia, is his home.
January 3, 1903, was the date of his birth.

Exception: When the word *of* or the phrase *of the year* connects the month and the year, no commas are used.

(9) The second (occasionally the first, when negative) of two members of a compound subject, complement, object, or dependent construction if the second member is intended to be somewhat less prominent, significant, or emphatic than the first. (See also P 3c.)

Compound subject: Today a "roughneck" in the oilfields, or any common laborer in modern industry, has a larger real income than the most highly skilled artisans received a few generations ago.

Compound subjective complement: Spun-glass cloth is a valuable new textile, but hardly a successful fabric for clothing.

Compound objective complement: Senator Blackstone called the proposed pipeline to the East a military plan, not primarily a measure to supply civilian needs. (*Note:* The word *not,* although an adverb rather than a conjunction, may be loosely regarded as a compounding word in such constructions.)

Compound object of verb: Arabian scholars advanced algebra, and also some other branches of science.

Compound object of preposition: He objected to the thesis, but not the style, of Robson's article.

Compound prepositional phrase: He objected, not merely to the style, but to the thesis of Robson's article.

(10) Explanatory elements attached to direct quotations: *he wrote, the statement says,* etc.

Caution: Several of the foregoing classes—especially (1), (2), (3), (4), and (10)—frequently occur between independent clauses, and therefore may be adjacent to a semicolon that supplants one of the two commas ordinarily needed to set off a semiparenthetical element. Guard against commission of the "comma splice" through faulty retention of both commas in this situation. See Explanation (3) under P 4; cf. the last two sets of examples given under P 4a.

2b. Nonrestrictive modifiers. Practically all sentences contain modifiers, and *every* modifier is either restrictive or nonrestrictive. Single-word qualifiers (adjectives and adverbs) usually are restrictive and therefore seldom are set off by commas. Most phrases also are restrictive; however, participial phrases are in the main nonrestrictive. Since clauses give by far the most trouble, they will be used for illustration. Never forget that it is *nonrestrictive* clauses, and *nonrestrictive* modifiers generally, that are set off.

Definitions: A restrictive modifier is one that is necessary to convey the intended meaning of the *word or words qualified.* (That is why it is not set off by commas.) A nonrestrictive modifier (the kind set off by commas) is not necessary to convey the intended meaning of the word or words qualified but, instead, conveys *additional* information. Another way to express the same distinction is to say that a nonrestrictive modifier could be removed without changing the meaning of *that part* of the sentence on which it depends.

Caution: Restrictive and nonrestrictive modifiers can be identified only on the basis of sound and clearly understood definitions. Avoid gaining the erroneous impression that either type could be omitted without changing the content of the sentence *as a whole.* Because every part of a properly written sentence contributes meaning, only *redundant* elements can be removed without reducing the total thought. (Cf. Chapter III: D 19 and 20.)

Note: The statement (sometimes given in textbooks) that a nonrestrictive modifier could be omitted without changing the main or "essential" thought of the sentence is true, but misleading because the same can be said of restrictive modifiers that qualify minor rather than major parts of sentences. For instance, in the preceding sentence the phrase "in textbooks" is a *restrictive* modifier of the participle "given"; nevertheless, the phrase could be removed without affecting the principal thought. Many restrictive modifiers are not part of the "essential" meaning of the sentence in which they occur.

Study the following sentences and comments:

(*Nonrestrictive adjectival clause*) He was educated in Chicago, where he later practiced architecture. (The meaning of the modified word, *Chicago,* is self-contained. If the information given in the dependent clause were removed, the communication of the sentence as a whole could of course be reduced by about half, but the meaning of *Chicago* would not be in doubt.)

(*Restrictive adjectival clause*) Chicago is the city where I am now employed. (What is meant by "the city"? The reader would have no idea if the *where* clause did not inform him.)

(*Nonrestrictive adjectival clause*) All freshmen, who are required to enroll in person, must present their certificates of admission. (Cf. the example following.)

(*Restrictive adjectival clause*) All freshmen who have not taken mechanical drawing in high school are enrolled in a slow section. (Not *all* freshmen, but only certain ones, are placed in the special section. Notice how a restrictive element literally *restricts* the meaning of what it modifies.)

Note: Of the relative pronouns, *which* and *who*(*m*) can introduce both restrictive and nonrestrictive adjectival clauses; *that,* only a restrictive clause. *When* and *where* as the initial words of adjectival clauses are called relative adverbs. (More commonly, of course, *when* and *where* act as subordinating conjunctions and introduce adverbial clauses.)

(*Nonrestrictive adverbial clause*) The thermal efficiency of the engine is nearly constant, as the graph shows. (The predicate of the main clause, "is nearly constant," is clear in itself; the dependent clause merely directs attention to evidence of its truth.)

(*Restrictive adverbial clause*) Proceed as the arrows point. ("Proceed" without the modifying clause would fail to communicate the intended meaning.)

Importance of discrimination. The distinction between the term *restrictive* and its contrary, *nonrestrictive,* is crucial for correct punctuation, as the meaning of whole passages often depends upon discrimination between the two kinds of modifiers. Where legal documents, such as specifications and other contracts, are concerned, very great care should be exercised, for the same words variously punctuated can actually say entirely different things. In illustration, consider the following sentence in its two forms:

(A) All lighting fixtures, which shall be of design approved by the National Electric Association, shall be installed by a licensed electrician. (By the specification as here written, all lighting fixtures must meet the standards of the National Electric Association and also be installed by a licensed electrician. Note, incidentally, that the *which* clause certainly could not be omitted without seriously reducing the meaning of the sentence as a whole, although it does not limit the meaning of "All lighting fixtures" and is therefore nonrestrictive.)

(B) All lighting fixtures which shall be of design approved by the National Electric Association shall be installed by a licensed electrician. (The writer has omitted two important commas. Now *only* those fixtures that meet the standards of the National Electric Association need be installed by a licensed electrician, since "All lighting fixtures" is restricted to that one class. If a janitor strings up bare wire to a homemade wall socket and burns down the building, no violation of the contract has occurred.)

Exception 1: Long adverbial phrases and clauses that *precede* the part of the sentence on which they depend, instead of following in normal position, are set off by commas, regardless of whether they are restrictive or nonrestrictive. If such a modifier is inserted between the introductory word of a clause and the rest of that clause, the first comma for setting off the modifier may be omitted. Use of both commas is correct if no awkwardness results.

UNDESIRABLE (because awkward): Mechanics know that, when the jets of the carburetor are clogged with sediment, the owner of the automobile often suspects the distributor of being at fault.

RIGHT: Mechanics know that when the jets of the carburetor are clogged with sediment, the owner of the automobile often suspects the distributor of being at fault.

Note 1: No definite rule can be stated on how long a restrictive adverbial clause or phrase in the "inverted" (introductory) position must be to require setting off. The decision rests upon the individual judgment of the writer of the sentence. Because clauses normally have more words than phrases, a "long" phrase might actually contain fewer words than a clause deemed "short."

Note 2: Bear in mind that *nonrestrictive* modifiers *always* should be set off by commas, irrespective of their position in the sentence or their length, and of whether they are adjectival or adverbial. *Exception 1* also permits use of commas with certain restrictive elements (otherwise not set off) that are at the same time (a) long and (b) ahead of their regular syntactical position. It may be regarded as an instance of P 3.

Exception 2: Clauses beginning with *provided* or *provided that* normally are set off by commas even though their force is restrictive. In contracts they usually are paragraphed separately, started with a capital *P,* and connected in series by semicolons. Long phrases and clauses beginning with *except* (*for*), *except that,* or *except with* also tend to be punctuated as if nonrestrictive.

3. Wherever commas would definitely improve the clarity of a sentence, they may be inserted. (Principle III)

By this principle, commas are employed in several typical situations not covered by either Principle I (P 1) or Principle II (P 2).

3a. To prevent the momentary mistaking of the function of a word.

Everything he had, had been itemized in a previous schedule.

After eating, a boa constrictor passes into a quiescent state.

When we entered, the room already was crowded.

(Without commas, these sentences would each contain a stumbling block for the reader.)

3b. To show omission of part of a construction parallel with a preceding construction.

In the proposed curricula the chemical engineering course would last five years; the petroleum, six.

But: Some live by their brains and others by their wits. (No comma is required for clarity.)

3c. To set off the second (occasionally the first, when negative) of two members of a compound construction in order to improve smoothness of reading or ease of comprehension.

This rule permits the use of commas with the types of compound constructions in which the mark would not ordinarily be employed either for separation (P 1) or for setting off one member from the

87

rest of the sentence (P 2). Cf. Explanation (3) under P 1 and Class (9) under P 2a.

RIGHT: Please come to my office any morning, or any afternoon by special appointment. (The comma indicates that "by special appointment" restricts the second member of the compound, "any afternoon," but not "any morning.")

3d. To separate from a verb an unusually long substantive phrase or clause that functions as its subject.

Whether a block in a railway system should be a few hundred feet or several miles long, is determined by the traffic.

Caution: Do not abuse Principle III by scattering commas in positions where they have no genuine clarifying value. Moreover, do not think of it as a convenient substitute for Principles I and II, which are far more important and which it supplements without in any way replacing. Finally, do not *habitually* attempt to clear up obscure constructions by introducing extra commas, for very often a fundamental revision would be preferable. Below is shown, as an example, a sentence that a writer tried to perfect with a comma. Although the sense is clearer with the punctuation than it would be without it, the phrasing remains unwieldy.

AWKWARD: The cushions on the capitals of the Municipal Art Museum and the Erechtheum also, are divided vertically by eight narrow pearl beadings.

IMPROVED: On the capitals of both the Municipal Art Museum and the Erechtheum, the cushions are divided vertically by eight narrow pearl beadings.

SEMICOLON (;)

4. Where two independent clauses or two groups of words containing independent clauses are joined without a coördinating conjunction, a semicolon is regularly used for separation. (Principle I)

Your time is limited; so begin at once and work steadily.
Some power always is dissipated when energy is transformed in a machine; if this loss is less than half, the machine is over 50 per cent efficient.
East-bound Number 15 was on time; west-bound Number 15 was ten minutes late.

EXPLANATIONS

(1) *Definitions:*

Independent clause: A clause * which, so far as grammatical correctness is concerned, could stand by itself as a separate sentence. Independent clauses either have no special introductory words or else are introduced by:

    (a) coördinating conjunctions (see below)

    (b) conjunctive adverbs (the most common are *however, thus, so, then, nevertheless, also, besides, hence, moreover, furthermore, consequently, therefore, accordingly, still,* and *otherwise*)

    (c) transitional phrases (such as *for instance, for example,* and *of course*)

    (d) transitional clauses (chiefly *that is,* the abbreviation *i.e.,* and the expanded form *that is to say*)

Coördinating conjunction: See definition under P 1.

(2) Concerning three or more independent clauses in series when the last two are joined by a coördinating conjunction, see *Note 2* under P 1a. If no coördinating conjunction is used in the series, semicolons are regularly employed to separate all the clauses.

(3) Use of the comma instead of the semicolon required by P 4 is a serious error known as the *comma splice* (abbreviated *C. S.*). Observe that this term does not mean all faults of the comma. The comma splice often results from confusion of conjunctive adverbs (see list above), which introduce independent clauses, with subordinating conjunctions (such as *when, where, unless*), which introduce dependent clauses. Mere omission of the comma does not correct a comma splice; on the contrary, it creates another serious blunder known as the *fused sentence.*

4a. A comma splice can be corrected in any of four ways: (1) substitution of a semicolon for the comma; (2) substitution of a period, thus creating two sentences from the original one; (3) insertion of a coördinating conjunction; (4) revision of the sentence in such manner as to subordinate part of it, leaving only one independent clause in place of the original two. Usually (4), subordination, is best, since the author probably supposed one of the two independent

---

* Every clause is either independent or dependent. A clause is a logical and structural unit that contains a subject and a predicate; other logical and structural units are called phrases. All phrases and dependent clauses *depend,* directly or indirectly, upon an *in*dependent clause in the same sentence.

clauses to be dependent when he first wrote and punctuated the sentence.

WRONG (comma splice): Rain water can soak into the marshy ground to only a slight depth, thus it mostly drains into ditches and ravines.

WRONG (fused sentence): Rain water can soak into the marshy ground to only a slight depth thus it mostly drains into ditches and ravines.

RIGHT (so far as punctuation goes): Rain water can soak into the marshy ground to only a slight depth; thus it mostly drains into ditches and ravines.

IMPROVED (by subordination): Because rain water can soak into the marshy ground to only a slight depth, it mostly drains into ditches and ravines.

The comma splice is most likely to occur: (a) before a conjunctive adverb (see the example just above) or a transitional phrase or clause; (b) between two independent clauses of a quoted sentence when an explanatory element, referring to the quotation, is inserted at that point.

WRONG: The water wheel is a prime mover, in fact, it probably was the first of all prime movers.

RIGHT: The water wheel is a prime mover; in fact, it probably was the first of all prime movers.

WRONG: "The range of the Spitfire is very short," he wrote, "that of the Thunderbolt is nearly three times as great."

RIGHT: "The range of the Spitfire is very short," he wrote; "that of the Thunderbolt is nearly three times as great."

The correct position of the semicolon is after the interrupting element. The comma preceding "he wrote" helps to set off that element as semiparenthetical; this comma has no organic relation to the first clause, with which it is associated in appearance only. (For the position of the comma before rather than after the quotation marks, see P 13.)

ALSO RIGHT: "The range of the Spitfire," he wrote, "is very short; that of the Thunderbolt is nearly three times as great."

The interrupting element is now completely set off by commas, for it does not split the quotation between independent clauses. The semicolon naturally reverts to its original position immediately at the end of the first clause.

5. Semicolons may replace commas between coördinate elements to improve the clarity of a sentence. (Principle II)

Main division made evident in presence of other commas:

I respectfully direct your attention to Title I, Section A, Subsection 1, Paragraph (3); and to Title II, Section C, Subsection 1, Paragraph (8).

Men and machines, under certain conditions of modern industry and warfare, have sometimes been mutually destructive; but men and machines, united for peace and construction, can be the best of friends.

The Mechanical Engineering Society elected the following officers: President, John Smith; Vice-President, Henry Arthur; Secretary, Albert Morton; Treasurer, James Goodson; Corresponding Secretary, Jay Brook; and Sergeant-at-Arms, Joseph Alling.

Indication of shift from indicative to imperative mood, or from a statement to a question:

We have given you the facts; but do not act upon them hastily.

We must have facts; for what is action without knowledge?

Because semicolons are employed in modern punctuation to separate sentence members of equal rank, they cannot replace commas to set off a nonrestrictive or semiparenthetical element from the rest of the sentence. If a construction of that kind is not clear with commas, either the phrasing should be revised, or, occasionally, dashes (P 7) may be used. Adopt the working rule, which admits few exceptions in good contemporary style, that what lies on the right of a semicolon should be grammatically equal to what lies on the left.

COLON (:)

Only one fundamental principle governs the colon. A few minor uses, more or less arbitrary, are so well understood as to require no discussion (e.g., indications of time, as 2:25 p.m.), or else are unimportant for technical writing.

6. The colon is a formal sign that something of significance, referred to or implied in what has just been said, is to follow directly.

Note: The first word after the colon should not be written with an initial capital unless it is a normally capitalized expression or opens a new sentence. Even an independent clause, if the writer wishes it to be taken integrally with the preceding introductory expression, should begin with a small letter.

In accordance with the basic principle (P 6), colons are employed:

6a. After introductory expressions containing follow(s) or following.

Among other instruments, the following were available for use by students: an ultramicroscope, a refractometer, an interferometer, and several electrometers.

6b. Before semiparenthetical expressions of introduction such as namely, viz, for instance, for example, and e.g., but only if a formal sign to introduce the coming matter is especially wanted. Ordinarily terms of this kind are preceded merely by a comma, or by a semicolon if they stand between independent clauses. Whatever the mark of punctuation before them, they are regularly followed by a comma, *not* by a colon.

Even the most primitive races possess elementary tools, for example, knives and instruments for boring.

The South American Indians had many artistic crafts; in particular, weaving and pottery-making were brought to a high degree of perfection.

A great invention marked the dawn of the useful sciences: namely, the invention of the wheel. (The colon here is used as a more formal introductory sign than the comma. The semicolon would be wrong, because *namely* does not introduce a second independent clause.)

Caution: The expression *such as* is neither preceded nor followed by a colon. A comma goes before *such as* (and also after the entire construction being introduced, unless the latter ends with the sentence or at some other mark of punctuation) if the examples cited are nonrestrictive (i.e., given only for illustration), but no comma follows *such as*. Commas are not placed either before or after *such as* if the examples are restrictive (i.e., given to limit the principal word to a certain subclass).

RIGHT (nonrestrictive): A commission house handles all kinds of fruits, such as apples, bananas, lemons, and berries.

RIGHT (restrictive): The ranch produced fruits such as lemons, oranges, and grapefruit in prodigious quantity, but its soil was unsuited to any except citrus crops.

6c. To introduce a list or a citation. A colon may be employed for this purpose even without a formal introductory expression. (Cf. 6a and 6b.)

Hundreds of men of all degrees of skill worked in the shop: designers, machinists, welders, riveters, painters, helpers, and wipers.

One creation, among all recent developments and refinements of the munitions of war, is unique: the atomic bomb.

6d. After the salutation of a business letter. A comma usually follows the salutation of a personal letter, but the colon always may be used with propriety.

A semicolon is never correct after the salutation of any kind of letter.

6e. Regularly, before a quotation of more than one sentence; sometimes, for added formality, before shorter quotations.

6f. Between two independent clauses when the second clause explains or exemplies what has been said in the first. Substitution here of the colon for the normal semicolon (cf. P 4) is not positively required. The colon can on occasion be of real service to the reader by showing at a glance that the second clause clarifies a preceding thought instead of adding a new one.

In modern times precise measurement has replaced the search for ultimate causes as the chief end of science: instead of asking "Why?" we now ask "Exactly when?" and "Exactly how much?"

DASH (—)

The dash is not, as some careless writers appear to imagine, a general substitute for commas, semicolons, and other marks. It has definite, limited functions; frequent occurrence of dashes is a sign of either loose syntax or slipshod punctuation.

Do not confuse the dash (a long mark —) and the hyphen (a short mark -). They are unrelated except in similarity of appearance.

All uses of the dash of any significance for technical writing are summed up in a single principle, as follows:

7. Within a sentence—that is, anywhere except at the beginning—elements may be set off by dashes to indicate that they are partially but not completely parenthetical.

EXPLANATIONS

(1) The principle is illustrated by the sentence in which it is stated: the element reading "that is, anywhere except at the beginning" is partially parenthetical but not completely so. Material put between dashes is less completely abstracted from the sentence, and therefore is more emphatic, than if it were enclosed in parentheses.

(2) Dashes can replace commas to set off semiparenthetical elements having internal commas. At times, also, they replace commas to set off nonrestrictive modifiers having internal commas. (For explanations of the terms, see P 2a and P 2b; cf. discussion under P 5.)

Note: A parenthetical independent clause should not be set off by commas. Either dashes (P 7) or parentheses (P 8) should be used. Concerning semiparenthetical clauses such as *that is,* see Class (3) of P 2a and *Caution* at end of P 2a.

PARENTHESES (( )) AND BRACKETS ([ ])

Both parentheses and brackets are employed to enclose parenthetical material. The important difference between their respective functions is easy to grasp by comparison of P 8 and P 9.

8. Parenthetical material originally included within a writer's own statements is enclosed in parentheses, and remains so enclosed if the passage is quoted. (Principle I)

9. Parenthetical matter inserted into a quotation or paraphrase of the statements of another is enclosed in brackets. (Brackets would also be used by a writer to insert a parenthetical remark into the quotation of a previous statement of his own.) *(Principle II)*

James Truslow Adams (1878–1949; an eminent American scholar) writes: "Rhythm in the universe is fundamental in its effect upon our minds. For example, certain rhythmical waves of energy (to use a loose term), of long wave length and low frequency, make themselves known to us as heat;

94

increase the rhythm a little by shortening the wave length and increasing the frequency, and we become aware of them as color; continue the process [it is clear that Mr. Adams is referring to the electromagnetic spectrum], and we get electricity; do so again, and we get a phenomenon which we can use but cannot perceive by our senses, the X-rays; and so on. . . ."

(The brief identification of J. T. Adams is entered in parentheses; however, the explanation inserted into the quotation is placed in brackets, which sharply distinguish it from the phrase, "to use a loose term," enclosed in parentheses by Adams himself when he wrote the passage. Note that no extra quotation marks are employed, for the brackets themselves are a signal of "time out" from the quotation, whereas the parentheses (within a quotation) are understood to enclose a part of the original matter.)

Note: Brackets also can be employed to enclose parenthetical matter inside other parenthetical matter. Since this usage conflicts with the basic distinction between parentheses and brackets, some writers prefer a second pair of parentheses even within an outer set of the same marks.

Special rules. The following three rules concern both parentheses and brackets in relation to adjacent punctuation:

9a. Defer any mark of punctuation that would normally occur at the same point where parenthetical matter is inserted into a sentence, and place that mark after the second parenthesis or bracket. Do not place an extra comma, semicolon, or other mark before the first parenthesis or bracket.

WRONG: Sir Isaac Newton, the father of classical physics, (his dates are 1642–1727), has been much degraded by the silly popular legend about the falling apple.

RIGHT: Sir Isaac Newton, the father of classical physics (his dates are 1642–1727), has been much degraded by the silly popular legend about the falling apple.

Exception: P 9a does not apply to a mark of punctuation, such as a comma or colon, that precedes a number, letter, or other symbol enclosed in parentheses and used to introduce one of the items in a series.

9b. In parenthetical matter within or at the end of an enclosing sentence, omit all punctuation before the second parenthesis or bracket except a question mark, an exclamation point, quotation marks, or the period of an abbreviation. Even though parenthetical matter inside an enclosing sentence is an independent clause and, therefore, potentially a complete sentence, it is not followed by a period other than one used to mark an abbreviation; also, the first word is not capitalized.

A force pump is used (see Figure 1).

(Observe the small *s* and the position of the one period, *after* the closing parenthesis, when the writer wishes the parenthetical matter to be regarded as part of an enclosing sentence.)

9c. When parenthetical matter is a separate sentence or a series of sentences, punctuate it according to all normal rules. Be sure to distinguish between 9b and 9c.

The distributors will handle the entire account. (See your invoice.)

(Observe the capital *S* and the position of the second period, *before* the closing parenthesis, when the writer wishes the parenthetical matter to be regarded as a separate sentence.)

PERIOD (.)

10. Do not place a period after a dependent element that is not joined to an independent clause. (Principle I)

EXPLANATIONS

(1) This error is called the *period fault* (abbreviated *P. F.*). Observe that the term does not mean all faults of the period.

(2) Every sentence must contain at least one independent clause.* See Explanation (1) under P 4 for definition.

(3) A group of words lacking a finite verb (i.e., a verb form other than an infinitive, a gerund, or a participle) is not a clause, either independent or dependent. Thus the presence of a finite verb is a

---

* Authorities differ on the question of whether this term is appropriate to a simple sentence, such as "The engine is being repaired." Conservative grammarians would say that the quoted sentence consists of an independent predication, rather than of one independent clause; however, the distinction is of little importance.

necessary, though not a sufficient, condition of a complete sentence. Since dependent clauses also contain finite verbs, the period fault can occur even when a finite verb is present; *however, where there is no finite verb there is no sentence.* Obvious exceptions, like sentences consisting of the single word "Yes" or "No" in answer to a question, need hardly be mentioned.

WRONG: The circuit reduces the middle frequencies. The seeming effect being the same as though the low and high frequencies were amplified. (The second group of words has a finite verb, "were" or "were amplified," but the verb serves in a dependent clause, introduced by "as though.")

RIGHT: By reducing the middle frequencies, the circuit has the seeming effect of amplifying the low and high frequencies.

11. When a declarative or imperative sentence ends with an abbreviation,* one period is used for closing both the abbreviation and the sentence. (Principle II)

A fuller course of engineering could be taken in the V–12 program than in the wartime N. R. O. T. C.

Exception: If the last word of parenthetical matter at the end of an enclosing sentence is abbreviated, two periods are used, one before and one after the parenthesis or bracket. See the first sentence of Explanation (1), P 10, for an example.

QUESTION MARK (?)

12. The question mark is used primarily to indicate a direct question. It has one minor function: it may be inserted (usually enclosed in parentheses) to indicate doubt as to a preceding detail.

The invention of the Archimedean screw, an ancient device for raising water, is attributed to the Greek philosopher Archimedes, B.C. 287(?)–212. (The date of Archimedes' birth is conjectural.)

Caution: Avoid careless use of the question mark after *indirect* questions (characteristically beginning with *whether,* but also with many other introductory words). Avoid, too, the device of calling attention to humor or irony by means of question marks and exclamation points.

* Concerning omission and inclusion of the period in technical and nontechnical abbreviations, see Chapter V, M 33.

Note on interrogative phrasing of requests: Correspondence (rarely any other kind of writing) may contain requests or suggestions which, formally, are questions. Sound punctuation demands that the question mark be employed. If, on the other hand, the logic of the sentence is felt to conflict with use of a question mark, the phrasing can easily be changed.

WRONG: Will you please send me your latest price list.

RIGHT: Will you please send me your latest price list?

ALSO RIGHT: Please send me your latest price list.

QUOTATION MARKS: DOUBLE (") AND SINGLE (')

The following two special rules pertain to both double and single quotation marks:

13. A period or comma *always goes to the* left *of all adjacent quotation marks. Any other mark of punctuation is placed inside the quotation marks if it is a part of the quoted matter; otherwise it is placed outside.* Thus commas and periods have a fixed, conventional position with respect to quotation marks (always preceding them), whereas all other marks of punctuation take a logical position.

"First," announced the lecturer, "we shall consider the word 'engine'; second, the word 'motor.' "

Note 1: When an enclosing and a quoted sentence come to a simultaneous close, only a single terminal mark is used. If one sentence is interrogative and the other declarative, the question mark rather than the period survives.

The lecturer raised the question, "What is the difference between the word 'engine' and the word 'motor'?"

Did you hear the lecturer say, "There is an important distinction between the word 'engine' and the word 'motor' "?

Did you hear the lecturer ask, "What is the difference between the word 'engine' and the word 'motor'?"

Note 2: The quoted sentence, rather than the enclosing sentence, determines whether the question mark is entered inside the double quotation marks; review the second sentence of P 13, above.

14. When a quotation continues through more than one paragraph, all quotation marks that remain in force between successive paragraphs

are again written at the beginning of each new paragraph. The effect of this rule is to remind the reader that a quotation (indicated by double quotation marks) or, perhaps, a quotation within a quotation (indicated by double quotation marks followed by single quotation marks) extends into the new paragraph. For a possible exception, see P 20, including Explanation (3). (See an occurrence on pages 408–409.)

Caution: Except, of course, where a quotation ceases, no quotation marks are placed at the end of paragraphs.

15. Double quotation marks enclose direct quotations of what has previously been written or spoken, either by others or by the writer himself. (Principle I)

Note 1: The first word of a quoted *sentence* is written with an initial capital, but not the first word following an interrupting element unless it is normally a capitalized word. In general, only those capital letters present in the original matter appear anywhere in a quoted passage.

RIGHT: "Selection cannot produce new genes," writes Dr. Altenburg; "it can only isolate Mendelian classes which contain desired genes."

Note 2: An indirect quotation (commonly, but not always, introduced by *that*) is not enclosed in quotation marks. Occasionally, however, a writer calls special attention to a partial retention of the original wording by quoting a passage within an indirect quotation.

RIGHT (indirect quotation): The assistant promised (*or:* promised that) he would meet us in the laboratory.

RIGHT (indirect quotation with partial direct quotation): He tells how he was summoned to what he calls "the den of lost hopes" to present his plan. (Observe that no initial capital letter and no preceding comma are necessary for directly quoted passages embedded in an indirect quotation.)

16. In citations of titles, double quotation marks enclose the title of a piece of writing not published separately (in particular, the title of an article). (Principle II)

By the middle of next week, you should have read the following two articles: "Gravity" in *The Encyclopedia Scientifica* and "Dynamic Measurement" in the current number of the *Engineering Epoch.*

EXPLANATIONS

(1) An article is published, not separately, but *in* a larger publication: in a periodical, encyclopedia, or other composite work. The same principle applies to short stories, essays, and the like.

(2) Note that the titles are not originally placed in quotation marks at the head of the actual piece of writing. They are quoted only when they are *cited* elsewhere, as in a footnote.

(3) Titles and names of separate publications (e.g., books and journals) are italicized (underscored) when cited. This distinction between separate publications and writings not published separately is important; it should not be obscured by indiscriminate use of quotation marks for all titles.

Note: If the title or name of a publication cited in italics, according to Explanation (3), should happen to contain an italicized expression, that expression would be written with double quotation marks in the citation.

17. Double quotation marks enclose substandard expressions (e.g., slang) used within a dignified composition; and also at least the first occurrence of purely technical vocabulary, or of standard words used in an abnormal sense, within a composition intended for nontechnical readers. (Principle III)

A "Christmas tree" is more serious to oil production than its gay name may suggest.

EXPLANATIONS

(1) Substandard diction in general, including slang, should be enclosed in quotation marks if used in serious compositions, but good style ordinarily excludes such expressions.

(2) Purely technical writing employs many words from standard English that are given a special sense, as well as many terms wholly unknown to the general language. Expressions of this kind, if in good standing within the technical field, are freely written without quotation marks in writings intended for specialists. In a composition for the lay reader, however, they should be quoted (and of course also clearly explained) the *first* time each occurs; subsequent use of quotation marks is then optional.

Note: Do not employ single quotation marks for substandard and technical diction, on the incorrect assumption that double quotation marks are reserved for direct quotations.

18. Double quotation marks may enclose words, letters, and figures that merely name themselves, especially when the elements so marked really are being quoted. (If quotation marks are not employed, italics are used instead.) *(Principle IV)*

He carelessly pronounced his "and's" (or: *and's*) without the final "d" (or: *d*) sound.

Is that a "7" or a "9"?

Note: Both quotation marks and italics may be omitted with figures, but not with words and letters, used in this way.

19. Double quotation marks already present *in quoted matter are changed to single quotation marks; conversely, single quotation marks already present in quoted matter are changed to double quotation marks. (Principle V)*

Occurrence of single quotation marks may be observed in the examples under P 13 and *Note 1* to that rule. If the lecturer quoted in the examples had simply written down his remarks, instead of being quoted by someone else, he would have put "engine" and "motor" in double quotation marks (cf. P 18).

Note: P 19 assumes that the writer of the matter being quoted has followed the standard system outlined in the first four principles. If he has used the opposite (chiefly British) system of employing single quotation marks for P 15, P 16, P 17, and P 18, with double quotation marks only for a quotation within a quotation, the quoter retains the original marks *without change* (besides, of course, surrounding the quoted passage with the usual double quotation marks).

20. An extended quotation of two or more paragraphs, or of a single paragraph or less running to several lines, may be given without enclosing quotation marks by being separated from the main text and set in from the left margin. (It may be set in from the right margin, also.) (Principle VI)

Numerous examples of this usage will be found in other chapters of the book. See, for example, the quotations beginning on pages 2 and 161.

EXPLANATIONS

(1) P 20 furnishes a convenient method of giving occasional or frequent long quotations by way of illustration, elaboration, or proof.

(2) Such indented quotations are always single-spaced on the typewriter, except that like all other single-spaced matter, they should be double-spaced between paragraphs.

(3) P 20 supersedes P 19: that is, all single and double quotation marks of the original passage are retained without change. Furthermore, P 14 is suspended, in that no quotation marks are added to those of the original passage (if there are any) at the beginning of paragraphs.

21. Omissions from quotations. An omission within a quotation is indicated by marks of ellipsis, which consist of three dots (. . .); if they happen to follow a period, four dots in all are used, the period included. Omissions before and after a quotation of one or more complete sentences need not be shown by marks of ellipsis, though the marks may be included if the writer wishes to point out that the passage quoted is not the whole of the original text. When a quotation begins in the middle of a sentence, either of two devices may be employed: (1) marks of ellipsis may be entered and the first word written without capitalization (unless it is a normally capitalized expression), or (2) the initial letter of the first word may be capitalized and enclosed in square brackets.* If a quotation ceases before the end of a sentence, marks of ellipsis are required; punctuation (such as a comma) occurring at that point in the excerpt may be either retained or dropped before the marks of ellipsis.

HYPHEN (-)

22. A word split between two lines of writing, typing, or print must be broken   at a point of syllabic division   by means of a hyphen placed at the end of the first line (never at the beginning of the second). (Principle I)

Note: A *long* numeral written in figures may similarly be divided. Numerals are split only after one of the commas preceding a group of three digits; the hyphen follows the comma at the end of one line, and the remaining figures (without a second hyphen) continue at the beginning of the next line.

* Marks of ellipsis are optional when the second method is followed. As an example, see the beginning of the selection from Everett E. Thompson, page 4 of Chapter I.

Use the dictionary. A word that is to be divided between lines must be looked up *in a dictionary.* Do not guess where a word is divided. Is *knowledge,* for instance, correctly broken after the *w* or after the *l; engineer* after the first *n* or after the *g,* and after the *i* or the *n?* Look up those two words as a brief exercise in using a dictionary to verify the syllabic division of words. If you do not know what symbols your dictionary employs to indicate syllabication (various dictionaries employ different systems, but each has a consistent method), find out at once by consulting the explanations given in its preliminary pages. In general, a word may be split wherever the spelling (not pronunciation) entry includes any indication of division: viz., accent, hyphen (or equivalent mark), or dot.

Take note of the following restrictions:

22a. A word of one syllable, no matter how many letters it contains (e.g.,   straight, strength, twelfth),   is never divided.

22b. The inflectional endings "(e)d" and "(e)s" commonly are assimilated in sound with the last syllable of the stem (e.g., "revoked," "assembled," "knives"), but sometimes they are separately sounded (e.g., "repeat·ed," "apparatus·es," "wash·es"). Words may not be divided before either ending unless it is   pronounced   as a separate syllable.

For a rule applying to the syllabic division of words originally ending in a consonant, expanded by the addition of a suffix beginning with a vowel, see Chapter III, *Note 5* to D 5.

22c. To split a word after the first or before the last letter is regarded as bad style. If the word has no other syllabic division (e.g., "a·bout," "ston·y"), it should be kept intact on one line or the other. (Likewise, a figure should not be split after only one digit.)

23. Numerous compound words are hyphenated as part of their regular spelling, regardless of their position in the sentence. (In general, such compounds can be found in dictionaries.) **(Principle II)**

Caution: Most of the standard American dictionaries do *not* employ the ordinary hyphen to show that a word *contains* a hyphen.* Know

---

* Some use the hyphen to indicate simple syllabic division. In those dictionaries it must not be mistaken for a sign of hyphenation (except when the word happens to be split between two lines of text; cf. Principle I: P 22.

the mark by which your own dictionary indicates a hyphenated word: e.g., a double hyphen (=) in the *Century,* a very heavy dash in the Merriam-Webster series, a similar but lighter mark in the *New College Standard Dictionary,* and a tilted double hyphen in the previous Funk & Wagnalls dictionaries.

Expressions falling under P 23 belong to many classes. The hyphen sometimes distinguishes two words otherwise identically spelled (e.g., *re-creation* from *recreation*), one part of speech from another (e.g., the verb [*to*] *filter-press* from the noun *filter press*), or a combined form from its component elements taken separately (e.g., the adjective *over-all,* optionally written *overall,* from the preposition *over* plus the substantive *all*). Sometimes the hyphenated expression has few or no close analogues, as *loud-speaker, give-and-take,* or the pair *toxin-antitoxin* and *toxin-anatoxin.* Sometimes, on the contrary, an entire group of related words is uniformly written with hyphens, notably the whole series (other than a few like *selfish*) beginning with *self.* Compound units of measurement—e.g., *foot-pound, volt-ampere-hour, kilowatt-hour*—are usually hyphenated unless connected by *per* (*miles per hour, revolutions per minute,* etc.).

Note: Since even the largest dictionaries cannot include all possible instances of certain classes belonging to P 23, writers must rely partly upon observation and generalization. In particular, compound adjectives consisting of an adjective plus a participle (e.g., *bitter-tasting, white-veneered*), an adverb not ending in *ly* plus a present participle (e.g., *fast-drying*), or a noun plus a past participle (e.g., *firebrick-lined*), unless entered in the dictionary as solid words, may be assumed to be automatically hyphenated.

23a. Compound numbers. Both cardinal and ordinal compound numerals from *twenty-one* (*twenty-first*) through *ninety-nine* (*ninety-ninth*), including the same forms occurring in worded fractions (e.g., *three twenty-seconds*) and worded longer numbers (e.g., *five hundred and thirty-six billion*[*th*], are written with the hyphen.*

23b. Repeated vowels. Words in which the same vowel (usually *e* or *o*) is written and pronounced twice in succession (e.g., *re-election, co-operate*) generally are hyphenated. When the repeated vowel is *o* (seldom when it is *e*), a diaeresis (formed with two raised dots)

---

* On the question of when numbers and fractions are spelled out and when they are written with figures, see M 25–32 in Chapter V.

over the *second* vowel often is alternative to hyphenation (e.g., *co-ordinal* or *coördinal*). A form with neither hyphen nor diaeresis sometimes also is permissible as a third choice (e.g., *co-ordinate, coördinate,* or *coordinate*), and in certain scientific terms (e.g., *zoology, microorganism*) is the usual spelling.

23c. Changing forms. Normally, the history of compounds in English begins with two words (e.g., *horse power* or *basket ball*) that after some time acquire a hyphen (e.g., *horse-power, basket-ball*) and eventually may solidify into one word (e.g., *horsepower, basketball*). Determination of the correct form at any given time may be difficult because of variant usage, but a good recent dictionary will record the current practices of careful writers. As modern scientific style shows a certain antipathy to hyphenation, new compounds like *air-conditioned* usually (but not invariably) soon follow the many existing prototypes (e.g., *airtight, fireproof*) and fuse to single words. Technical nouns of the general type of *hookup* and *shutoff,* formerly hyphenated, now are almost all written solid. Notice, however, that the same combinations are two separate words (*hook up, shut off,* etc.) when the first element is a verb.

24. Two or more ordinarily separate words are hyphenated when used as a compound adjective (i.e., with a single adjectival force) preceding the modified noun. (In general, such compounds are not entered in dictionaries.) **(Principle III)**

> The builder of the bridge, a *much-respected* ENGINEER, wore ordinary overalls of *light-blue* DENIM, and continually puffed *two-for-a-nickel* CHEROOTS. (Each of the hyphenated compound adjectives precedes the noun it modifies, shown in capitals.)
>
> *But:* The builder of the bridge, who was much respected as an engineer, wore denim overalls of ordinary light blue and continually puffed cheroots of the kind sold two for a nickel. (This sentence contains no compound adjective preceding modified nouns.)

Principle III (P 24) pertains only to individual words that *acquire* a hyphen or hyphens by coming together as a compound adjective preceding a noun which they modify as a unit. It has no reference to the following classes of expressions that generally can be found entered in dictionaries: (1) compound adjectives belonging to P 23 (e.g., *up-to-date, self-contained, happy-go-lucky*) and hence automatically hyphenated in *any* position, before a noun or elsewhere; (2) solid words used adjectivally (e.g., *streamlined* [locomotive], *waterproof* [fabric], *teardrop* [shape]). In addition, it does not apply to: (3) an uncompounded adjective preceding and modifying a noun phrase that consists of more than one word. (Observe the difference between *high-power tube,* in which *high-power* is a compound adjective modifying *tube,* and *high power output,* in which the *high* is a single adjective modifying *power output.*) Review the discussion of coördinate and noncoördinate adjectives in *Exception 2* to P 1b.

Importance in technical writing. Compounds of the type found under P 24 are especially common in technical writing (e.g., *two-cycle engine, wrought-iron grille, end-to-end arrangement*). Because the compounds usually are specially constructed for each individual occurrence (e.g., *a one-inch board, a 2½-inch board*), or else consist of words normally joined in other constructions without hyphenation (e.g., *end to end, wrought iron*), such expressions have little tendency to consolidate into single words. Cf. P 23c; see also *Exception 2,* below.

Exception 1: The hyphen is not commonly used: (a) when the first member of the combination is an adverb ending in *ly* (e.g., *a beautifully finished print, newly coined silver*); (b) when the group consists of two proper nouns (e.g., *Cape Horn waters*) or a proper adjective joined with a proper noun to form a name (e.g., *United States citizens*). This exception does not, however, operate to suppress the hyphen following an adjective or noun ending in *ly* that serves as the first element in a compound adjective. Most such compounds (e.g., *sly-faced rascal, friendly-looking natives, fly-infested region*) fall under Principle II and are explained by the *Note* to P 23.

Exception 2: When an adjective-noun combination is very strongly felt to retain its independence and normal meaning while temporarily functioning as a compound adjective, the hyphen is optional: e.g., *high-school credits* or *high school credits, twentieth-century science* or *twentieth century science.*

Note 1: The hyphen is always correct in such expressions, and very commonly it is preferred to stress their adjectival function.

> *Exception 2* is given in order to explain the absence in readings of certain hyphens that would appear to be required by P 24. Students are advised, however, to follow the principle rather than the exception.

Note 2: A numeral and a unit of measurement preceding a noun (e.g., *a five-foot pole, a 125-mile channel*) constitute a pure adjective, as shown by the singular *form* of the unit of measurement even when the sense is plural. Therefore, other than according to *Exception 3,* below, the hyphen should not be omitted.

Exception 3: When a hyphenated number combines with one or more other words to form a compound adjective, further hyphenation is optional: e.g., *a thirty-five-foot well* or *a five-eighths inch bit* (but *a 1⅝-inch bit*).

24a. Fractions. Fractions used adjectivally demand the hyphen by Principle III (P 24). Thus a hyphen is written in the expression *a one-third payment,* but by many writers not in *one third of the money.* (Hyphenation of fractions used as nouns is optional.) The hyphen in a compound ordinal numeral (*twenty-first* through *ninety-ninth*), whether or not employed as part of a fraction, is required by P 23. Thus two hyphens (the first by P 24 and the second by P 23 as well as P 24) would be necessary in *a two-twenty-fifths part,* but only one hyphen (by P 23) in *an increase of two twenty-fifths.*

24b. Suspensive hyphens. In a pair or series of compound adjectives modifying the same noun, often the second element of all but the last compound can be dropped. To mark each omission, a so-called suspensive hyphen, which makes evident the nature of the construction and thereby prevents possible ambiguity, is a convenient device. Although generally avoided in literary style as awkward, suspensive hyphens are customary in technical composition.*

RIGHT: The company operates steam-, gasoline-, and Diesel-powered equipment.

APOSTROPHE (')

The apostrophe is employed for three entirely different purposes. Most errors occur as violations of P 26, which should be studied with particular attention.

25. In a contraction an apostrophe replaces the omitted letter or letters. (Principle I)

---

* *Solid* compounds also may be written with the suspensive hyphen: e.g., *mega-* and *microcephalic*). Sometimes other parts of speech, besides adjectives, take suspensive hyphens: e.g., *milli-, centi-, and deciliters.*

EXPLANATIONS

(1) When the omission of one or more letters is at one position only, the apostrophe is placed there: e.g., *doesn't* for *does n(o)t.*

(2) When letters are omitted at more than one position, the place of the apostrophe is determined by custom, aided by the analogy of similar contractions: e.g., *shan't* from *sha(ll) n(o)t.*

(3) Contractions must be distinguished from abbreviations, normally (but often not in technical style)* written with periods; and from so-called short forms, not marked with either periods or apostrophes (e.g., *plane* for *airplane, math* for *mathematics, taxi* for *taxicab*).

Note 1: Keep in mind that *it's* is a contraction, not a possessive form. Never write *it's* for *its* (meaning "belonging to it").

Note 2: Because most contractions and short forms—see Explanation (3), above—are colloquialisms, they are infrequent in formal writing.

26. The apostrophe marks the possessive case of all nouns ** and of indefinite pronouns; it precedes a final s that is added only because the word is possessive, but otherwise follows the whole word. (Principle II)

EXPLANATIONS

(1) The indefinite pronouns that occur in the possessive case end in *one* (including the word *one* itself employed in an indefinite sense), in *other* (including the word *other,* its plural, and *another*), in *body* (but the word *body* alone is a noun), and in *either* (including, besides *either* itself, only *neither*). Most indefinite pronouns are singular; the sole possessive plural of an indefinite pronoun is *others'* (singular, *other's*).

(2) No other kind of pronoun or pronominal adjective shows possession by means of the apostrophe.

WRONG: who's (for *whose*); her's; it's (for *its*—a very common error); our's, ours'; your's, yours'; their's, theirs'. (These forms typify the same kind of blunder as would be committed in writing "hi's" for *his.*)

---

* See the discussion and table of technical abbreviations in Chapter V: M 33–38.
** Not every noun, however, normally occurs in the possessive case. Cf. Chapter II, G 18.

(3) The following procedure, which takes advantage of the fact that pronouncing a possessive word is easier than writing it, will quickly reveal the correct position of the apostrophe in the possessive case of any noun or indefinite pronoun.

A. First, write the nonpossessive (i.e., the common nominative and objective) form, singular or plural as desired:

| *Singular:* | man | dog | ox | deer | beau | mouse | father-in-law | other |
| *Plural:* | men | dogs | oxen | deer | beaux | mice | fathers-in-law | others |

B. Second, add an apostrophe at the right, thus:

| *Singular:* | man' | dog' | ox' | deer' | beau' | mouse' | father-in-law' | other' |
| *Plural:* | men' | dogs' | oxen' | deer' | beaux' | mice' | fathers-in-law' | others' |

C. Third, pronounce the word (or combination of words) in the sentence you are trying to write, where it functions as a possessive. If, but only if, a "z," "ez," or "s" sound is heard *in addition to* the letters already present, write in an *s* after the apostrophe.

| *Singular:* | man's | dog's | ox's | deer's | beau's | mouse's | father-in-law's | other's |
| *Plural:* | men's | dogs' | oxen's | deer's | beaux' | mice's | fathers-in-law's | others' |

Exception: Possessive proper nouns in geographical and organizational nomenclature tend to reject the apostrophe: e.g., *Pikes Peak, Engineers Club, Peoples Trust Company.* Consult a dictionary, atlas, or gazetteer for a place name; and the advertising matter or official stationery of an organization.

27. The apostrophe and an *s* form the plural of: (1) a word or letter written as the name of itself; (2) a figure or symbol. (Principle III)

Dot your *i's* (*or:* "i's") and cross your *t's*; round your *8's* and distinguish your *to's* from your *too's.*

The square of 2 is both the product and the sum of two 2's.*

¶'s or ¶¶ (Some symbols have an alternative plural formed by doubling.)

Note: The plurals of certain capitalized abbreviations that contain more than one part—in particular, those referring to academic degrees and collegiate groups—also are written with the apostrophe. The period of the last abbreviation is placed in its normal position, not after the added *s*. (Discretion should be exercised in the use of such abbreviations in formal writing, as many are either colloquialisms or slang.)

* Concerning italics and quotation marks for words, letters, and figures that merely name themselves, see P 18.

Twenty M.D.'s and five D.D.S.'s were awarded.

C.E.'s and Ch.E.'s take few advanced courses in common. (*Or:* Civil and chemical engineers take few advanced courses in common.)

The I.Q.'s of all applicants will be tested by the Department of Psychology.

CHAPTER V

MECHANICS AND FORM IN TECHNICAL MATTER

Students and practitioners of the pure and applied sciences are concerned largely with forms: of nature and of human invention, singly and in static or dynamic arrangement. To say that their compositions should tend to reflect this special interest in form and mechanics is not just a figure of speech, for a cast of mind can show itself in many different ways. The accuracy, neatness, economy, and conformity to standards that would be expected, for example, in the design of a structure are qualities, also, of good technical composition.

GENERAL STANDARDS

MATERIALS

Paper. In reports, in manuscripts for the press, in business letters, and in student themes, paper measuring eight and a half by eleven inches should be used unless a different size is required for some specific purpose. For all compositions in longhand other than handwritten letters, so-called theme paper, ruled with lines one-fourth inch or slightly more apart, is convenient. For typescript and letters, unruled paper must be employed. Cheap paper in ruled and unruled sheets is obtainable everywhere, but should be tested with an ink eraser to make sure that it does not readily rub into holes. For more important writing, such as articles submitted for publication and business correspondence, a heavier and more highly glazed stock is desirable. Under no circumstances should onionskin be used except for carbon copies; even then, it is of no particular value in making a single duplicate unless the small saving of file space is an advantage. (A carbon copy should never be submitted in place of the original.) Prepared plotting paper for graphs can be bought in sheets of the

111

same size as those used for manuscript or typescript. Drawing paper of good quality, with sometimes a thinner (but tough) stock for tracings, is a necessary auxiliary to technical composition.

Writing instruments. The best way to write almost anything is to typewrite it, using a black ribbon. For longhand, use only black or blue-black ink (desirably of the permanent kind); if you insist on a more brilliant color, avoid any except blue. Select a pen that flows freely without blotching or scratching, and that does not tire your hand after a few pages of steady copying. Use a steel pen and India ink for drawing and similar work. Never submit any part of a formal composition, or send any business letter, written in pencil.

THE FINAL DRAFT

Practically never will the first and last versions of a writing be identical; usually, several intermediate drafts should be composed, criticized, and modified in a series of efforts (if possible, on more than one day). When you are ready to prepare the final copy, clear your desk or table of objects not related to that task. If you typewrite, make certain that the typeface is clean and the ribbon sufficiently fresh. Have everything needed, including a good dictionary, ready to hand. Then, take your time, with accuracy, legibility, and neatness as objectives, and with constant realization that you will be judged solely by the document you are then drawing up.

1. Margins and spacing. Approximately equal margins, from one inch to an inch and a half in width, should be left blank on all four sides of fully written or typewritten sheets. If the paper is to be bound or stapled within a folder, enough additional space (up to about an inch extra) must be allowed at the left so that the margins will *appear* equal with the folder open for reading. The title at the head of the first page of a composition (or of a new chapter or section) usually is dropped more than the regular distance from the top; in typescript, around two inches or more. Single-spacing with the typewriter is acceptable for most purposes, but double-spacing normally is required in material intended for publication, and often, also, in student papers submitted for marking by an instructor. Even when generally single-spacing, *always double-space between paragraphs.* (When double-spacing, do not triple-space between paragraphs.) Block style, with paragraphs beginning at the left margin instead of being indented in the conventional manner, is correct (but optional) only in single-spaced texts, since an indication of a new paragraph is furnished by the extra spacing between lines. Use of block style in handwritten papers is not recommended.

2. Page numbers. The first page may be left unnumbered, or (except in letters) the figure *1* in parentheses may be centered near the bottom of the sheet. Subsequent pages are numbered *2, 3,* etc., without parentheses, at the upper center or right of the sheets. In business letters the numbers of all pages after the first are properly indicated at the upper left, as part of a heading containing also the name of the addressee and the date. (See also pages 194, 274, 282.)

Note: If a titled chapter or section starts on a new leaf, the page number may be omitted, or centered at the bottom, as on the first page of the whole composition. Every chapter (except in a *printed* book or report) usually has its own separate pagination, but pages ordinarily are numbered consecutively throughout a series of sections.

3. Illustrations. Drawings and similar matter should be carefully prepared, with attention to neatness, accuracy, clarity, proportion, and general good form including the mechanics, spelling, and grammar of lettering. If relevant, scale and compass bearing should be clearly indicated. Guide lines and other pencilings must be cleanly erased. Sketches, diagrams, photographs, blueprints, and the like are inserted into manuscripts in two different ways:

(1) If small, they may be placed directly upon the regular pages, either between lines of writing or in box inserts flush with either margin. They should have at their bottom the designations "Figure (*or:* Fig.) 1," "Figure 2," etc., with or without descriptive captions.

(2) In general, the more satisfactory method is to interleave separate sheets (not numbered as pages) of drawing paper, or other appropriate material, as near to the related text as possible. (Sometimes illustrations are assembled at the end, a position less convenient to a reader, but usual in manuscripts prepared directly for the printer.) Extra sheets of illustrative matter have at their bottom the designations "Plate I," "Plate II," etc., usually with descriptive captions. Plates commonly include two or more related parts, which on each plate should be designated as "Figure 1," "Figure 2," etc., and which also may have individual captions.

Note 1: A separate sheet not divided into several parts sometimes is designated as a figure rather than a plate, and as such is numbered in rotation among the figures entered on the pages of writing. However, the term "plate" probably has better sanction for any extra page of graphic matter.

Note 2: Cross references in the text, which should be given even when the visual material is in close proximity, take such forms as "See Figure 7," "See Plate I," "See Plate IV, Figure 1," "See Figure 4 of Plate II." Descriptive captions of figures and plates may also be mentioned in the cross references.

Note 3: Observe the use of Arabic numerals for figures, and of Roman numerals for plates.

Note 4: A table commonly is treated as a figure or plate, but numerous tables occurring in the same paper may be separately designated and referred to as "Table 1," "Table 2," etc.

4. Proofreading. The proofreading, a most important stage of making the final draft, should never be done hurriedly or carelessly. It must be *thorough*. Even if you have the copying done by someone else, you alone assume responsibility for the corrections of any paper you submit or any letter you mail. In the text, carefully verify quotations, specifications of quantity, and punctuation and spelling; in drawings, tables, and so forth, check spelling and references of lettering, completeness of lining, and accuracy of calculations and formulae. A moderate number of changes in ink (not pencil) or on the typewriter are permissible, but a page requiring extensive revision should be recopied. (Do not forget to proofread the new draft.) To delete a letter, word, or passage, draw a horizontal line through it, black it out, or erase it; do *not* enclose it in parentheses. To insert a word, letter, or (short) passage, type or write it directly above the line and indicate the position of entry by a caret ($_\wedge$). To correct a misprint, first delete it (preferably by erasing) instead of merely writing the new character or word over the old.

5. Cover and title page. Most short papers require neither a cover of special material nor a title page; longer ones may have the latter without the former; full-length reports usually have both. Uniform specifications suited to all kinds of compositions are impossible; however, students should follow closely all directions given by their instructors, and others should follow accepted models or style manuals in their particular fields. A title page always states the title and the individual or group authorship; in addition, it may give such other information as the person or authority to whom the paper is presented, and the date and place of submission. A pleasing arrangement, involving balanced spacing and varied use of capitals, small letters, and italics (underlining), is best worked out by experiment. A stiff cover can be obtained at small cost. The sheets should be stapled or stitched within the bend, or (as a makeshift) clipped to the top of the back leaf. (More expensive covers contain loose-leaf binders, which usually require that the sheets be punched twice at the left margin.) Some indication of subject (not necessarily the full title, if long) and authorship should appear on the cover; an instructor may require a definite form of endorsement, typically including the course and section number and the date. Decoration seldom is desired; cleanness always is.

CAPITAL LETTERS AND ITALICS

CAPITALIZATION

6. Capitalize the first word of any sentence, including a directly quoted sentence.

RIGHT: "The attendant's room in the modern filling station," writes G. B. Bailey, "is a problem in glass." He adds: "It must, to quote Burnett's article again, 'instantly show the approaching customer to the attendant and the sales display to the approaching customer.'" (*Note:* The words "is" and "instantly" are not capitalized, because they are not the first words of sentences.)

7. Capitalize all words except *articles (a, an, the),* **short prepositions, and (at the writer's option) long prepositions and short conjunctions, in titles of books, articles, periodicals, and other writings and publications.** For examples, see M 21.

8. Capitalize proper nouns and proper adjectives. For examples, see M 10–16.

Definition. A proper noun or adjective is one that names or refers to a *particular* person, organization, place, thing, or concept as opposed to a class of persons, organizations, etc. We call *man* a common noun, *Darwin* and *Darwinism,* proper nouns; *Darwinian,* a proper adjective. The word *doctrine* (common noun) is of general application, but we capitalize *Monroe Doctrine* (proper noun).

115

Note on capitalized verbs: The capitalization of verbs (mostly ending in *ize*) derived from names tends to be discontinued when the origin is no longer strongly felt. However, a verb of this class (especially one based on the name of a nation) may retain its initial capital permanently. In doubtful instances, a recent dictionary should be consulted.

RIGHT: pasteurize; mesmerize; bowdlerize; (to) japan. *But:* Americanize; Anglicize *or* anglicize (first form preferable); Bessemerize *or* bessemerize (both forms equally acceptable).

9. Problematical expressions. Although the definition under D 8 is easy to state and exemplify, it is for two reasons difficult to apply in detail. First, "general" and "particular" are relative rather than absolute terms; second, there is a large element of the arbitrary and conventional in the discrimination of capitalized and uncapitalized expressions. To illustrate, everyone capitalizes the name of any make of motorcar, such as *Oldsmobile* or *Dodge,* regarding it as a *particular* (proper) noun, even though from another point of view it should be conceived as the name of a class of automobiles, and therefore as a common noun. Originally *Diesel* (from the name of the inventor of that engine, Rudolf Diesel) was always capitalized, but an increasing tendency to drop the capital is now evident. Eventually, perhaps, the word will be universally written with a small *d,* just as *china* (porcelain), *morocco* (leather), *ampere, macadam,* and numerous other terms from proper names have long since lost their capitals. Scientific nomenclature abandons the initial capital much more readily than does general vocabulary. The process does not always proceed evenly; in particular, a proper adjective may cease to be capitalized earlier than a name on which it is based. Occasionally, glaring inconsistencies can be pointed out; for instance, we print in *roman* type but supplement Arabic figures with *Roman* numerals.

Note: Technical and semitechnical proper nouns and adjectives generally come to be written with small letters at about the same time as corresponding, closely related verbs (see the *Note on capitalized verbs* under M 8): e.g., *pasteurization* (cf. *pasteurize*); *mesmerism, mesmerist,* and *mesmeric* (cf. *mesmerize*); *japan* (lacquer), noun and adjective as well as verb.

Aids to decision about capitalization. The following generalizations will be found helpful. Many times, however, whether a word should or should not be capitalized can be determined only by consulting a recent dictionary or closely observing authoritative current writings.

10. Nouns and adjectives indicating definite, or fairly definite, geographical regions are capitalized, but nouns of mere direction and the corresponding adjectives are not.

RIGHT: We enjoyed the paradox of sailing west and arriving in the Far East.

He lives in the Middle West but is familiar with Southwestern life.

We steered a northwesterly course.

11. Names of professions and trades are not capitalized.

RIGHT: My colleagues included physicians, biologists, and chemical engineers.

12. Names of subjects of study are not capitalized, except those of: (1) specific, individual courses; (2) all languages.

RIGHT: I did not like science when I studied it in high school, but I have found the Physics 10 course in college extremely interesting; chemistry, however, has been hard for me, perhaps because I was placed in Chemistry 11B, an advanced section.

She is majoring in French, with English history as her minor subject.

One brother is taking a premedical course; a second, civil engineering; the third, architecture.

13. Names of plants, animals, minerals, chemical substances, medicines, and diseases are not capitalized, except: (1) registered trade names; (2) personal or place names serving as part of names of diseases and of natural substances; (3) terms of biological classification other than the names (written in small letters) *of species and of subspecies or varieties.*

RIGHT: Samples of calcium, lime feldspar, and hydrated ferric oxide are available.

In treatment of hay fever and asthma, ephedrine is prescribed as a palliative.

RIGHT: The housefly (genus *Musca,* species *domestica*); plaster of Paris; Hodgkin's disease.

14. *A noun may be capitalized when it is used as a substitute for, or as a reduced form of, a proper name.*

RIGHT: He carried on research at the Foundation for three years.

        The President has the right of unlimited time on any radio channel.

15. *Nouns like* street, building, club, park, mountain(s), *or* river *are capitalized when they form part of specific names.* (The practice of printing them with a small letter is a journalistic mannerism which has little support in the best general and technical usage.) The word *the* occurring with such expressions is not, however, capitalized.

RIGHT: Main Street; Grant Park; Mount Pleasant; the Cape of Good Hope; the Engineering Club; the Atlantic Ocean.

16. *Expressions like* Rule I, Figure 3, *and* Plate II *are specific; therefore the noun should be capitalized.* In a few such expressions (mostly with abbreviated forms), however, a small letter is customary or optional: e.g., *p.* (plural, *pp.*), *vol(s).* or *Vol(s).*, *no(s).* or *No(s).*

17. *Use of initial capitals to emphasize or dignify certain words that would not otherwise be capitalized is, in general, poor style.*

18. *Full capitals and small capitals.* If, in a heading on a title page, or elsewhere, a writer wishes the printer of his manuscript to set an entire word or passage in FULL CAPITALS, he underscores that portion with three straight lines. If he wishes a word or passage to set in SMALL CAPITALS, he underscores it with two straight lines. For SMALL CAPITALS WITH MAIN INITIAL LETTERS IN FULL CAPITALS, he underlines the initial letters three times and the rest twice. (A normal initial capital occurring in ordinary text need not, of course, be underscored or marked in any other special way; it is simply written or typed in the large form.)

ITALICS

19. *Italics are indicated in longhand and on the typewriter by a single underscoring, with a straight line, of the words or characters to be italicized.*

Note: **Bold-faced type** is indicated by a wavy line. See also M 18, *Full capitals and small capitals.*

Italics are used for several different purposes:

20. *To emphasize a word or passage.* Do not rely largely on this easily overworked means of emphasis, which loses force if employed to excess.

21. *To refer to names of books (including encyclopedias and other composite works), periodicals, and works of art.* Titles of articles, essays, stories and the like, normally published *in* books or periodicals, are placed within quotation marks. (Use of either italics or quotation marks indiscriminately for all classes of titles would obscure an important bibliographical distinction.)

RIGHT: On the reading list for the first week were the article "Gravity" in *The Encyclopedia Scientifica,* one called "Dynamic Measurement" in the current number of the *Engineering Epoch,* a clipping from the Tinville *Courier* (*or:* from the *Tinville Courier*) headed "Scientists Learn New Facts from Local Mine," and some quotations in E. L. Baro's *A Millennium of Master Builders* from the notes of Leonardo da Vinci, who (besides creating such masterpieces as *The Last Supper*) was interested in both practical and speculative science.

Note: Usually the word *the* and the name of a town or city are not italicized preceding the name of a periodical, but a preliminary article (*A, An, The*) is treated as part of the title of any other publication (e.g., a book) or of the name of a work of art. Observe the examples in the sentence marked RIGHT, directly above.

22. *To write a foreign expression, or its abbreviation, that has not become naturalized to standard English.* The genus and species in biological nomenclature are regarded as belonging to this class.

RIGHT: *mot juste; ibid.* (abbreviation of Latin *ibidem*); *Apis mellifera* (honeybee). *But* (naturalized expressions): et cetera (*or:* etc.); vice versa; aileron; phlox; ion; gneiss.

23. *To indicate words, letters, and figures that merely name themselves.* Quotation marks may be employed in place of italics, especially for words that really are being quoted from another context.

RIGHT: He dotted the *e* in "receive" (or: *receive*) with the same motive that caused him always to form his *6's* and *5's* as nearly as

possible alike. (Because "receive" is quoted from a certain sentence or paper, just as here it is quoted from the example, there is special reason for placing quotation marks around the word even though italics are employed elsewhere in the sentence. However, italics or quotation marks throughout would be correct.)

Note: Both italics and quotation marks may be omitted with figures, but not with words and letters, used in this way.

24. To write the name of a particular vehicle or craft, whether of land, air, or water.

RIGHT: He arrived on the Burlington *Zephyr.* The Zeppelin *LZ–46* fell in flames. The *Sally Anne* is a trim schooner. (Note that the word *the* and such names as *Burlington* and *Zeppelin* are not italicized —except in rare situations, like the present sentence, where they merely name themselves as words. Cf. M 23.)

THE WRITING OF NUMBERS

25. Basic rule: In general, use figures for any number that cannot be written in one or two words. Do not, however, start any sentence with a figure; either spell out the numeral or bring it to a different position by recasting the sentence. (For use of the hyphen in compound numbers and in fractions, see Chapter IV: P 23a and P 24a.)

RIGHT: 101; 121st; 132d (*or:* 132nd); 143d (*or:* 143rd); 154th; 3,649,501.

Note: Commas mark off each three digits, beginning at the right, or at the decimal point, of numbers expressed in figures. Use of a comma with a four-digit number (e.g., *7485* or *7,485*) is optional.

RIGHT: Seven; fourth; thirty-six; seventy-second; one hundred; nine hundredth; eighty-five thousand (the compound element counts as one word, making a total of two for the whole expression); twenty-three thousandth; eight billion; forty billionth.

Fractions. The basic rule for expressing numbers includes fractions and mixed numbers as well as integers.

RIGHT: $1/101$, $8\frac{3}{4}$.

RIGHT: one half; seven eighths; three twenty-fifths.

Note: The expression *a half* (as opposed to *one half*) can be regarded either as a fraction or as an ordinary article-and-noun group.

Thus *three and a half* or *3½* would each be acceptable as conforming to the basic rule. The same principle, of course, holds for *a third, a fourth* (or: *a quarter*), etc.

Special rules.

26. Science is most hospitable to figures. In purely technical style (i.e., in compositions written by specialists for reading by other specialists), numbers above ten seldom are spelled out unless they represent approximations.

27. Worded numbers almost never occur in drawings, graphs, tabular matter, and the like (except occasionally to prevent confusion, as *one 4-ply tire*); or before abbreviations; or after such expressions, whether abbreviated or not, as *vol., page* (or: *p.*), *no.,* and *Figure* (or: *Fig.*).

28. In a sentence, paragraph, or other unified passage where, according to the basic rule, both figured and worded numbers might occur, all numerals may be given consistently in either figures or words. When this practice (which is optional) is followed, literary style generally prefers words; technical, almost invariably, figures.

29. Figures are employed (often in parentheses) to indicate divisions or classifications of subject matter.

30. Decimals, with any associated integers, and Roman numerals obviously can each be written in only one way.

31. Exact percentages commonly are expressed by figures.

32. Figures ordinarily are used for any date or street address. However, words may be employed for the *name* of a street (e.g., *78 West Fourth Street*).

Note: Indications of pronunciation, in the form *st, nd, rd, d,* or *th,* need not be added to the figure expressing a date of a month, but should be placed after a street name that is a long number conventionally expressed in figures.

RIGHT: July 26.   901 East 125th Street.

ABBREVIATIONS

Technical standards. The system of abbreviations proposed by the American Standards Association has been so generally accepted that technical students should consider the *American Standard Abbreviations for Scientific and Engineering Terms* * a necessary professional handbook. As preliminaries to the following list of frequently needed forms, which by permission has been adapted from the recommendations of the Association, several explanations are necessary:

33. Although, in general, periods are omitted, they are used in a few expressions to prevent possible ambiguity (e.g., *car.,* rather than *car,* for *carat*). In addition, retention of periods is desirable in long-established nontechnical abbreviations (*e.g.* is an instance), a type not included in the bulletin.

34. Except when the contrary is explicitly indicated (only in certain nontechnical or semitechnical terms), the given form of abbreviation represents both the singular and the plural. Thus, *cu ft* signifies either *cubic foot* or *cubic feet; kva,* either *kilovolt-ampere* or *kilovolt-amperes.*

35. At least in sentences, abbreviations for names of units of measure should be employed only after numerals. (The question is not likely to arise in tabular matter, where numbers are almost certain to precede such abbreviations.)

36. An abbreviation should be used only if its meaning will be clear to the intended reader. When in doubt, do not abbreviate; or else construct a less compressed form of abbreviation, as *cu ft per min* in place of *cfm.*

37. Abbreviations are properly read aloud by pronunciation of the full words for which they stand. (If these words are Latin, as *id est,* represented by *i.e.,* it is customary to substitute the English translation, as *that is.*) Seeming exceptions like *log* are to be regarded as colloquial "short forms," analogous to *math, phone,* and *lab,* rather than as abbreviations in the strict sense.

* Published as American Standard Z10.1–1941 (price: forty-five cents) by the American Standards Association, Incorporated, 70 East Forty-fifth Street, New York 17, N. Y.

38. List of Abbreviations Frequently Employed in Technical Writing.

absolute—abs

air horsepower—air hp

{ alternating current—ac

alternating-current

(adjective)—a-c

amount—amt

ampere—amp

ampere-hour—amp-hr

angstrom unit—A

antilogarithm—antilog

approximate(ly)—approx

atmosphere, -pheric—atm

atomic number—at. no. *or* Z

atomic weight—at. wt

{ audio frequency—af

audio-frequency

(adjective)—a-f

average—avg

avoirdupois—avdp

barrel—bbl

Baumé—Bé

board feet—(*See* feet board

measure.)

boiling point—bp

brake horsepower—bhp

British thermal unit—Btu *or* B

bulletin—bull. (*plural:* bulls.)

calorie—cal

candlepower—cp

capacity (electric)—k

carat—car.

centigrade—(*See* degree centi-

grade.)

centigram—cg

centiliter—cl

centimeter—cm

chapter—ch. *or* chap. (*plural:*

chs. *or* chaps.)

chemical—chem

chemically pure—cp

coefficient—coef

cologarithm—colog

compare—(*See* confer.)

compound—comp

concentrate(d)—conc

confer (i.e., compare [with])

—cf.

constant—const (mathematical

symbol, k)

cosecant—csc

cosine—cos

cotangent—cot

cubic centimeter—cu cm, cm^3, *or*

(liquid, meaning milliliter) ml

cubic feet per minute—cfm

cubic feet per second—cfs

cubic foot—cu ft

cubic inch—cu in.

cubic yard—cu yd

cycles per second—(spelled out,

or:) c

cylinder—cyl

decibel—db

degree—deg (symbol, °)

degree centigrade—C

degree Fahrenheit—F

diameter—diam

{ direct current—dc

direct-current (adjective)

—d-c

ditto (i.e., the same)—do. (in

tables sometimes symbolized

as ")

double—dbl

dozen—doz

efficiency—eff

electric—elec

electromotive force—**emf**

123

equivalent—equiv

et cetera (i.e., and so forth)
—etc.

Fahrenheit—(*See* degree
Fahrenheit.)

farad—(spelled out, *or:*) f

feet board measure (board feet)
—fbm

feet per minute—fpm

feet per second—fps

Figure—(only preceding a numeral; usually capitalized:)
Fig. (*plural:* Figs.)

fluid—fl

foot—ft

foot-pound—ft-lb

for example—e.g. (*exempli
gratia*)

frequency—(spelled out)

fusion point—fnp

gallon—gal

gram—g

henry—h

high-pressure (adjective)—h-p

horsepower—hp

horsepower-hour—hp-hr

hour—hr (in astronomical
tables, h)

inch—in.

inch-pound—in-lb

inches per second—ips

indicated horsepower—ihp

inside diameter—ID

joule—j

kilocycles per second—kc

kilogram—kg

kiloliter—kl

kilometer—km

kilovolt—kv

kilovolt-ampere—kva

kilowatt—kw

kilowatthour—kwhr

linear foot—lin ft

liquid—liq

liter—l

logarithm (common, or Briggs-
ian)—log

low-pressure (adjective)—l-p

mass—(spelled out)

maximum—max

mean effective pressure—mep

megacycle—(spelled out)

megohm—(spelled out)

melting point—mp

meter—m

micron—mu (symbol, μ)

miles per hour—mph

miles per hour per second
—mphps

milliampere—ma

milligram—mg

milliliter—ml

millimeter—mm

million gallons per day—mgd

millivolt—mv

minimum—min

minute—min (angular meas-
ure, ′; time in astronomical
tables, m)

miscellaneous—misc.

molecular weight—mol. wt

negative(ly)—neg (symbol, —)

normal strength—N

notice particularly (note well)—
N.B. (*nota bene*)

number—(only preceding a numeral; often capitalized:) no.
(*plural:* nos.)

ounce—oz

outside diameter—OD

page—(only preceding a numeral:) p. (*plural:* pp.)

parts per million—ppm
*p*H or pH—(read as a symbol
 rather than an abbreviation, by
 pronouncing the letters)
positive(ly)—pos (symbol, +)
potential (*and* potential difference)—(spelled out)
pound—lb
pound-foot—lb-ft
pound-inch—lb-in.
pounds per cubic foot—lb per
 cu ft
pounds per square foot—psf
pounds per square inch—psi
power factor—(spelled out, *or:*)
 pf
quart—qt
{radio frequency—rf
{radio-frequency (adjective)
 —r-f
resistance (electric)—r
revolutions per minute—rpm
revolutions per second—rps
secant—sec
second—sec (angular measure, ″;
 time in astronomical tables, s)
shaft horsepower—shp
sine—sin
specific gravity—sp gr

specific heat—sp ht
square centimeter—sq cm *or* cm²
square foot—sq ft
square inch—sq in.
square yard—sq yd
stere—s
tangent—tan
temperature—temp
tensile strength—ts
that is—i.e. (*id est*)
versus—vs. *or* v.
vice versa—v.v.
videlicet (i.e., namely) viz. *or*
 viz.
volt—v
volt-ampere—va
volume—(only preceding [often
 capitalized] or following a numeral:) vol. (*plural:* vols.)
watt—w
watthour—whr
wave length—wl
weight—wt
which see (used in referring by
 name to an item more fully described elsewhere in the same
 list)—q.v. (*quod vide*)
yard—yd

39. *When to abbreviate.* If a graph could be drawn to plot frequency of abbreviation against a graduated scale of styles, probably it
would show something like an even slope, rising from a minimum
of very few abbreviations in purely literary writing to a high maximum in purely technical writing. Business letters would stand perhaps
midway on the scale; however, because of their subjects, many would
occupy a technical level and, consequently, show greater use of
abbreviation. The writer on topics of pure or applied science must
govern his use of abbreviation largely by his relation to the intended
or probable reader. A report, for instance, might contain many abbreviations if it were submitted to, say, the engineer in charge of an

operational department, or to the instructor of a professional course; another submitted to, say, a public authority not composed of engineers, or to the instructor in a course in English, might be almost free of strictly technical abbreviations (or, at least, of the more unfamiliar ones) and comparatively free of others. Common sense should warn anyone against saving a few strokes of the pen or typewriter at the cost of partial failure to communicate.

SIGN WRITING

40. *Value; formation.* Every field of technical knowledge and practice develops many signs and symbols, which become indispensable by preciseness of reference combined with convenience. Although many consist of (or at least take their origin from) alphabetical letters, they are extralingual, not really part of English or any other language. Commonly they are arbitrary in form; usually they are international in acceptance. All students of theoretical or applied science must become familiar with numerous devices of this kind. The section on "Arbitrary Signs and Symbols" in *Webster's New International Dictionary* (greatly abridged in the *Collegiate*) is worth knowing, as are similar sections on "Signs and Symbols" in the *Winston* and *American College* dictionaries.

41. *Use.* Like abbreviations, but to less extent, sign writing is habitually employed in technical communications intended for readers of professional training and experience. Its greatest use is in formulae, tables, graphs, and drawings. Within paragraphed discourse, even that of a purely technical style, considerable restraint is observable in the best models. If a familiar expression in words or a standard abbreviation is available, a sign or symbol generally is undesirable because of the break it causes in the verbal flow. Thus, as examples, in textual matter *number, no., Number,* or *No.* is preferable to #; *inductance,* to *L; and so forth, et cetera,* or *etc.,* to *&c.*

CHAPTER VI

THE MAJOR FUNCTION OF TECHNICAL DISCOURSE:

EXPOSITION

The four functions of discourse. The word *discourse* signifies sustained, ordered, purposive language, in distinction from emotional exclamations and aimless chatter. All technical compositions, both written and oral, are forms of discourse. According to its several functions, discourse is divided into four basic types, or "modes": **exposition, description, narration,** and **argumentation.** Definition and analysis of the last three named will be reserved to the following chapter.

Exposition. In scientific communications exposition has larger place than any of the other forms of discourse, possibly than all the other three together, and therefore may unquestionably be termed the major mode of technical discourse. The word *exposition* is practically equivalent to *explanation,* but is more explicit because the latter word, through common use, is rather loosely employed. For instance, in ordinary speech "an explanation of what happened" might refer to a simple recounting of events (i.e., a narrative), rather than to an exposition (i.e., an explanation in the strict sense). Exposition is a principal instrument of teachers, of lecturers, and of informative writers on every subject. Almost all textbooks (this one, for instance) are basically expository; in fact, many of them are as nearly pure examples of the type as could be found among extended works. The man on the street and the woman in the home may employ narration (perhaps also description) more often than exposition; a salesman or a lawyer may earn his livelihood mainly through argumentation. But serious-minded students of science will find their staple linguistic need, certainly during their university days and probably also in later life, to be a command of clear, forthright, soundly organized expository discourse.

Composite discourse. From the outset, an important fact must be clearly understood: the different kinds of discourse are much more usually found in combination than in isolation. Indeed, a completely unmixed occurrence of any of the four is rare, for normally they interpenetrate and support one another. Like elements of matter, however, they can be isolated by analysis for separate study.

Purpose determines classification. Much as in Chapters II and III English was broken down to its constituents of grammar and diction, so in this and the next chapter the problem is to view language according to its primary functions. The terms "exposition," "expository paper," and the like should be interpreted as referring to compositions (or parts of compositions, as, for instance, a separate section of a report) of which the underlying purpose—but usually not the whole content—is expository. Incidental descriptive, narrative, and argumentative passages, serving a fundamentally explanatory intention, might well be called expository description, narration, and argumentation, respectively; or descriptive exposition, narrative exposition, and argumentative exposition.

Example. Technical discourse very frequently involves explanation of theories underlying the operation of processes and mechanisms. The student paper that follows was written, by assignment, to expound the principle of a scientific instrument unfamiliar to the assumed readers. Although, necessarily, the author included some description (partly accomplished by means of a sketch, not here reproduced), this short composition comes close to being unalloyed technical exposition.

THEORY OF THE ULTRAMICROSCOPE

When very small particles are suspended in a liquid, the resultant mixture is known as a sol. Some sols (or their coagulated forms, called gels) are important articles of commerce; as instances, everyone is acquainted with gelatin, glue, and ink. At times it is necessary to determine the dimensions of the particles in a sol. Although the particles themselves are far too small to be measured directly, this information can be obtained by indirect methods: equations have been derived for computing the dimensions of a particle if the number in a definite volume of a sol is known. The ultramicroscope was invented for the specific purpose of counting the number of particles in the given volume of sol.

The complete instrument consists of an ordinary microscope, a source of intense light, a slit arrangement, a focusing lens, and a container to hold the sol to be examined. These five parts are arranged as in the diagram.*

This special microscope requires such delicate adjustments that a skilled technician is necessary. Nevertheless, the theory on which it operates is simple and readily grasped.

The ultramicroscope is based on the principle that light is reflected in all directions when it strikes a very small particle. This is the same principle that explains why floating dust is visible in a beam of light shining into a darkened room. Each particle that is struck reflects some of the light in the direction of the microscope, which magnifies the tiny beam coming from the particle and thus makes it visible to the eye of an observer. When this reflected beam is magnified, a point of light is spread over a much larger area and the intensity is greatly reduced. For that reason, the original source must be very strong, an electric spark usually being employed because it can be made to produce an intense beam of light.

The slit arrangement is used to adjust the size of the beam, which is then focused through a biconvex lens to illuminate a much smaller volume of sol than the unfocused light would show. Without a great reduction in this manner, counting of the particles would be impossible. (To count the number contained in a small jar of jelly would take several lifetimes.) The illuminated volume must be calculated with exactness if practical results are to be obtained, for on the basis of the particles counted in a known volume the final computation of dimensions is made.

A. THE ANALYTICAL SENTENCE OUTLINE

(1) GENERAL CHARACTERISTICS

Purpose. Good planning lies at the root of successful exposition. In some instances the plan may be constructed only mentally, but unless one definitely exists in some form prior to composition, chaos instead of order is certain to result. The normal procedure, especially for a student working under the supervision of an instructor, is to draft a formal outline on paper. Of all the types, by far the best for expository writings is the sentence outline, which assures in advance a logical harmony of all major and minor thoughts. Not realizing that a large portion of the working time on any composition should be devoted to planning, students sometimes regard the construction of a sentence outline as an unnecessary delay. On the con-

* Sketch omitted.

trary, their effort is being most efficiently distributed; for material is relatively easy to arrange at this blueprint stage, but becomes very difficult to rearrange after it has been expanded into continuous text.

Note: The assumption is made throughout Section A that the outline under discussion is being drawn up as a means of planning. To outline an existing article composed by someone else has, at times, some value; the problem then is to *discover* the definite plan from which the original author worked. However, students who first write their own papers without method and afterwards attempt to outline them, "because we have to turn in an outline," usually are simply wasting time, paper, and energy—not to mention the patience of their instructors.

Definition. An outline is a schematic representation of a composition. The **sentence outline** (often, particularly as applied to exposition, called the **analytical sentence outline**) indicates logical relationships by means of single declarative sentences, ordered in a system of symbols and indentations.

Note: The **topical outline,** which shows relationships by the same system of symbols and indentations, differs radically in employing words, phrases, and elliptical ("telegraphic") constructions in place of complete sentences. Planning of technical description is often satisfactorily accomplished by means of a topical outline, but generally the sentence type is preferable for the final plan of any except very brief expository papers. Whereas a topical outline, through vague entries such as "Importance," "First step," "Conclusion," and the like, can easily be a hollow shell concealing actual ignorance, the making of a sentence outline enforces detailed knowledge of a subject down to its foundations. (Treatment of various types of outlines suited to nonexpository composition will be found in Chapter VII, including discussion and illustration of the topical outline on page 158 ff. Oral composition has special problems of planning and outlining, to be considered on pages 347 ff. of Chapter XI.)

Length. The length of sentence outlines varies greatly, not only with the size but also with the complexity of the compositions being planned. In general, the proportion between the number of words in an outline of this type and in the finished paper should fall within the limits of about one tenth and one fifth.

Preliminaries. Before starting work on the sentence outline as such, the writer must first choose a specific, limited subject which can be adequately treated in an article of the contemplated size; then he must set about assembling the needed information by thought or investigation. Usually a broad, tentative division of material begins to take shape in his mind almost from the start, followed by jottings on paper in the form of a series of topical outlines, variously rearranged as the subject matter becomes progressively fuller and clearer. The first sentence outline may be attempted about midway of the whole study; however, a perfected draft, showing the completed plan of organization, is not achieved until immediately before composition proper begins.

Note: Revisions may even become desirable still later, during the actual writing of the paper, should new interpretations occur or new material be discovered. If, however, sufficient time has been allotted to the preparatory period, nothing more than minor alteration of the outline should be necessary at this stage.

Submission. As scaffoldings are torn down following a construction, outlines usually are discarded after they have served their purpose. In books and in lengthy articles and reports, the outline normally is replaced (on publication or submission) by a table of contents, which is more compact and, from the viewpoint of a reader, more convenient. Students often are asked to submit outlines for criticism and grading, either with assigned papers or separately. An outline accompanying a theme or report should be placed at the beginning rather than at the end.

(2) CONTENT

(1. THESIS SENTENCE)

Function. The first part of a sentence outline, and the most important single entry, is the thesis sentence, which *states the unifying idea of the composition in one sentence.* The thesis is the paper in miniature, a reduction of the whole plan to a single sentence in which every thought to be developed is present in germ.

Note: The thesis sentence may or may not occur in the paper as well as in the outline, but if present it is not necessarily the first sentence of the paper, as it is of the outline. This one sentence is so broad in view as to scan, by implication, the whole discussion; like the topic sentence of a paragraph, it can appear almost anywhere in the composition, or even be repeated (most probably with some modification of phrasing) several times.

Basis. The ability to draft an efficient thesis sentence rests upon the original choice of a genuinely unified subject. For example, if a writer were inadvisedly planning to treat the history, mechanics, manufacture, uses, and probable future of the airplane in one article, undoubtedly he would find great difficulty in composing a satisfactory thesis sentence in brief form; but the unity of a more narrowly cir-cumscribed topic—e.g., jet propulsion in the Second World War—could be revealed in a sentence of moderate length. A good thesis sentence is, in fact, evidence that the ultimate paper will be properly unified, and, with the outline as a whole, greatly helps the writer to exclude extraneous discussions.

Caution: The thesis sentence does not make a statement *about* the paper; it actually *is* the paper, compressed to one sentence. Formulas such as "This report will discuss . . ." or "I plan to investigate . . .," being little more than repetitions of the title, serve no useful purpose. Only a writer who knows his subject thoroughly can draft a genuine thesis sentence. Observe the model (page 138); cf. also Rule 4 (page 134).

(2. BODY)

Logical structure. Beyond the thesis sentence, the drawing up of a sentence outline is a process of successive subordinations and coördinations by logical analysis.

Main topics. Since the thesis is the whole composition in minia-ture, the first analytic step is to divide that basic, unifying thought into its component parts. Sometimes this step is practically dictated by the statement of the thesis; for instance, "Radical extension of the life of stationary-lathe cutting tools has been effected by two new methods," stated as a thesis, obviously calls for either two main topics (one for each method) or else three (one on the problem and one each on the two methods of solution). Ordinarily, however, the divi-sion demands considerable thought, inasmuch as the same subject usually can be divided in different ways, among which the writer must choose the one best suited to his purposes and material. For example, a discussion of the uses of the radio could be broken into commercial uses, military uses, educational uses, and uses for enter-tainment; or into the uses of the radio telegraph, of the long-wave radio telephone, of the short-wave radio telephone, of television, and of radar and other specialized adaptations; or, chronologically, into early uses of the radio, uses between the last two wars, and uses since 1939. Time, place, structure, importance, purpose, and comparison or contrast are typical bases of division. Whatever principle may be selected, the main topics must cover fully, and cover only, that range of material implied by the thesis sentence. If, say, there are four main topics, their relationship with the thesis may be expressed quasi-mathematically, thus:

$$\text{Thesis} = I + II + III + IV.$$

Note: Sentence outlines do *not* contain sections labeled "Introduction" and "Conclusion." As a matter of fact, formal introductions and formal conclusions—apart from such essentially independent elements as letters of transmittal, abstracts, and appendices—have little or no value in technical writing. (They are, however, usually desirable in speaking. On all special problems of oral composition, see Chapter XI.)

Sequence. Having laid down his main topics, the writer must arrange them in a suitable order. Here, again, different plans often are possible for the same material, such as progress from earlier to later time, from nearer to more distant place (or vice versa), from simple to complex, from smaller to larger, from familiar to unfamiliar, and the like. Sometimes convention (that is, an established pattern) determines the order of treatment; occasionally, but by no means usually, the arrangement must be arbitrary because no special sequence seems better than any other. The general principle, however, is to arrange the topics in as logical order as possible.

Greater subtopics. The next process is to divide each of the main topics into its component thoughts, in the identical manner by which the thesis was broken into main topics. Precisely analogous directions for this division and for the arrangement of the resulting large subtopics should be assumed, and the same type of quasi-mathematical equations should be obtained. Thus, for example:

$$I = A + B + C. \qquad \text{(Three greater subtopics.)}$$
$$II = A + B. \qquad \text{(Two greater subtopics.)}$$
$$III = A + B + C + D. \qquad \text{(Four greater subtopics.)}$$

Lesser subtopics. In turn, each of the greater subtopics may now be divided into its component thoughts in the form of lesser subtopics, and these may themselves be further divided in the same way. The drafting of the body of the outline thus continues as a process of successive logical analyses, from each main segment of thought down to the smallest elements. In practice, the series seldom needs to be carried beyond a fourth or fifth degree of subdivision. **Cf.** Rule 6 (see especially *Note 2*) on page 135.

(3) RULES OF FORM

1. The title of the paper should be laterally centered, at least two spaces above the thesis sentence and at least an inch below the top of the page. The word "Outline" need not be included, but if written it should be enclosed in parentheses and laterally centered, at least two spaces under the title and at least two spaces above the thesis sentence. Neither the title nor the word "Outline" (if given) should be followed by a period. See the model beginning on page 138.

2. Every entry must be a single, complete, declarative sentence. Each sentence of the outline closes with a period.

Note 1: Do not employ a "telegraphic" style: that is, do not omit articles (*a, an, the*), subjects, verbs or parts of verbs, or any other sentence elements that would be present in normal written discourse.

Note 2: Do not substitute one tense for another. In particular, do not substitute the present for the past.

Note 3: Do not capitalize words that would not be capitalized in other kinds of writing.

Note 4: Do not substitute a question for a declarative sentence.

Note 5: Do not mistake a phrase or a dependent clause for a sentence.

Note 6: Do not write two sentences in a single entry.

3. The thesis sentence is preceded by the word   Thesis (*not* by the two words "Thesis sentence") **and a colon.** See the model.

4. Do not mistake a statement of the importance of the subject for a thesis. Beware of words like "important," "essential," "necessary," and "interesting." The thesis sentence is a brief summary of the paper; unless, therefore, the paper itself is definitely to be upon the importance or interest or necessity of something, such words are illegitimate. Temptation is strong to write: "It is desirable that everyone should understand the principle of the four-cycle gasoline engine," for a sentence of this kind can be dashed off with no thought whatsoever. Nevertheless, if the theory of the engine (not the importance of understanding it) is the topic being planned for discussion, it must also be the subject of the thesis sentence.

5. Particularly in the thesis and larger topics, prefer positive to negative statements. Violation of this rule is permissible when an idea to be presented is essentially negative in bearing.

6. The process of logical division should be continued as far as may be necessary for full analysis of the subject.

Note 1: Without exception, it should be carried at least one step beyond each main topic. A thought which does not require any subdivision is hardly to be regarded as a *main* topic of the discussion.

Note 2: All the coördinate items (entries of the same rank, as "A" and "B"; or "1," "2," and "3") of any one set are not necessarily divided at all, or into the same number of subordinate items. Analysis stops when, at any point, it reaches what the planner regards as logical bedrock. Observe differences in amount of coördination and degree of subordination in the first and third sections of the model.

7. Because nothing can be divided into only one part, there must be at least two main topics; and, similarly, at least a second coördinate subtopic wherever there is a first subtopic at any stage of the outline. A "I" without a "II," an "A" without a "B," a "1" without a "2," an "a" without a "b," a "(1)" without a "(2)" or an "(a)" without a "(b)" is inadmissible because illogical. If other parts are not discoverable or significant, then presumably the one part is *equal* to the idea next above it and, therefore, should be absorbed into the statement of that thought. For instance, do not write:

    C. A pinion is a small cogwheel.

        1. It is the smallest member of a train of gears.

Either write:

    C. A pinion is a small cogwheel.

        1. It may function as the smallest member of a train of gears.

        2. It may gear with a rack.

—or write:

    C. The smallest cogwheel of a train of gears is a pinion.

Exception: Since no logical necessity compels the citing of more than one instance in support or illustration of a statement, a single example sometimes is given without any parallel example or examples.

8. The number of main topics, or of subtopics in any one set, should not be excessive. No definite limits can be stated, but a number over five or six is seldom desirable. When a great many topics have been tentatively listed, upon further thought they can usually be grouped and made subtopics of a small number of more comprehensive headings. Thus, instead of being enumerated as one continuous series, the many uses of X rays might be sorted so that a few would fall under each of several sentence headings, indicating various *classes* of application (perhaps experimental, therapeutic, and industrial).

9. So far as possible, state coördinate topics in similar grammatical constructions. The principle of parallel structure for parallel thoughts is even more binding in an outline, which is not designed primarily for reading, than in the composition itself, where numerous balanced constructions might be objectionably monotonous.

10. Consistently follow a standard system of symbols. The forms shown in the model are generally accepted. At its upper and mainly used levels, this system labels entries as follows: thesis sentence, Thesis; main topics, I, II, . . . ; first subdivisions, A, B, . . . ; second subdivisions, 1, 2, . . . ; third subdivisions, a, b, ...

Note 1: When division is carried further, Arabic figures in parentheses, small letters in parentheses, Arabic figures in square brackets, and small letters in square brackets may, in turn, be employed for additional stages of subordination.

Note 2: All symbols are followed by periods. When parentheses or brackets enclose a number or letter, the period follows the second parenthesis or bracket.

11. Indent approximately equal distances for each successive degree of subdivision beyond the main topics. All symbols of the same rank should be aligned, not merely in each set but throughout the entire outline. Excessively wide indentations must be avoided, especially in handwritten outlines, as they quickly result in overbalance toward the right of the sheet.

Note: The word "Thesis" preceding the thesis sentence and the Roman numerals preceding main topics are written even with the regular left margin, except that slight compensations may be made for varying widths of Roman numerals as in the printed model.

12. When an entry runs to more than one line, begin the second and succeeding lines even with the first word of the first line.

Note: The first word of the thesis is the opening word of the sentence proper, excluding "Thesis." See the model.

13. In typewriting, single-space the individual items of the outline internally, but double-space between items.

Note: In handwritten outlines on ruled sheets, no lines need be skipped. In handwritten outlines on unruled paper, the single-spacing and double-spacing of the typewriter should be imitated.

14. Subordination and coördination in the outline must truly represent logical subordination and coördination. It is illogical to write:

C. Texas produces the largest cotton crop in America.
    1. The United States is a great cotton-producing country.
    2. The United States has several important rivals in the production of cotton.

(Topics "1" and "2" are not logically subordinate to Topic "C.")

It also is illogical to write:

C. The United States is a great cotton-producing country.
    1. Texas produces the largest cotton crop in America.
    2. The United States has several important rivals in the production of cotton.

(Topic "2" is not logically coördinate with Topic "1.")

15. The members of any set of coördinate items must be mutually exclusive in content. There must be no overlapping of ideas between an "A" and a "B," between a "1" and a "2," or the like. It is illogical to write:

C. The United States is a great cotton-producing country.
    1. The South is the principal cotton-producing region.
    2. Texas produces the largest cotton crop in America.

(Topics "1" and "2"overlap.)

16. The members of any set of coördinate items must fully develop the thought of the topic to which they are subordinate. It is illogical to write:

C. The United States is a great cotton-producing country.
    1. Texas produces the largest cotton crop in America.
    2. Mississippi produces a large cotton crop.

(One of three changes should be made: an entry or entries covering the other American cotton-producing regions should be added; "C" should be revised to show that the discussion is to concern only two states; or "2" should be rephrased to indicate that Mississippi is mentioned as important or typical *among* the great cotton states, apart from the most productive one.)

(4) MODEL

The sentence outline given below, which was submitted by a student with a term paper some five thousand words in length, has been slightly edited to serve as a model of form and general method. It is not, of course, presented for detailed imitation. Different subjects naturally raise widely different questions of content and organization; every outline, therefore, is an individual problem.

THE HONEY ANTS OF MANITOU

(Outline)

Thesis: The honey ants living in and near the Garden of the Gods store a form of honey, obtained from parasites or parasitic conditions of plants, in the enormously distended abdomens of specialized worker ants immobilized in underground vaults.

I. Honey ants build large nests in the sandstone ridges outside Manitou, Colorado.

  A. The type of honey ant observed in and near the Garden of the Gods is a regional variety.

   1. It is a pale yellow ant, about half an inch long, classified as *Myrmecocystus hortideorum*.

   2. Its habitat is Colorado, where it is best known in the vicinity of Manitou, and New Mexico.

  B. This ant digs, in a sandstone ridge, a large nest, with a single large entrance and vaulted rooms.

   1. Its nest is dug in a hard sandstone ridge, usually near dwarf oaks.

   2. Its nest may occupy as much as thirty-six cubic feet.

   3. The single large entrance, set in a low mound, leads to branching galleries.

   4. The vaulted rooms have smooth floors and rough ceilings.

II. The ants obtain a clear, sweet honey directly or indirectly from other insects.

  A. Their sources of supply are oak galls, aphids, and coccids.

1. The ants lap up, during the night, drops of honey produced by oak galls.
   a. They enter nearby groves of dwarf oaks at sundown and pass from one gall to another.
   b. The cause of the galls is the presence of larvae of a gallfly.
2. The ants "milk" aphids living on wild rosebushes.
3. The ants obtain honey from coccids, including scale insects and mealy bugs.

B. The amber honey is clear and palatable.
   1. It is uniform.
      a. It never crystallizes.
      b. The color is a clear amber.
   2. It is edible.
      a. It is a solution of various fruit sugars.
      b. It has a sweet, slightly aromatic flavor.
      c. It formerly was eaten by Indians.

III. Numerous repletes—specialized, enormously distended, almost helpless workers hanging in the underground rooms —store the honey for the colony.

A. Repletes are formed from young workers by a swelling of the crop.
   1. They begin life as unhardened workers.
   2. The crop greatly distends and pushes the other organs toward the back.

B. The repletes' function is to store honey and regurgitate it when it is needed by the colony.

C. With their abdomens distended to huge spheres, the repletes hang from the ceilings of the honey-chambers.
   1. A large nest may contain three hundred repletes, suspended from the ceilings of the honey-chambers.
   2. Their abdomens become great amber spheres.

D. The repletes, being limited in movement, are largely cared for by the other ants.
   1. They can do little for themselves.
   2. They are cleaned and massaged by the other ants.

B. EXPOSITORY PRESENTATION

All the topics treated at length in the previous chapters of this book bear upon the presentation of expository material. In particular, acceptable written exposition is impossible unless grammar (Chapter II), spelling (Chapter III, pages 47 ff.), and punctuation (Chapter IV) are correct. See also, concerning principles of logic, pages 168 ff. in Chapter VII.

(1) RELATION OF PLAN AND COMPOSITION

The "blueprint" analogy. Near the beginning of Section A of the present chapter, the outlined plan of a paper was referred to as the "blueprint stage." If taken as more than a figure of speech, the implied analogy would be misleading. Since the plan for a physical construction shows spatial relations in exact proportion, it necessarily must be precisely followed by the builder. A sentence outline, however, represents *logical* relations, which are impossible to reduce to an arithmetical scale. In some parts the completed article may be only slightly amplified from the outline; in others it may require many times the original number of words, because of the terse, unemphatic style in which major and minor topics are alike outlined. Moreover, the sentence outline arranges everything in one fixed pattern. Starting always from a comprehensive idea, it works down to smaller and smaller subordinate thoughts and data. Obviously, this single pattern (which is characteristic of topical as well as sentence outlines) is not the only sound manner of organization.

Elasticity of method. The fact is that the outline serves as a place of departure and return during actual composition. In being expanded from a sentence outline, an expository writing is likely to follow a somewhat less rigidly schematic method, anticipating, deferring, adding, or combining certain points for emphasis, suspense, or other purposes of effective presentation. It may, for instance, reverse the uniform procedure of the outline by frequently passing from lesser ideas to larger; * insert some incidental material (for instance, an illustration, a summary, a transitional passage, or an introductory or concluding remark) not explicitly represented in the outline; occasionally transpose topics for special effects; and, in general, employ whatever means are most expedient in particular situations.

The outline as a control. Nevertheless, with the outline before him as a chart, the writer at all times knows exactly where he is with respect to the whole subject. He may purposively take bypaths, but he does not wander in a maze. As a rule, radical divergence from the *general* scheme shown in the outline is neither necessary nor desirable. If a paper drifts away from the basic plan, probably there are logical flaws in either the outline or the composition—or, very likely, in

---

* See the next subsection: DEDUCTIVE AND INDUCTIVE METHODS.

both. No matter how much variance is permitted in detail, the following test of over-all content always is valid: *Nothing in the outline should fail to be presented in the composition; conversely, no essential topic or major body of material in the composition should fail to be indicated in the outline.*

(2) DEDUCTIVE AND INDUCTIVE METHODS

Two diametrically opposed methods of presentation, called **deductive** and **inductive,** received their names from corresponding terms of logic.* The words are, however, more easily understood by direct reference to their Latin etymologies.

Etymological explanation. The prefixes *de* and *in* signify, respectively, "(away) from" and "into"; the root common to the words *deductive* and *inductive* is the verb *ducere,* meaning "to lead." Besides the nouns *deduction* and *induction* (the latter, incidentally, having specialized meanings in electromagnetism), English possesses also the verbs *deduce* and *induce,* together with various derivatives developed from these primary forms or their Latin originals. Usually only the adjectives and adverbs—*deductive*(*ly*), *inductive*(*ly*)—are employed in the sense here under consideration.

Difference. The deductive method starts with a comprehensive thought and "leads away from" it toward evidence, details, subordinate ideas, examples, or applications. The inductive method, on the contrary, begins with instances, evidences, analogies, problems, or minor points and builds toward ("leads into") a generalizing conclusion. Progress from the commonplace, concrete, and practical to the unusual, abstract, or theoretical is the typical inductive pattern. The deductive pattern typically exhibits or explains the familiar and ordinary in the light of an initially stated generality.

Individual value. Both procedures, the inductive and the deductive, have special advantages. Particularly for the instruction of laymen and elementary students, a technical theme often is best approached circuitously, that is, inductively. A standard arrangement is to give several instances (preferably from everyday experience) in order of increasing complexity, meanwhile pointing out in a loose way their similarity of structure or behavior, before at last formally stating the underlying scientific principle. More advanced learners, on the other hand, especially if the subject is not unusually difficult, ordinarily would prefer to have a general truth laid down in advance

* The significance of the terms *deduction* and *induction* in logic will be explained in Chapter VII. See pages 170–171.

of demonstration or application, as a frame for fitting together individual elements of the ensuing discussion.

Combination. Sentence and topical outlines are strictly deductive in method; that is to say, entries invariably follow the larger topics to which they are subordinate, and precede their own subtopics. The expository composition written from the outline is just as likely, however, to be wholly inductive as wholly deductive. Actually, unless it is extremely short, it is still more likely to combine both methods. For example, a lecturer or textbook writer might commence an explanation by phrasing, rather informally, the law of conservation of energy or the principle of the lever; then give simple instances and analogies from daily life, followed by more complicated exemplification from structural design, mechanics, or theoretical physics; and finally restate the law or principle in formal terms. An even more usual compromise between the two plans places the general law, truth, or principle near the middle of the discussion, by first establishing it inductively and afterwards applying or further explaining it deductively.

Variation. Selection of a basically inductive, deductive, or combined inductive and deductive pattern, for presentation of expository material, sometimes can be made in relation to a total composition, especially one that is to treat a narrowly limited subject briefly or with only moderate fullness. Generally, however, the question must be separately considered in different parts, often in every paragraph. Suppose, for instance, that Newton's laws of motion were to be explained. Almost certainly they would be taken up one by one, and if so the same method would not necessarily be employed for each. The relatively simple first law perhaps could be successfully presented deductively, but when the more difficult third came under consideration, at least an initially inductive approach very possibly would be preferable. (If the reader is inclined to inquire which method should be employed for the second law, he is missing the real point, which is merely that variation within a composition often is desirable. The purpose of the example is not to explain how the Newtonian laws of motion should be expounded; choice of technique for each of the three would depend partly on the exact purpose of the writer or speaker, partly on the mentality and educational background of those addressed.)

(3) PARAGRAPHING

Three criteria. Among the principles of good composition in general, three standards apply notably to the expository paragraph:

unity, coherence, and **emphasis.*** Each paragraph should treat one definite section of thought (the test of unity). It should, in addition, follow an orderly sequence in the presentation of material (the test of coherence; the word *cohere* literally means to "stick together"). Finally, it should focus the reader's attention most sharply upon the main element of the thought, and upon other elements in due proportion (the test of emphasis). Although certain characteristics of paragraph structure relate more or less directly to unity, coherence, or emphasis (e.g., transitional devices to coherence), these principles operate in conjunction, and are expressed by the whole development of a well-written paragraph.

(1. LENGTH)

The scale of unity. The question of the right size of paragraphs cannot be settled by a formula. Length might, on first consideration, appear to follow directly from the requirement of unity, each paragraph being exactly long enough to contain its segment of the general topic. Although this presumption is true enough, so far as it goes, it ignores the factor of discretion in the assignment to any particular paragraph of a relatively large or small subsection of the total composition. If, for example, several causes or results of a condition were to be explained, each could be presented in a separate paragraph or all could be treated together in one. Every expository composition is, in effect, a pyramid of progressively higher orders of unity, from the individuality of subordinate thoughts and facts at the base up to the comprehensive oneness of the whole subject. Therefore, according to the scale chosen, discussion of the same theme can be developed in many paragraphs and again in very few, yet in neither version violate the principle of unity.

Custom. Stylistic convention helps to determine the length of paragraphs. Newspapers relegate the smallest particulars of fact or event to separate paragraphs, which usually are noticeably short even though set in narrow columns. In present-day literary writing, passages of dialogue not considered, the average size is perhaps somewhere between 150 and 250 words, but a hundred years ago the figure would have been larger. Technical style, as will be seen, tolerates great latitude in paragraphing.

Faults. Purposeless fluctuation of paragraph size within a single

---

* These standards are not less important in descriptive, narrative, and argumentative paragraphs, but on the whole are much harder to achieve in exposition than in the other three modes of discourse.

paper of any kind is of course unwarranted, as it suggests, and may really indicate, needless shifts also of style and point of view. Some variation is, however, desirable—indeed, positively necessary—to lend due weight to different portions of a discussion. Successive blocks of massive paragraphs, each many hundreds of words in length, and a string of very short paragraphs are alike presumptive evidence (though not, to be sure, conclusive proof) of a shirking, in opposite ways, of the problem of paragraphing. Abnormally short paragraphs used habitually are in most contexts offensively "choppy"; at the other limit, abnormally long ones tend to obscure the natural divisions of thought and, consequently, to put a strain upon the reader's attentiveness and power of comprehension.

Variations in technical style. Nevertheless, a "right" length of paragraphs for technical discourse is impossible to state, for the range is almost unlimited. The short type, sometimes only one sentence long, is common in the clauses of specifications, and also often serves special purposes such as introduction, conclusion, summary, and especially transition. Long paragraphs, too, have legitimate functions in many kinds of scientific treatises that entail elaborate explanations. Everything considered, the proper extent of a paragraph of technical writing is much better judged by unity and clear development of subject matter than by conformity to artificially imposed limits of size.

(2. TOPIC SENTENCE)

Value. Expository paragraphs generally contain what is known as a **topic sentence,** a device that relates primarily to unity but contributes also to coherence and emphasis. The topic sentence, like the corresponding thesis sentence of an analytical outline, evidences a unified conception and sets a point of orientation for the entire organization of the paragraph. Although excellent paragraphs of exposition can be written without a topic sentence, they always are under the control of an implicit, even if unexpressed, central idea. Students do well to acquire the habit of invariably embodying this dominant thought in the definite form of a sentence, as proof of their awareness of a precisely delimited topic under treatment in each paragraph, and as a touchstone for the exclusion of irrelevant material. Occasionally, provided the core thought of the paragraph seems to be sufficiently clear, by inference, from the other sentences taken together, the tentative topic sentence will be dropped in the course of final drafting.

Note: Topic sentences are useful to paragraphs in other forms of discourse as well as in exposition. They are especially common in argumentation and fairly so in description, but have only limited applicability to narration.

Position. When a topic sentence is included in a paragraph, it most commonly is placed at or near either the beginning or the end, since these are the positions of greatest inherent emphasis. It may, however, be anywhere within the paragraph, at whatever location best suits the author's purposes. Not infrequently it is repeated or, rather, stated again in different words—usually being phrased first more concretely or loosely; afterwards, following an intervening discussion, more abstractly or definitively.* The proper placing of topic sentences in paragraphs is determined by the choice of inductive, deductive, or combined inductive and deductive method. That problem has been treated at some length on pages 141–142, which should be reviewed.

Examples. The four paragraphs below, adapted from papers by different students, illustrate several typical positions of topic sentences (italicized).

(1) *Two principles of wing lift govern heavier-than-air flight.* In the first place, air going over the curved top of the wing travels farther, in a given length of time, and thus moves faster than that passing below. Since, by a well-known physical law, any fluid loses pressure when its velocity is increased, a partial vacuum is created above the wing, causing the craft to rise. Second, the air traveling under the wing exerts upward thrust because of the angle of incidence—or, more properly expressed, the angle of attack—at which the leading edge of this airfoil is set. The same two principles are applied also in the elevators of the tail assembly.

(2) The fuel consumption per hour was found to be nearly constant, irrespective of load. The fuel consumption per brake-horsepower-hour was about three times as great at one-third as at full load, with the sharpest decrease between one-third and two-thirds load. The thermal efficiency increased almost directly as the load. Mechanical efficiency also increased with loading, tending to level off toward the top. *All values obtained showed that for greatest economy the tested engine should operate only on heavy loads, not less than 66⅔ per cent of rated capacity.*

(3) The average commercially manufactured radio, because

---

* As the fourth example appended to the next paragraph shows, the second topic sentence instead of the first may be the more concrete.

audio systems usually are fully responsive only to vibrations between about two hundred and three thousand cycles per second, is poor in tonal quality. Ordinary tone-control devices merely permit further reduction of response to the upper ranges of sound, so that more bass tones seem to be present. The result is most unsatisfactory, for high-frequency notes and overtones are essential to faithful reproduction. *What is really needed, a means of simultaneous intensification in both the very low and the very high regions, can be obtained in a specially designed tone-compensation unit.* The feedback circuit employed makes use of the fact that a large inductance offers great impedance to high frequencies but allows lower ones to pass through, whereas a condenser offers very little on the higher levels but heavy impedance to low frequencies. Inserted in a radio receiver as a single amplifier stage, this unit increases the relative sensitiveness of the audio system to frequencies less than two hundred and greater than three thousand cycles. It can be so adjusted as to yield an output signal of constant magnitude over the entire range of sounds perceptible to the human ear.

(4) Just how was a beating heart to be imitated? *As an experienced studio technician, I was sure that the real sound would not convey the right effect.* For example, a small fire actually burning and crackling results in nothing more than a dull roar if broadcast, yet a piece of cellophane expertly twisted causes hearers of the program to imagine a roaring blaze. Once I had created a magnificent rainstorm by swishing water around in an old basketball. *Whatever technique I might finally invent for simulating a heartbeat, I could assume from past experience that connecting a stethoscope to the microphone was definitely not the solution to my problem.*

(3. ORGANIZATION)

Problems. The relative position of a stated *topic* of discussion (in an expository paragraph normally conveyed by a topic sentence) and the subordinate *material* of discussion—that is to say, the question of selecting an inductive, a deductive, or a combined inductive and deductive method—has just been considered. Another major problem of paragraph organization concerns the *arrangement of coördinate details* of expository matter with respect to one another. Actually, this question is largely settled in advance if a good sentence outline is drafted, for each paragraph of the composition is likely to be developed from one of the items of the outline, including the subdivisions of that entry. Almost always the order of these subtopics in the paragraph is exactly the same as in the outline, where they already are—or should be—grouped according to a rational scheme. Sometimes, however, a whole paragraph is expanded from a simple, undivided entry; in that situation, obviously, the outline merely indicates content without throwing much, if any, light on either the details or their organization.

Development. Among the numerous ways of developing paragraphs are the following, which can be employed singly or in combinations of two or more methods within the same paragraph. All are common in technical exposition: progression through time (an essentially narrative method that may incidentally serve an expository function); progression through space, as from up to down or outside to inside (an essentially descriptive method that, too, may incidentally serve an expository function); analysis into phases, characteristics, functions, or the like; listing of evidences, instances, or applications in order of increasing complexity or decreasing familiarity; relation of cause(s) to effect(s), or of effect(s) to cause(s); comparison, contrast, or analogy.

Special arrangements must, of course, be worked out individually to suit the exact material contained in various paragraphs, for none of the generalized methods suggested above can be completely standardized. In a comparison or contrast, for instance, two essentially different plans are available: (1) each member may first be separately presented in full, and a summary of similarities or differences may then be given, or else simply left to be inferred; (2) the whole paragraph, or the whole other than a summarizing topic sentence, may consist of a point-by-point comparison or contrast. In the second of these procedures, which is often the better, corresponding parts, aspects, or qualities are examined in succession, both (or all) members being constantly treated together.

(4. *TRANSITION*)

Importance. Whatever the content and order of a paragraph, the prime consideration is that the reader should be made aware of a logical unfolding; in other words, all details should emerge in clear and reasonable relation to one another, to the unifying thought of the paragraph as a whole, and to other parts of the larger composition. This end cannot be achieved unless, in the first place, a logical plan has been adopted, but it also cannot be accomplished without skillful transition.

Between paragraphs. A few pages above, topic sentences of paragraphs were said to be "most commonly . . . placed at *or near* either the beginning or the end, since these are the positions of greatest inherent emphasis." The main reason for the qualification "or near" is that frequently the first or last sentence of a paragraph is transitional, having the task of establishing a connection with the preceding or following subject matter. Sometimes a separate transitional paragraph, usually rather brief, marks a main division of topic, often by summarizing what has just been said, what is about to be said, or both. Again, only part of the opening or closing sentence of a paragraph, which may or may not be the topic sentence, serves for transition. Occasionally no explicit transitional element is needed, as when a given paragraph obviously constitutes the next member of an already-established and continuing series (e.g., of parts or rules). In general, however, some device is employed—perhaps only an introductory word like "Second," "Next," or "Finally"; or, in some situations of technical writing, a number (commonly in parentheses) preceding each of a specially related group of paragraphs.

Within paragraphs. Internal transition is as important as the linking of successive paragraphs. Several methods of transition within the individual paragraph are at the command of a resourceful writer: (1) balanced (parallel) structure for similar thoughts or facts; (2) transitional words, phrases, and clauses (e.g., "nevertheless," "again," "on the other hand," "that is to say"); (3) complete sentences at points of major transition (e.g., "We now pass to a radically different effect"); (4) numbers or letters (commonly in parentheses) preceding either a series of specially related sentences or, as here illustrated, a list within a single sentence; (5) reference words (i.e., pronouns and pronominal adjectives); (6) repetition of significant words. On the whole, the second method (use of transitional words, phrases, and clauses) is the most important. Fortunately, the English language is rich in expressions for every class of connective idea.

Cautions. Because the methods of transition listed just above as (5) and (6) hold special dangers, they must be employed with care. Pronouns and pronominal adjectives (in particular, *this, that,* and the corresponding plurals, *these* and *those*) lose their peculiar value if they are even slightly or momentarily vague in reference. Repetition provides, not transition alone, but also emphasis; therefore only *key* terms should be so constantly and closely reused as to become noticeable. Similar dinning of minor words into the consciousness of the reader, forcing attention upon trivialities, is unwise.

Note: Merely structural elements in unforceful positions, such as articles, conjunctions, and prepositions, of course have to be repeated frequently. Nevertheless, even they can grow objectionable when occurrences of the same word are excessively clustered.

C. TECHNICAL DEFINITION

Definition is a specialized form of exposition that is important in every field, above all in the sciences.

The method of formal definition. From the Greek philosopher Aristotle (384–322 B.C.), who originally analyzed the process of definition, the traditional method still sometimes is called "Aristotelian," as well as "logical" or "formal." A completely developed formal definition includes four parts: (1) **term** (or **subject of definition**); (2) **verb** (usually a form of *to be,* but often of *to mean, to signify,* or the like); (3) **genus;** and (4) **differentia** (or **specific difference**).

Genus and differentia. Together, the genus and differentia are the heart of any formal definition. The genus names a class to which the term being defined belongs, and the differentia discriminates that particular term from all other members of the same class. Selection of a relatively broad genus obviously places a heavy burden upon the differentia. If, for example, "A prime mover is a thing which . . ." were the opening words of a definition, how conveniently could a differentia be formulated to distinguish *prime mover* (term) from every other kind of *thing* (genus)? Surely *mechanism* or, still better, *engine* would be a more serviceable choice of genus. Immediately, however, another and opposite danger is apparent: when the genus is narrowed, it may lack clearness and so defeat the purpose of definition. The ideal is a genus large enough to be instantly comprehended by the reader (or listener) and yet small enough to permit a differentia of reasonable brevity. If, as often happens, this goal is unattainable, a chain of two or more definitions becomes necessary; that is, the restricted genus of the primary definition must be defined in terms of a larger genus, which itself may have to be defined in terms of still a third, and so on through as many supplementary steps as happen to be required.

Qualifiers. The subject of definition, the verb, and the genus may be limited by modifying words, phrases, or clauses. Thus: "A *floating* bridge, *as the term is used in military history,* means a *movable* structure *in two levels,* which . . . [the differentia follows]." Whether adjectives and prepositional phrases grammatically qualifying the

genus should not be regarded, logically, as part of the specific difference, sometimes is a difficult theoretical question. Similarly, grammatical qualifiers of the verb actually may have the effect of narrow-
ing the field covered by the term under definition.

Synonymous definition. A common method of dictionary definition (in pocket dictionaries the usual technique) is the listing of several approximate synonyms of the term in question. Occasionally in
a formal definition the genus may be replaced by an *exact* synonym
of the subject (i.e., an expression of identical denotation); no differentia need then be given. Thus: "*Equus caballus* is the horse." "Pyrite
is native iron disulphide." (Concerning the function of the adjective
"native" in this example, see the paragraph labeled *Qualifiers,* immediately above.) "The sternum is the breastbone." Further information
on synonyms, including the distinction between denotation and connotation, can be found in Chapter III: D 11c and D 11d.

Errors. Three pitfalls should be avoided in definitions:

> (1) *"Circular" definition.* A term may not properly be de-
> fined by means of itself or any form of itself. "A triangle is a
> triangular figure," "An appendix is an appended member,"
> and "A voltage drop is a drop in voltage" are crude instances
> of "circular" definition.

Exception: While always theoretically at fault, this method is acceptable in practice when the meaning of the repeated word can be assumed to be entirely clear (e.g., "A cantilever bridge is a type of
bridge consisting . . ."). Also, the error can be overcome, if necessary, by a supplemental definition of that part of the subject term
repeated in the genus.

> (2) *False genus.* The genus must name a class to which the
> subject wholly belongs. "A hypothesis is a *truth* that is not yet
> established" is a faulty definition. Hypotheses are not neces-
> sarily true; many are found to be false as further evidence is
> examined.

> (3) *Inadequate differentia.* The specific difference (except,
> of course, in synonymous definition) must *fully* discriminate
> the defined term from all other species of the same genus.
> Most unsatisfactory definitions fail in this respect, but cor-
> rection often involves revision of the genus as well as the
> differentia, since these two elements stand in a reciprocal
> relation to each other. The following are examples of defini-
> tions with insufficient differentiae: "Gauges are instruments

used in scientific tests." "The meter is a basic unit of linear measurement." "A catalyst is a substance that accelerates a chemical reaction." "Optical torque is an effect produced on light by certain transparent bodies." Although inadequate in themselves, propositions of this kind are often of service in definitional discussions (see below), when joined with other explanatory statements. They should not, however, be mistaken for formal definitions and regarded as self-sufficient.

Value of formal definitions. The Aristotelian mode of definition has been subjected to much unfavorable criticism, especially by modern semanticists. (The science of meanings is called semantics.) That formal definitions have only limited utility for the transmission of knowledge, cannot be denied. Indeed, the natural way of defining by striking attributes, reinvented by every child ("A holiday means you don't have to go to school and can stay home and play"), can at times be much more communicative. Nevertheless, there is equally no doubt that formally and logically constructed definitions, as a means of *organizing* knowledge, are indispensable to science. They are, also, incidentally valuable as checks of a student's personal comprehension of technical and scientific terms. Although recitation of phraseology taken from lectures or textbooks may prove nothing except industry or the faculty of memory, ability to compose an original and, at the same time, correct definition is very nearly conclusive evidence that a concept has been mastered.

Definitional discussion. A definitional passage, either separate or contributory to a longer paper or speech, has as its purpose the clarifying of one or more terms by every available means. Only seldom is the process limited to Aristotelian definition. (Sometimes, in fact, no strictly formal definitions are given.) Among auxiliary methods often helpful are exemplification, analogy, contrast, resolution into parts or properties, etymology (attention to the source and basic significance of words and their elements), and what for want of a better name may loosely be called expanded definitional discussion. In general, an abundance of specific data and concrete imagery is desirable, to compensate for the characteristic abstractness of formal definitions.

Topics for students of technical English. Definition of the specific terms of the various sciences and technologies is part of the usual class work in those subjects. Highly appropriate to the course in technical English are general scientific words that, crossing the boundary lines of different fields, are vocabulary requirements of all: e.g., *hy-*

pothesis, theory, axiom, postulate, phenomenon, analysis, formula, deduction. In seriously attempting to define terminology of the kind just listed, the student is certain to make three significant observations:

(1) Numerous terms (e.g., *law*) have common meanings apart from their technical sense in the natural sciences. Those other meanings are likely to figure most largely among the definitions entered in ordinary dictionaries; therefore (if for no other reason) encyclopedias, dictionaries of limited fields, textbooks, and similar reference works also should be consulted. (Concerning library materials for technical research in general, see Chapter IX, pages 235–244.)

(2) Some terms have more than one scientific application. Thus *equation* may be given at least two definitions (mathematical and chemical); *induction,* several (logical, mathematical, and electromagnetical).

(3) The line of demarcation between terms of nearly allied meaning, as drawn even in careful usage, often is indeterminate. Just when, for instance, does a speculation or guess become a hypothesis, then a theory, and finally an established truth? What is the exact difference between a law and a principle? Are formulas (other than chemical) a special type of rule, or something essentially separate? Is engineering fundamentally a science or an art? Can the postulate be precisely discriminated from the axiom? These and like questions, as meeting grounds of science and language, are proper topics for discussion in a class of technical students.

D. SCIENTIFIC CLASSIFICATION

Another specialized form of exposition, closely related to definition, is classification. This chapter, for example, began with a definition of discourse, which thereupon was classified, on the basis of its several functions, into four types or "modes."

Two ways of classifying. Classification is the process by which related data are sorted into meaningful groups. The resultant categories have either *simple* or *hierarchical* structure. In the first they are distributed on one level of mutually exclusive classes; in the second, graduated in a series of levels, the divisions on each being mutually exclusive groupings of all the categories or individuals on the next lower level. Classification of levers into three types, according to whether the fulcrum, the lifted weight, or the applied force is between the other two elements, exemplifies the simple order. The biological system by which the whole animal and vegetable kingdoms are divided, redivided, and minutely subdivided, from phyla down to subspecies or varieties, provides a remarkable illustration of hierarchical classification. Every science makes large use of both forms.

Classification in science. An ideal scientific classification fulfills four conditions: (1) It is **complete,** finding a place for every part of the subject matter originally included. (2) It is **methodical,** being consistently developed from a logical plan, with no overlapping between any categories of a simple classification or between any on the same level of a hierarchy. (3) It is **natural,** rather than artificial; that is to say, the object is to discover and reveal a pre-existent order. (4) It is **comprehensive,** taking into account all significant particulars.

Classification in student composition. Classification lies in the background of many compositions on scientific technique or knowledge, but is more often implicit than explicit. Students sometimes are assigned a separate paper or oral report on one of the established classifying systems (e.g., the periodic table), or on an original or semioriginal application of principles of classification to a limited topic (which might be a phase of almost any practical or theoretical question, from tools to minerals or from radio hookups to the branches of mathematics). Exercises of this kind can be very instructive. If occasionally arranged in sets, they are a useful method of demonstrating the multiple form (involving treatment of the same subject from several different points of view) often necessary in a comprehensive classification. Thus, one student could classify dyestuffs by chemical composition (nitroso, nitro, quinoline, etc.); a second, by method of impregnation (direct, mordant, ingrain, etc.); a third, by suitability for particular materials (wool, silk, etc.); a fourth, by imparted color and shade. Similar problems in variant classification, for presentation in series by either a single student or a group, are readily devised.

CHAPTER VII

THE MINOR FUNCTIONS OF TECHNICAL DISCOURSE:

DESCRIPTION, NARRATION, ARGUMENTATION

In what sense "minor"? Communications pertaining to science and technology are chiefly explanatory; thus exposition (including definition and classification) constitutes the major part of technical composition. For two reasons, however, students of science dare not neglect the other three types of discourse. In the first place, primarily expository articles, letters, and reports almost always contain passages of narration or description, or both, and sometimes of argumentation as well. In the second place, many compositions on scientific and technological subjects are basically descriptive, narrative, or argumentative rather than expository. These three functions, then, are very far from being insignificant. They are minor only in a relative sense: that is, as severally and collectively set over against the major form of technical discourse, exposition.

Mingling of types. Just as exposition is seldom found in an absolutely pure form, at least in discussions of any considerable length, so the three types of discourse here under view can be mixed with each other, as well as with exposition, in any proportion. Argument is practically certain to require explanations (exposition), and description often involves both expository and narrative material. In the three following sections the terms "technical description," "technical narration," and "technical argumentation" will refer to the *primary intention* of compositions on scientific themes; this division by function, for the sake of discussion, is not to be taken as meaning that any rigid separation of the modes of discourse usually occurs, or should occur, in actual writing.

A. TECHNICAL DESCRIPTION

False meanings of "description." In a loose, popular sense, to "describe" is to carry on discourse in general, with the possible exception of argumentation. One hears: "He *described* the process of excavating the tunnel" (narration); "I shall now *describe* the physical laws underlying gyrostabilizers" (exposition); "to *describe* a laboratory procedure" (narration, usually mixed with description in the limited sense and with exposition). Indiscriminate usages of this nature are excusable, perhaps, in informal writing or speech; nevertheless, they should not be allowed to obscure the important specific province of description.

The sensory basis of description. Fundamentally, description is concerned with observable physical characteristics: both so-called primary qualities (those regarded as residing in the object itself), such as size, shape, and mass; and so-called secondary qualities (those mainly significant in relation to the senses of the beholder), such as color, sound, and taste. To these two, a third class of attributes, especially important in technical description, must be added: certain essential facts or relations not directly perceived, but apprehended by the mind acting upon the immediate data presented by the physical senses. If this synthetic process is complex, requiring intellectual subtlety, communication of the results would be expository rather than descriptive (as, for example, in the development of the theory underlying a mechanism). However, any particulars that are almost instantaneously grasped like ordinary primary or secondary characteristics, are among the proper material of description. They frequently include quantity, proportion, gradation, harmony and blending, contrast, large or general principles of design (as opposed to a principle of operation, which belongs to the province of exposition), and empty spaces (which are not unimportant parts of technical structures).

(1) ENUMERATION

Itemized lists. The simplest order of description, one constantly employed in technical writing, is enumeration. In most reports and articles dealing with laboratory research or with practical work in shop or field, occasion arises to itemize materials, equipment, and sometimes products also. When the form of presentation is tabular, a formal caption (e.g., *Apparatus*) often is used; captions are especially serviceable for dividing enumerated data into several categories (e.g., *Wood, Hardware, Hand Tools, Power Tools*). If the lists are not embedded in, and essentially part of, the continuous written text, tables should be treated in the manner explained in Chapter V (see M 3, *Note 4*). Sometimes a long and minutely detailed list is set apart at the end of the paper, as an appendix, to which the reader is directed by cross reference at the appropriate place (or places) in the general discussion.

Special rules of style. Two practices are customary to help compress itemized material, particularly that given in tabular form:

(1) All numbers normally are given as figures.

Exception: To avoid confusion, when two kinds of numerals precede the individual items of a list (typically stating, respectively, quantity and a specification such as size), one set of numbers (commonly the first) is written in words and the other in figures—e.g., *six 6-penny nails* (not 6 *6-penny nails*).

(2) Both abbreviations and symbols (such as the signs for inches, feet, yards, degrees, and percentage) are employed much more freely than in expanded passages of description. (See Chapter V: M 33–41.)

(2) EXPANDED DESCRIPTION

Purpose. Technical description (like all other types of composition) is of course selective. Its aim is clear, objective portrayal of a unit or system in all important phases. Sometimes simple enumeration of quantities and specifications is sufficient; often, however, more expansive description is necessary.

Pictorial aids. Drawings and photographs, obviously, are greater aids to description than to any other kind of writing. While they ought to be admitted liberally, they do not—certainly not in papers prepared for courses of technical English—take the place of language; rather, they either fully or schematically present to the eye the same information that is set forth in words. Figures and plates should be made with care and clearly integrated with the text, in which they should be directly mentioned at suitable points.

See Chapter V: M 3, *Illustrations* (including the subparagraphs and appended notes).

Problems of descriptive style. Precision and avoidance of monotony are twin problems of worded technical description. They have a kind of inverse relation, for descriptive accuracy in covering large blocks of weighed and measured, but unadorned, physical material may encourage stereotyped expression. Precise specification, not literary grace, assuredly is the prime test of scientific description. Still, conflict between these ideals really is unnecessary. If you will set down aggregates of small details frankly as lists (whether in tabular, sentence, or paragraph form), the remaining composition, being less encumbered with particulars, can attain greater fluency of style. Indeed, descriptive passages concerned with configurations, with general relationships among parts or of parts to wholes, and with transitions between enumerated data can test and reveal your best talents for writing. Incidentally, they also will challenge your power of imagination, for despite the importance of massed factual details, description fails when clear visualization is lacking.

Organization: division. Two principles of division, operating separately or together, normally govern the organization and paragraphing of expanded technical descriptions:

(1) *Reduction to parts.* The sextant, for instance, might be divided, for purpose of description, into the alidade, graduated arc, telescope, horizon glass, and handle; or a plant for contact manufacture of sulphur trioxide, into the melting pit, burner, converter, economizer, and cooler.

(2) *Varied approach.* As many points of view should be taken as the significant aspects of the subject demand. Among standard ways of describing technical apparatus and constructions are the over-all view; front, side, back, and top (plan) views; and various sections (cross, longitudinal, etc.) and "cutaway" views.

Organization: order. In outlining and composing, a descriptive writer should place himself mentally in the position of the prospective reader. Accordingly, he should attempt to find that order which, as the full description unfolds, will correspond most nearly to the latter's developing curiosity and understanding. So far as possible, spatial patterns are always desirable in description. Among common principles of sequence in space are the following: passage from top to bottom, or from bottom to top; passage from one side to another; passage from outside to inside, or (less usually) from inside to outside; circular or peripheral motion; and direct, spiral, or concentric movement from a center outward, or from a perimeter inward. Nonspatial patterns occasionally are preferable, chiefly to show the order in which individual pieces of apparatus or parts of a mechanism actually are engaged in an operation.

Outlining. To plan an expanded technical description, either a sentence outline or a topical outline is serviceable. The latter type, which has the advantage of being simpler and more rapidly prepared, is likelier to prove adequate for description than for exposition, since logical analysis is much less fundamental in descriptive than in expository papers. In style the topical differs from the sentence outline in two important respects: (1) a formally stated thesis is optional rather than obligatory; (2) the entries are words and clipped phrases, or if some sentences are employed, they too are stripped to "telegraphic" style by omission of articles and possibly other words (even subjects or verbs). The system of indention and labels (Roman and Arabic numerals and capital and small letters, with and without parentheses) is exactly the same as in the sentence outline.

For a detailed discussion of the sentence outline see Chapter VI, Section A.

Form and content. The principal entries of a normal outline (of either type) would indicate either the parts into which the object of description is being divided, or else the several approaches according to which details are to be organized and exhibited. In the former plan different approaches might, perhaps, constitute the largest subtopics (instead of the main topics, as in the latter). Next downward in the order of subdivision—that is, directly below the approaches; or, if only one is being taken, directly below the division into major parts —might come smaller parts, or categories of related descriptive data. Subdivision continues as far as may be desirable to clarify the writer's intentions to himself, and also to his instructor if he is planning the paper under supervision. Ordinarily, listing of the ultimate, minute descriptive details is superfluous, except for perhaps one or two examples at each point to show the kind of material that will be presented there. Whether the descriptive outline is in sentence or in topical form, usually it is shorter than an outline for a technical exposition of the same size; and, of course, a topical outline is always shorter—in number of words (not necessarily in number of items)— than a sentence outline for the same subject.

Examples. To show topical and sentence outlining of technical description, the same plan (based on an outline that was submitted in sentence form) is given below in both styles. Note that a paper written from these outlines would be truly descriptive, not expository; also, that the cathode-ray tube would be described demounted from its socket, rather than in use as it might be shown according to a different outline.

A Cathode-ray Tube

(Sentence Outline)

Thesis: One type of cathode-ray tube is a flared glass envelope containing eight functional parts, including a heater, six electrodes, and a screen.

I. In general form, the tube is a conical quartz-glass flask that has its curved large end internally coated; and, at the opposite end, has a greatly elongated neck containing a series of metal elements wired to external prongs.

II. The heater, nearest the base, is the first element.
   A. It resembles a hairpin wound into a double-helical coil.
   B. It is made of tungsten wire.

III. Surrounding and extending beyond the heater is the cathode.
   A. It is a small cylinder enclosed at one end.
   B. It is made of nickel coated with the emissive substance.
   C. It is held in place, away from the heater, by a glass stem attached to the closed end beyond the heater.

IV. Surrounding and extending beyond the cathode is the shield or grid.
   A. It is a larger cylinder with an opening at each end.
   B. It is made of nickel.
   C. It is held in place, away from the cathode, by the same glass stem that holds the cathode.

V. Two successive anodes follow.
   A. The first, or focusing, anode is the smaller.
      1. It is tubular and contains small holes in its ends.
      2. It is made of nickel or nickel-molybdenum alloy.
   B. The second, or accelerating, anode is the larger.
      1. It is a larger tube with an aperture at each end.
      2. It, also, is made of nickel or nickel-molybdenum alloy.

VI. Two successive sets of deflecting plates are the final electrodes.
   A. All the plates are rectangular but are bent at one end to flare toward the screen.

    B. They are made of nickel or molybdenum.

    C. The first pair is mounted parallel and opposed; the second pair, also parallel and opposed, is mounted beyond and at right angles to the first.

VII. The fluorescent screen is the last operational member.

    A. It covers the whole interior of the belled end of the tube.

    B. Varieties of willemite, producing different colors, are used for the coating material.

Note: The first main topic, representing an over-all view, permissibly violates two rules of expository sentence outlines, in that (1) it has no subdivisions and (2) it overlaps in content all the other main topics.

(Topical Outline)

I. Over-all view: conical quartz-glass flask having, at one end, internally coated curved surface; and, at opposite end, elongated neck containing electric elements wired to external prongs.

II. Heater nearest base.

    A. Coiled-hairpin shape.

    B. Material: tungsten.

III. Cathode surrounds and extends beyond heater.

    A. Small cylinder with one end closed.

    B. Made of nickel coated with emissive substance.

    C. Held away from heater by glass stem at closed end.

IV. Shield or grid surrounds and extends beyond cathode.

    A. Larger cylinder with opening at each end.

    B. Material: nickel.

    C. Held away from cathode by same glass stem holding cathode.

V. Two successive anodes.

    A. Smaller focusing anode.

        1. Tubular with small holes in ends.

        2. Material: nickel or nickel-molybdenum alloy.

    B. Larger accelerating anode.

        1. Larger tube with aperture at each end.

        2. Material: same as of first anode.

    VI. Two successive sets of deflecting plates.
- A. All plates rectangular—bent at one end to flare toward screen.
- B. Material: nickel or molybdenum.
- C. Each pair parallel and opposed; second pair beyond and at right angles to first.

   VII. Fluorescent screen.
- A. Covers whole interior of belled end.
- B. Material: varieties of willemite for different colors.

The over-all view. Illustrated by the first main topic in the foregoing duplicate outlines, a general picture makes an effective opening for many technical descriptions, and also may helpfully establish a frame of reference or basis of comparison for the limited aspects or parts afterwards to be described. (Sometimes, indeed, particularly when only brief description of some object is wanted in connection with a mainly expository or narrative account of a scientific topic, nothing further is required beyond a general pictorial survey of that object.) This part of the composition is given from a fixed stance, clearly implied if not definitely announced, or from a progressively shifting viewpoint to follow movements of the spectator or of the object as it is inspected. A machine shop, for example, could be portrayed as observed from an overhanging balcony or window; a stationary engine, as seen in the course of walking entirely or partially around it; a small model or piece of laboratory equipment, as held in the hand and revolved. When a mechanism is depicted in normal motion as it passes through its cycle of operation, a more distinctly narrative element is introduced into over-all description. Still another type of over-all view, encroaching on exposition, is abstract or generalized, rather than vividly particularized; this method is useful in representing setups and hookups of apparatus whose exact spatial arrangements are of secondary or minor importance.

The fundamental image. Once in a while in technical composition, a device known in literary description as the fundamental image —amounting to an expanded figure of speech—can be used to advantage, especially to suggest an over-all view. The sequence of details is then determined, at least in part, by the imaginative picture evoked. The "tilted isosceles triangle" in the following paragraph, which opened a descriptive paper written by a student, is illustrative.

      The pendulum tester is the machine most commonly used in measuring the tensile strength of paper, that is, the longitudinal force (expressed in kilograms) necessary to break a strip of paper fifteen millimeters wide. The instrument is actuated by a small electric motor. Its own proper parts are chiefly a slender rod rigidly mounted in a hollow screw that is moved up and down by a high-ratio reduction gear, a pendulum beam, and a graduated scale, together with supporting structures consisting of a flat base, a main vertical pillar, and a fixed beam carrying the outer end of the graduated scale. In outline, as seen from the front, the tester has very much the appearance of a tilted isosceles triangle, one leg being identified with the vertical pillar (continued, of course, below the triangle as a support), the other leg with the fixed beam, and the base with the graduated scale, which, however, is the arc of a large circle rather than a straight line. The triangle is subdivided by the pendulum beam, pivoted at the apex and free to move along the scale. Just outside the tilted triangle, mounted parallel with the vertical leg, are the hollow screw and inserted rod, with clamps and other auxiliary equipment for applying tension to the strip of paper under test.

B. TECHNICAL NARRATION

(1) CHARACTERISTICS, TYPES, AND PROBLEMS

Characteristics. Narration is the process of recording a series of events. Most personal writings (mainly friendly letters) and conversations are basically narrative, as are several literary forms (including the novel and short story). Whereas private and literary narrators sometimes seek to "tell all," yet at the same time are free from the obligation of a straightforward sequence, technical writers recount, almost always strictly in order, only those occurrences that are both relevant and important to problems, methods, or results. Characteristically, technical narration is thus **chronological** and **highly selective.**

A danger. At least, technical narration *ought* to be highly selective: it is so when well composed. Because telling a story is easier than explaining, describing, or arguing, a peculiar difficulty of narration is the curbing of detail. The critical question is not so much what to tell as what to omit. There is real danger especially when a narrative, instead of being independent, accompanies passages composed in the other modes of discourse. Unless checked it tends to become disproportionately large, and at the worst, like Aaron's serpent, "swallows up the rest." Subordinate or independent, a good technical narrative relates nothing merely for the reason that the doing of it cost the operator time and tedious effort; side excursions are not made into matters only casually related to the topic; no passages are expanded or inserted because words or recollected incidents come to mind with alacrity and serve to fill out a manuscript of predetermined length.

Particularized and generalized technical narration. Most narration is individual in subject, stating what happened on a particular occasion. The "procedure" section of a laboratory report and innumerable other technical narratives fall into this class. A second, opposed type of narration also is employed extensively for scientific subjects. This is the generalized narrative, concerned with typical rather than particular actions. It serves the two ends of (1) giving directions and (2) imparting knowledge regarding processes, especially routine processes such as manufacture or laboratory technique. In both functions, generalized narrative may be (in giving direction, it always is) as much expository as narrative in ultimate effect; still, the term "narration" is warranted by the fact that invariably a sequence of actions determines the organization.

An example of generalized narrative. Below is transcribed (with minor changes) a paper written to fulfill a class assignment in generalized informational narration, for a supposed reader specified as a college student not majoring in science. The first two paragraphs present necessary exposition; the third (which in the original was accompanied by a sketch, not reproduced) is descriptive. Although the remaining two comprise less than half the total number of words, the composition is, in fundamental purpose and nature, more distinctly narrative than descriptive; and, as was mentioned in the preceding paragraph, generalized narrative characteristically borders closely on exposition. (Review, also, the second paragraph of this chapter, labeled *Mingling of types.*)

ANALYZING FOODS FOR PROTEIN CONTENT

The determination of protein in foods has long been a common laboratory process, and the general procedure has become rather standardized. The proteins form a group of complex organic compounds of considerable variation in structure. They have, however, one property in common: incorporation of nitrogen as the element distinguishing them from other nutrient materials. Since they are the only nutritional substances that contain that element, food analyzed for nitrogen is, in effect, analyzed for protein as well. This relationship has been studied in great detail, and sixteen per cent of proteins in general is known to be nitrogen. Thus, for determination of the protein content of a given foodstuff, the percentage of nitrogen is found and multiplied by 6.25 (100/16).

The routine analysis for nitrogen is called the Kjeldahl determination, after the Danish originator of the process. The theory of this method is grounded in well-known chemical principles. When the material containing protein is heated (digested) with concentrated sulphuric acid, the carbon, hydrogen, oxygen, and nitrogen of the substance are converted into carbon dioxide, water, and ammonium sulphate. The last is a nitrogen salt that is easily decomponed by strong bases, forming ammonia, water, and an involatile salt. Therefore, concentrated sodium hydroxide is added and the mixture is boiled. The ammonia and water distilled are caught in a flask containing a definite volume of hydrochloric acid of known concentration. The ammonia neutralizes a certain portion of this acid, leaving an excess of acid in the receiving flask. This excess acid is determined with a standard base. Thus the amount of ammonia which has distilled over can be determined, and from this value the amount of nitrogen and subsequently the amount of protein in the sample can be calculated. The accuracy of the Kjeldahl analysis is reasonably good, considering the nonhomogeneity of food samples.

The apparatus employed include a Kjeldahl flask, distillation equipment, analytical volumetric glassware, burners, ring stands, and other ordinary laboratory paraphernalia. The long-necked Kjeldahl flask is made of fire glass; in appearance it is a huge test tube blown into a pear-shaped bulb at the bottom. The distillation equipment, standard for any laboratory, consists of a spray trap connected to a water-cooled condenser. The outlet tube of the condenser is connected to a delivery tube, which extends nearly to the bottom of a receiving flask for the distillate.*

A two-gram sample of the foodstuff to be analyzed is placed in the dry Kjeldahl flask. To this sample a small amount of potassium sulphate, copper sulphate, mercuric oxide, mercury, or any of several other chemicals is added to speed the ensuing reaction. Then approximately twenty-five milliliters of concentrated sulphuric acid is added to the mixture, and the flask and contents are supported on a ring stand over a small flame. The mixture is heated gently over this small flame for several minutes. At first it swells and froths, turning a dirty black. The

* Sketch and textual reference to it omitted.

frothing gradually stops, and the mixture becomes somewhat brownish in color. The flame is turned up, and the heating is continued for several hours. Finally the brown color passes away, and the mixture appears as an emerald-green liquid. The heating is continued for several minutes after the appearance of the brilliant green; then the flame is removed, and the flask and contents are allowed to cool. The green liquid, on cooling, solidifies to a mass of greenish-white crystals.

After solidification of the digested sample has occurred, the Kjeldahl flask is attached to the distillation apparatus. Into the receiving flask is put a measured volume of hydrochloric acid of known concentration, and the end of the delivery tube is adjusted so that it dips just below the surface of the acid. The solid cake in the Kjeldahl flask is dissolved with about two hundred milliliters of distilled water, and a small handful of granulated zinc is added to the solution. This is followed by about fifty milliliters of fifty per cent sodium hydroxide. The contents of the Kjeldahl flask are now heated, at first gently, until an even boiling occurs. The process is continued until about two thirds of the liquid has distilled over. Then the receiving flask is removed, and its contents are analyzed for excess acid with a standard base. From this analysis the amount of ammonia in the sample can be determined; from the amount of ammonia is calculated the amount of nitrogen; and from the amount of nitrogen the protein content of the original foodstuff is obtained.

Problems of narrative style. Generalized technical narrative regularly follows certain set patterns of verb forms, directions being stated in the imperative mood and information in the passive voice. The inherent monotony of these styles can be escaped only by the most skillful composition; so far as the verbs themselves are concerned, about the only release comes through variation of auxiliaries (*may, might, should, would,* etc.). In particularized narration on scientific themes, also, especially in reports and in articles prepared for professional journals, the third person of the passive voice is approved. (Thus: "One part of mercury is [was] dissolved in twelve parts of nitric acid, and to this solution $5\frac{1}{2}$ parts of ethyl alcohol are [were] added.") Textbooks of general English object to frequent occurrence of passive constructions on the grounds that they lack vividness; that they give the recipient of an action, often an inanimate substance, an undue position of prominence; and that they fail to name the doer, or else mention him inconspicuously in a mere prepositional phrase.

Technical writers reply that in their fields the things done and bodies or substances acted upon usually are more worth emphasis than the identity of the human agents; they insist, too, that the active voice in sustained use, with constant repetition of the same subject, is at least as monotonous for recounting a detailed procedure as the passive, with continually varied grammatical subjects. Naturally, technical narration does not reject the active voice and the first person when those forms are felt to be better suited to a topic or occasion than the essentially impersonal passive. In general, passive forms are better adapted to professional writing than to conversational or public speaking on identical topics. Also, written discourse in the "popular" and "middle" technical styles, as defined at the end of Chapter I, frequently (but by no means necessarily) employs the first person with active verbs. Students of technical English are advised to practice both passive and active phrasing of scientific procedures, in different compositions.

(2) ARRANGEMENT OF NARRATIVE MATERIAL

Organization. The planning of a technical narrative is relatively easy because of the directly chronological method. Normally, the account advances by a *series of steps* more or less obvious in the technique or process itself. When incidental narrative passages are to be contained in technical exposition, argumentation, or description, ordinarily they can be provided for within any type of outline drafted for the whole composition. On the other hand, a distinctively narrative paper, or a major section (as of an industrial report or scientific monograph) consisting principally or wholly of narration, requires its own special planning. For a short piece of work a brief topical outline (a type discussed and illustrated, in relation to description, earlier in the chapter) suffices well enough; however, for an article of extended length a paragraph outline is much more satisfactory.

The paragraph outline. This type of outline comprises a series of miniature paragraphs, of one or more sentences each, usually without subordination among the entries. When it is used to synopsize an already-written composition (in any of the forms of discourse), normally every item of the outline corresponds to a single paragraph of the original text. In employing it to *plan* a narrative, however, the writer should not immediately think in terms of paragraphs except as affecting the structural form of the outline itself. When each distinct step, or important partial step, of a process has been summarized in the outline, he usually will have little trouble in deciding which should be retained as individual paragraphs in the paper, which should be split into two or more separately paragraphed subtopics, and which should be blended into comprehensive single paragraphs.

Example. Below is a paragraph outline of a short narrative paper (actually, of the "procedure" section of a student report that had several other parts, including a set of drawings), on a problem of construction. Use of the first person singular and plural, with active verb forms, corresponds to the style of the original. (Cf. the paragraph labeled *Problems of narrative style*, page 165.)

How My Brother and I Built a Flat-bottomed Boat

(Paragraph Outline)

I. Our first step was to lay the keel, a long center board placed upright the length of the boat. We shaped the bottom, and cut notches on the top to hold other structural members.

II. We next built the frame on the keel. The frame consisted of a series of five U-shaped members, made of boards screwed together, graduated in size to taper the vessel from stern to bow.

III. We constructed a sternpiece the shape of a frame member but of solid board.

IV. The most difficult step was attaching the planking. First we screwed on the bottom planks, working forward from the sternpiece; then the side planks, also starting at the stern. We sawed off excess lumber to complete the actual construction.

V. We inserted caulking into all cracks, driving it in with a chisel and hammer, and covered it with tar.

VI. Finally, we poured water into the hull and let it remain overnight to swell the wood.

C. TECHNICAL ARGUMENTATION

How argumentation differs from exposition. Argumentation is the process of maintaining opinions and counseling actions in controversy with conflicting counsel or opinion. It is a form of combat in words, being directed against opposition, potential if not actual. It deals with conjectures, uncertainties, and probabilities, whereas exposition mainly concerns the positively knowable and demonstrable. A treatise on integral calculus, or an analysis of traffic on a section of highway, would typify pure, or nearly pure, expository composition; an article urging the need of a free bridge to join Louisiana and Mississippi, or one asserting the superiority of fluorescent over incandescent lighting (or vice versa), would be essentially argumentative.

Know when you are arguing. The line between these two forms of discourse is not always easily drawn. One difficulty is that arguments have a way of masquerading as exposition, for a controversialist can ask no better advantage than to have his contentions, especially the more doubtful ones, accepted as simple statements of truth. Moreover, argumentation almost invariably does contain expository (that is, explanatory) elements; on the other side, fundamentally expository discussions not infrequently include argumentative passages bearing on unsettled subsidiary issues. Though such mixtures are entirely proper, intellectual integrity demands that a writer or speaker always know when he is arguing points from which other minds may rationally dissent, and when, on the contrary, he is explaining what reason itself is bound to accept.

Persuasion and conviction. Textbooks on argumentation make a distinction between the terms *conviction* and *persuasion*, defining the former as a wholly rational process and the latter as an appeal to, or through, emotion. So far as controversies on scientific questions are concerned, one governing principle would appear very nearly self-evident: that any address to the emotions should be in thorough harmony with the factual evidence and with sound thought. In respect to science and technology, the means of persuasion are—or certainly ought to be—simply tact, discretion, and good manners accompanying an attempt at logical conviction.

(1) LOGIC

General importance. Logic is not, of course, peculiar to arguments, but is properly the guiding principle of all thought and communication of thought. Despite the fact that the subject is separately presented at this point, it is relevant to all the forms of discourse. In exposition, fully as much as in argumentation, logic is of paramount importance.

The natural source of logic. The science of logic is grounded upon natural laws of human reasoning and upon apparent relations between perception and external reality. For any race possessed of the merest glimmering of intellect, the laws of *sound* reasoning are the same as for the most advanced. We have no ground for believing that they have ever changed in any respect, though they have been discovered and formalized only gradually. Human kind always has been highly ingenious in misusing the brain; nevertheless, when the man on the street or the farm reasons accurately, he is employing the same logic as the man in the laboratory. Reread, on this subject of the universality of the laws of thought, the paragraph by T. H. Huxley previously quoted (Chapter III: under D 10, page 60); or, better yet, read in the library that selection in its context. The passage can be found, under the title "The Method of Scientific Investigation," in numerous collections of miscellaneous essays; in the works of Huxley it occurs in the first part of the third of six lectures "On Our Knowledge of the Causes of the Phenomena of Organic Nature," printed in the volume titled *Darwiniana* (vol. II of Huxley's *Collected Essays*).

(1. TYPES OF REASONING)

Basic forms. The fundamental modes of logic are discriminated under the terms **deduction** and **induction.** Together, these two complementary patterns of thought have enabled man to rise above the merely instinctive way of living that characterizes the lower creatures.

Admixture. In most processes of reasoning the two basic forms of thought are so inextricably mixed that only by abstraction can the identity of each (in particular, of deduction) be clearly perceived. To be sure, some periods or schools of thought are called "deductive" (e.g., the scholastic philosophy of the middle ages) or "inductive" (e.g., the modern age of experimental science); however, these designations merely point to a salient characteristic and do not imply, as an impossible condition, absence of the opposite manner of reasoning. Even geometry, closest to being a purely deductive science, tacitly appeals to inductive experience in its underlying postulates. Among the many important techniques by which scientists combine deduction with induction, is their manner of employing hypotheses, inductively obtained by tentative inference from observed facts, as what amount to syllogistic premises. By deduction, conclusions are then drawn that can be checked by further observation; unless those conclusions accord with the newly recorded facts, the hypotheses necessarily are abandoned or modified. Interesting examples of delicate interweaving of inductive and deductive methods, as applied to the study of natural phenomena, are to be found in accounts of the discovery of the planets Neptune and Pluto, which may be read in any recent textbook of astronomy or, respectively, in *The Encyclo-*

paedia Britannica (ed. 14, vol. XVI, pp. 226–227) and *The New International Year Book* for 1930 (p. 68).

(1) Deduction

Deduction "leads from" the general. By its nature, a generalization embraces a number of individual cases, from two to infinity. Therefore, *from* (Latin, *de*) a given general or universal truth, it is possible to lead (Latin, *ducere*) the mind either to a particular instance of that truth or to a group of such instances constituting a subgenerality. The conclusion thus reached can often, itself, be made the basis of another deduction, and this procedure sometimes is carried through many stages.

The syllogism. Deductive reasoning is best understood when it is reduced to the form of syllogisms. Fully expressed, a syllogism consists of three parts: a major premise, a minor premise, and a conclusion. Each of the premises contains two terms, but one member (the "middle" term) appears in *both* premises. This middle term is qualified in at least one (usually the major) premise by *all, no* (the negative form of *all*), or an equivalent; that is, a general truth is predicated of the middle term. The conclusion draws a logical inference that relates the other two terms of the major and minor premises, respectively. A great many special types of valid syllogisms are possible, but the most typical patterns are shown in the following examples:

I. **Major premise:** All engineers understand mathematics.
   Minor premise: Mr. Doe is an engineer.
     Conclusion: Mr. Doe understands mathematics.

II. **Major premise:** No modern astronomer accepts the Ptolemaic system.
   Minor premise: Mr. Roe is a modern astronomer.
     Conclusion: Mr. Roe does not accept the Ptolemaic system.

(2) Induction

Induction "leads into" the general. Study of individual cases can lead (Latin, *ducere*) to or into (Latin, *in*) a generalization. This procedure, known as inductive reasoning, obviously is the reverse of deduction. All of us make "inductive leaps" from the particular to the general in the course of our commonplace affairs. As children we discovered by experience that various glowing bodies produce a markedly unpleasant sensation to the touch; thereupon we reached, with the aid of words borrowed from our parents, the inductive conclusion that objects of a certain hue "burn" or "are hot." At this stage our belief was empirical, resting upon observation alone with no theoretical basis. Later the study of physical principles known from the experience and demonstrations of others, combined with further personal familiarity with hot substances, increased and improved our knowledge of the subject. Ultimately, however, at the root of all our ideas of heat are individual observations—whether our own or those communicated to us by other persons—inductively generalized.

Difficulties. No simplified, formalized routine, comparable to the syllogism, has been devised for regularizing inductive thinking. The difference between scientific or strictly logical induction, on the one side, and that practiced by the average man, on the other, is not of kind; but, rather, of degree of caution in inference and verification. Moreover, despite partially successful efforts to distinguish induction from empiricism (the grounding of knowledge flatly on experience), the boundary remains an indefinite field instead of a sharp line of demarcation. John Stuart Mill, the great nineteenth-century theorist of inductive logic, observed: "There is a point of generality at which empirical laws become as certain as laws of nature, or rather, at which there is no longer any distinction between empirical laws and laws of nature." The dominant skepticism, or reserved judgment, of our age is largely explained by the fact that the precise location of Mill's "point of generality" not only varies widely in different problems but is extremely hard to locate in the individual problem. In spite, however, of many practical as well as theoretical difficulties, for some three hundred years the prime mover of the scientific movement has been inductive reasoning. So far as technology is concerned, as Professor Allen H. Blaisdell remarks: "The engineering method . . . is essentially the application of the principles of inductive logic." *

(3) Analogy

How analogies combine induction and deduction. Both logical and illogical thinkers make use of a device, known as **analogy**, which in one seemingly instantaneous process blends elements of both induction and deduction. In schematic form, analogical reasoning goes as follows:

A has a certain cause, effect, or characteristic *C*.
B is similar to *A*.

* *Bulletin of the American Association of University Professors,* **XXXII** (1946), 272.

THEREFORE: *B* has the cause, effect, or characteristic *C*.

Breaking down the analogy into its inductive and deductive phases, we see that two steps are united, for a conclusion reached by induction is tacitly employed as the major premise of an incompletely expressed syllogism:

Inductive phase: *A* belongs to a class having the cause, effect, or characteristic *C*.

Deductive phase: *B* belongs to the same class as *A*.

THEREFORE: *B* has the cause, effect, or characteristic *C*.

Analogy in science. Research scientists ground belief on analogy only when the evidence admits no other form of reasoning. As a matter of fact, this condition rather often exists in all the sciences, especially those concerned with evidences of the geological or historical past. The reconstruction, from a few accidentally surviving bones, of extinct animals and the earliest races of men exemplifies the analogical process in biology. By comparison with present anatomical forms and with those of past creatures that have been more fully preserved, museums of natural history are able to expand scant remains into life-sized models regarded as accurate within close limits of probability. If an archaeologist should uncover, on a hill dominating the site of an ancient city, the foundation of a building much larger in floor area than the surrounding dwellings, he would be justified in announcing (taking the results of similar diggings as analogues) that he had found a buried temple. Of course, the analogy would be greatly strengthened if he succeeded in unearthing fragments of statues and other objects resembling material already collected from the ruins of known temples of antiquity.

(2. FALLACIES)

Any type or instance of erroneous reasoning is termed a **fallacy.** Everyone should be on guard against sophistry in his own thought, and at the same time should stand ready to resist—if not always to expose publicly—specious arguments of others.

Truth and validity. Before fallacies can be considered with full benefit to the student, a line of distinction must be drawn between **truth** and **validity.** Logic is concerned with relations between premises or evidence (the material of thought) and conclusions; when it is correctly employed the conclusions are said to be *valid,* for no fallacy has been committed. Nevertheless, the conclusions are not necessarily *true* unless the premises or data, as well as the techniques of thought, are sound. The difference between validity and truth is especially easy to see in the realm of deductive reasoning. In the middle ages strings of deductively valid but questionable "truths" were spun out of initial premises established by authority and tradition. As instances closer to our time, a generation ago no chemist or physicist would have hesitated to employ, as major premises for deduction, the principle of conservation of mass and the proposition that the molecular weight of water is always 18.016; but would present knowledge allow the same to be done today?

Types of fallacies. Some of the more common fallacies are analyzed and illustrated below:

(1) Faulty Deduction

Use of syllogisms to discover fallacies. Although few people ever hear the word *syllogism,* deductive reasoning always can be converted to syllogistic form. When the conversion is made, fallacies that might otherwise lie concealed are relatively easy to detect.

Purely negative premises. For example, all possibility of inference is nullified if each premise contains a negative word. Thus:

Major premise: No scientist is dogmatic.
Minor premise: Mr. Hoe is not a scientist.
Conclusion: ? ? ? ? ? ? ? ? ? ?

(No conclusion can be reached. Mr. Hoe may or may not be dogmatic; the premises throw no light on that question.)

Undistributed middle. A fundamental law of syllogisms is that the middle term (the one common to both premises) must be *distributed*: that is to say, it must state a characteristic separately true of all individuals denoted by that term. The following *reductio ad absurdum* (in which the middle term is signalized by FULL CAPITALS) illustrates the fault of the undistributed middle. (Note that the middle term is *not* "educated Hungarians," which appears in only one premise; it is "the Magyar language," which is common to both premises.)

Major premise: All educated Hungarians study THE MAGYAR LANGUAGE.
Minor premise: I am studying THE MAGYAR LANGUAGE.
Conclusion: I am an educated Hungarian.

The following deduction, however, is valid. The word by which the middle term ("Romance language") is distributed is "every."

Major premise: Professor Poe speaks *every* ROMANCE LANGUAGE.
Minor premise: Portuguese is a ROMANCE LANGUAGE.
Conclusion: Professor Poe speaks Portuguese.

Ambiguous terms. A main source of errors in deduction, but one against which precautions also must be taken in inductive reasoning, is the ambiguity of language. Consider again the syllogisms numbered "I" and "II" in the paragraph labeled *The syllogism,* on page 170; you may find that all the crucial terms in both are equivocal. Who are included in, and who are excluded from, the group called "engineers"? As variously interpreted, the word might mean all persons who so style themselves, without discrimination; those belonging to certain professional societies, or holding certain licenses or titles; or students along with practitioners of the technical sciences. What degree of knowledge does the verb "understand" imply? Does "mathematics" embrace not only algebra, geometry, trigonometry, and calculus, but also the higher, more theoretical branches? Just who are "modern" astronomers? Suppose, for example, that a star-gazer and astrologer accepts what he comprehends of the Ptolemaic system; is he, or is he not, "modern" by virtue of being now alive? (Furthermore, is he really an "astronomer"?) Does "accepts" mean "accepts fully and in detail" or "accepts in any particular whatsoever"? Is "the Ptolemaic system" to be understood as originally conceived in the second century, or as further developed in later medieval times? One of the most common fallacies in deductive thinking is use of the same expression with different implications in the premises and the conclusion.

(2) Hasty Generalization

An inductive fault. "Jumping to conclusions" is the layman's meaningful name for hasty generalization, a characteristic fallacy of loose inductive thinking. (In a general sense, however, "jumping to conclusions" refers also to false deductions.) A high school graduate, having taken courses in both Spanish and French, but not in Latin or any other foreign language, regarded the letter *s* as the "natural" sign of plural nouns; he was astonished, on going to engineering college, to learn that very few German plurals end in *s*. Another student was positive, from exactly one experience, that "women can't teach mechanical drawing."

Precautions. Everyone is inclined to the error of hasty, sweeping induction. Nevertheless, universal statements are intellectually safe only when they rest upon particular facts which are both *typical* and *sufficiently numerous* to preclude reasonable doubt that exceptions will be discovered. If the number of cases embraced by a generalization is relatively small, prudence suggests that all be individually considered. If selection is necessary because the number is large or infinite, the samples should fairly represent the whole field under consideration. Amateur investigators, at least, do well to take account of as many instances as possible before proceeding to a conclusion. The United States Census offers large-scale exemplification of the exhaustive method in its grouping of the population according to age, occupation, housing, and the like; numerous private and magazine polls illustrate the technique of sampling. (The Bureau of the Census now also employs a five per cent sample for obtaining certain information.)

Exceptions disprove the rule. Even the most solidly established propositions based on inductive reasoning must continue, indefinitely, to be regarded as in a sense tentative, so that they will not be dogmatically retained if unpredictable exceptions should later occur or come to light. Whenever a person appears to be more concerned with inference than with evidence, more inclined to seize upon instances that support his prejudices than to seek out and weigh all kinds of relevant data, regardless of the effect upon his position or cause, more ready to laugh off seeming exceptions as "only proving the rule" than to analyze them critically, he is under suspicion of hasty generalization. Even though what he asserts *may* be right, his conclusions should be rigorously tested before they are accepted.

Note: Citation of a random example sometimes clarifies an accepted truth, but it is not an adequate method of proof. It is, however, a perfect method of rebuttal against hasty generalization. If an opponent contends that *all* instances of X have the characteristic Y, demonstration that *one* instance of X does *not* have the characteristic Y is sufficient to refute his assertion.

(3) False Analogy

Analogies are dangerous. Because analogies can be, and often are, deceptive and erroneous as means of reasoning, they are employed only with the greatest care and restraint by disciplined minds. In popular usage, however, their very looseness and convenience make them a favorite method of arguing controversial issues, since an analogy can be set up to "prove" almost any point. Even when made by skeptical minds trained to scientific caution, analogical assumptions many times fail to square with actualities. For instance, Bode's Law —according to which the approximate distances from the sun of unknown planets were supposed to be analogically inferable (somewhat as unknown elements and their properties have been inferred from gaps in the periodic table)—was in part undermined by the discovery that the mean distance of Neptune from the sun is much less than that predicted, whereas the distance of Pluto is very nearly what would have been expected, not for a trans-Neptunian planet, but for Neptune.

Relation to hasty generalization. As was shown before, an analogy joins in one process an inductive and a deductive phase. In consequence, an indistinct line separates false analogy and hasty inductive generalization, for the latter is the usual cause of the former error. If the induction implicit in any analogy is untrue, then the analogy itself fails. Through unwarranted generalizations from the habits of civilized peoples, many acquired patterns of behavior were once mistakenly attributed to "human nature" and expected to be found in any society, but some are not practiced among primitive races visited in remote lands by modern anthropologists.

(4) Begging the Question

Meaning of "beg." A reasoner is said to beg the question when he takes for granted, or rather asks others to take for granted, the truth of the very proposition that is in dispute. This sophism can be contrived in various ways. Perhaps the most usual method operates through prejudicial language. Suppose, for instance, that the problem at hand concerns the value and practicability of various substitutes for natural rubber. If a speaker or writer on the subject begins by saying, "I shall discuss the relative merits of G.R.S. and the various inferior synthetic rubbers," he has assumed (by means of the word "inferior") precisely what he ought to be required to prove.

"Circular" argument. A more elaborate technique of begging the question, called arguing in a circle, consists in "proving" a proposition (the point at issue) by a second proposition and then "proving" the second, in its turn, by the first. Or the circle can involve more than two propositions: e.g., A is "proved" by B, then B by C, then C by D, and finally D by A, to complete the continuous chain. The reliability of a book on an erudite subject was urged on the basis of

the writer's authority in the special field; later it transpired that his alleged authority rested entirely upon that book. The situation was much the same as if two men, both under indictment, should offer to appear in court as character witnesses *for each other*.

(5) Evading the Issue

Issues must be faced. An issue is a point of controversy in an argument, and the issue is said to be evaded (or dodged) when a disputant refuses or fails to take or keep it under consideration. Shifting ground is a common method of evasion. A salesman tried to convince a prospective customer that, in the long run, annual purchase of a new automobile saves money. The customer gave facts and figures, from his wartime experience, tending to show the economy of retaining the same car over a period of years. Thereupon the salesman, instead of standing by the question he himself had raised, asserted: "Yes, but you have to figure in the added satisfaction of always having the latest model." He had artfully shifted from untenable to tenable ground, but in doing so he had evaded his own issue. A large proportion of "yes, but" and "just the same" arguments fall into this class.

The "argument to the man." Certain familiar manifestations of the fallacy of evading the issue go under the Latin name of *argumentum ad hominem*. The term is used in a double sense. Some authorities take it to mean an indirect attack on the validity of opinions through a denial of the personal integrity of a holder of those opinions. Another definition (see *Webster's New International Dictionary* at the entry on *ad hominem*) interprets it to signify an address to the emotions and particular viewpoint of the listener or reader. Instances of the latter meaning are furnished by that kind of political oratory directed at the self-interest of special groups, rather than at larger issues of permanent and general public welfare. The first sense is well exemplified by the Latin retort *tu quoque* (literally translated, "thou also"; more vulgarly rendered, "you're another"). In the heat of controversy, an opportunity to point out that an opponent violates his own theories in his private life can be very gratifying; usually, just the same, the real question to be settled does not in any way hinge on the personal character of the disputants.

(6) Mistaking the Cause

"After this: therefore because of this." Although to mistake the supposed effect of an observed cause is, of course, just as fallacious

as to mistake the supposed cause of an observed effect, the latter error is much the more frequent. It is often called the *post hoc: ergo propter hoc* fallacy, the Latin words signifying "after this: therefore because of this." The fact that two events occur in sequence is not even prima-facie evidence, much less conclusive proof, that the first is the cause of the second. The seasons succeed one another with yearly regularity; nevertheless, summer is no more responsible for autumn than for spring. We are prevented from the mistake of thinking so by our knowledge of the inclination of the earth's axis to the plane of the ecliptic, as the common cause of all seasonal changes; but in every other subject we are not so fortunate. At the present time, to cite an almost fantastic yet true example, a question has been seriously raised whether sunspots have a connection with business depressions, for the two have been observed to pass through strikingly similar cycles. Although some causal relation may be discovered, more probably later generations, after the astronomical and economic sciences have finally settled the matter, will smile at our conjecture as an instance of mistaking the cause.

Common forms. Most superstitions, much advertising, and many false notions concerning disease and other human problems rest upon *post hoc: ergo propter hoc* inferences. Perhaps more subtle, yet scarcely more intelligent, is the common feeling that the bearer or prophet of bad tidings is somehow partially responsible. Linguistic taboos among savages, and even among cultivated races, often originate in the delusion that to name evil might tend to produce or intensify it. Some people, for instance, are reluctant to use the word *cancer*. Material for an instructive research in the psychology of language could be garnered from the various euphemisms for *undertaker*; notice, in fact, the indirectness of that word itself: "one who undertakes" (something unspecified).

Difficulties. Some philosophers reject the entire cause-and-effect relationship, preferring to consider only existence and succession of phenomena; however, to carry skepticism to such limits hardly is necessary, and certainly is not helpful in practical matters. The most valuable single theoretical contribution to the subject was made by John Stuart Mill in Book III of his great *System of Logic*. All serious students of the sciences should at some time acquaint themselves with this passage (especially Chapter VIII), despite the fact that it is lengthy and very far from being light reading. Also, they should thoughtfully observe, in their laboratory courses and background studies, the extensive use of control experiments by modern science in the effort to avoid mistaking causes.

(2) FUNCTIONS AND CHARACTERISTICS OF TECHNICAL ARGUMENT

(1. FUNCTIONS)

Science does not escape argument. All men must argue, including men of science. Truth has ever proved an elusive quarry, and in some of its aspects appears permanently unknowable as well as at present unknown. Very generally, proponents of revised or new scientific beliefs restrict themselves to clear, forthright explanation accompanied by studious marshaling of evidence. Still, scientists cannot remain always on that even plane; technologists, in particular, are continually required to lend aid and advice on problems involving what amounts to an argumentative decision.

Technical arguments. Of two or more proposed machines, sites, techniques, agencies, or the like, oftener than not one is more economical of time, another of expense; one more efficient in the mechanical or thermal sense, another in the common meaning of reaching desired ends; one better over short periods, another over longer; one difficult of installation, another of operation; one sound in theory but impractical with the means at hand, another feasible in spite of theoretical deficiencies; one cheap in initial cost, another still cheaper when allowance is made for upkeep and replacement; one desirable but subject to patent restrictions, another less serviceable although freely available; one slow yet dependable, another fast but erratic; etc. Unless discussion of such problems is rigidly limited to expository presentation of facts, expounding readily passes into argument. Exposition, in its own right, sometimes reaches conclusions as to which proposal or possibility is, on the whole, better or the best, all facts being considered and duly weighed. If, however, the conclusions receive an emphasis equal or superior to that of the analysis itself and if, in addition, strong demand is made that they be accepted or acted upon, the point of balance moves (as, of course, it often should) from exposition to argumentation.

"What ought to be?" A curious and extraordinarily significant fact is that pure logic is incapable of settling any question that turns upon "should" or "ought." The adage that "of tastes there is no disputing" (*de gustibus non est disputandum*) might better be inverted to state that of tastes there is nothing *except* disputing. All matters of

preference are open to discussion; none, to certitude. Virtually all the unsolved problems of social living (anarchic international relations, inadequate education, and periodic economic depressions with accompanying lowered wages and maldistribution of consumer goods, to name some of the most obvious) fall within that class: they involve not merely questions of "What is?" but likewise of "What ought to be?"

The factor of choice. Many practical problems in the fields of technology have similar, though usually less self-evident, factors of choice. As an instance, erecting a fifty-story building is not solely a matter of constructional engineering. Questions such as location must first be settled; and behind them is the much more fundamental issue of whether the rearing of skyscrapers, with the resultant increased centralization of urban life, is a socially desirable practice. When technical people are asked to present opinions relevant to public or industrial decisions, to a large extent, of course, what is sought is simply their knowledge of facts, of mathematical relationships, of physical principles; to that degree their statements are (or are expected to be) strictly informational. A great many reports, indeed, are altogether of this nature. On the other hand, expert advice very frequently is expected also to bear directly upon the decision itself: that is to say, to go beyond verifiable fact and scientific law into the realm of judgment or choice. Hence, technical opinion may be arrayed against other technical opinion, as often happens in cases at law.

Science and society. In any practical problem, no one doubts that professional counsel, whatever its deficiencies and even contradictions, is most apt to be reliable. Not quite so universally recognized, however, is the obligation of technically trained men and women to channel their thoughts toward the more basic social implications of technology, regarded both generally and in connection with the particular activities on which, as experts, they may be engaged. An essay entitled "The Scientist in an Unscientific Society," written by Henry A. Wallace while he was Secretary of Agriculture, is at once a model of argumentative writing and a call to an aroused social consciousness on the part of twentieth-century scientists. It may be read in full in *Scientific American,* vol. CL, no. 6 (June, 1934), pp. 285–287. Here is the concluding paragraph:

> It is difficult to see how the engineer and the scientist can much longer preserve a complete isolation from the economic and social world about them. A world motivated by economic individualism has repeatedly come to the edge of the abyss, and

this last time [i.e., the great depression] possibly came within a hair's breadth of plunging over. Yet science, all this time, has been creating another world and another civilization that simply must be motivated by some conscious social purpose, if civilization is to endure. Science and engineering will destroy themselves and the civilization of which they are a part unless there is built up a consciousness which is as real and definite in meeting social problems as the engineer displays when he builds his bridge. The economist and the sociologist have not yet created this definite reality in their approach; can you who are trained in engineering and science help in giving this thought a definite body? *

(2. CHARACTERISTICS)

The aims: truth and utility. In argument, no less than in exposition, the legitimate aims of the scientist or technologist are truth and human betterment. Therefore, on problems for which information is partially unascertainable and in which certainty is impossible, or only relatively possible, he is obligated to bring to bear good will and trained judgment.

Qualities. Good technical argumentation is characterized by **sincerity, objectiveness, fairness, courtesy, reasonableness,** and **relevance.**

(1) Sincerity

Intellectual honesty. The very first principle of technical dispute is sincerity—intellectual honor. Ideally, students of the sciences never should be required to enter into arguments in favor of beliefs they do not really hold. They should learn, rather, the important lesson that the purpose of controversial discussions, at least within their intended professions, is not to "win" disputes but to enlarge man's knowledge or mastery of himself and of his environment.

(2) Objectiveness

The common ground. As has been mentioned, arguments commonly involve expository elements that establish a basis of demonstrable fact and law. Reason is best served when disputants are able to agree upon such matters, thus limiting their controversy to questions of judgment, interpretation, and application, while avoiding contention over the measurable or ascertainable. You may sometimes

* Excerpted by permission of *Scientific American.*

undergo the unhappy experience of having to oppose those who refuse to take a similarly objective attitude toward facts or natural laws, but for your own part you should hold respect for truth as of greater account than cleverness in manipulating evidence to defend a prejudiced attitude.

(3) Fairness

"Every argument has two sides." When intelligent men engage in sincere dispute, seldom is one utterly right and the other utterly wrong. Indeed, the whole tradition of intellectual freedom is grounded upon accumulated experience that no one man or group is wise enough to know the whole truth. The sensible controversialist treats his antagonists with respect and genuinely tries to understand their position, even though it should appear to him untenable or be poorly presented. Incidentally, no scientist worthy of the name is ashamed to acknowledge that he has been wrong, should he be convicted of error; actually, the confession is a token of strength rather than weakness, for it reflects added credit upon those opinions he continues to hold.

(4) Courtesy

Importance. Discourtesy is both ineffective and inexcusable. Tolerance and good humor are much better arms for technical controversy than a sharp tongue or pen: the disputant who keeps steady control of his temper and his manners, no matter how strong the provocation to discourtesy, generally is master of the situation. Furthermore, courtesy is an end in itself, as well as the natural accompaniment of objectivity and fairness. Incivility, discreditable to any profession, is disgraceful in those pretending to scientific balance.

(5) Reasonableness

A necessary condition. Controversy among poor logicians (which can be heard on any corner of the street) does not advance scientific knowledge. Notwithstanding the fact that arguments involve many questions unanswerable by purely logical techniques, rationality is a necessary—even though not a self-sufficient—condition of argumentation intended to advance abstract knowledge or to solve practical problems. (See the extended discussions of sound and fallacious reasoning, beginning at page 168.)

(6) Relevance

Reject the extraneous. No form of discourse should be more pointedly focused, less diffuse, than argumentation. A piece of information, so far as argument is concerned, has no *intrinsic* worth. That its truth is demonstrable is not a direct measure of its significance. The pertinent question is how it bears upon the topic at issue; or, in one word, how it is *relevant.* (Review "Evading the Issue," page 177.) Criticize closely the material you may gather in preparation for an argumentative paper or talk; probably a great part, doubtless in itself interesting enough, will have to be rejected as extraneous. Use of a brief for outlining (see immediately below) is of great value as a guard against irrelevance.

(3) PLANNING AND PRESENTATION

(1. THE ARGUMENTATIVE BRIEF)

Form. The customary type of outline for formal argumentative compositions is known as the brief. As in a sentence outline, entries in the body of a brief are sentences whose coördinate and subordinate relationships are indicated by series of initial figures and letters and by progressive degrees of indentation. The important peculiarity is that every statement, except of the lowest rank in any sequence of subordination, is followed by the word *for* to bind it definitely to its substatements, which constitute the evidence supporting it. (Observe the scheme under *Pattern,* on the following page.)

Value. The drafting of a brief is an unexcelled discipline for forcing the mind to think through an argumentative problem, to view propositions in clear relation to one another, to exclude irrelevant or repetitious data, and to fit each specific piece of evidence into a total structure of proof. A carefully briefed case may be factually weak (since no form of outlining can produce or change facts), but it hardly can be illogical.

Logical relationships. If the brief schematically represented below is logically constructed, "I," "II," and "III" prove or, at least, tend to prove the major proposition being affirmed or denied; "A" and "B" prove or tend to prove "I"; "1," "2," "3," and "4" prove or tend to prove "A"; and so forth down to the smallest arguments. The order in any group of coördinate items—e.g., "I," "II," and "III"; or "(1)" and "(2)"—is not haphazard but, rather, is a logical sequence of evidence to substantiate the covering assertion. Note that the number of items of any given rank, as well as the depth of subordination necessary before argumentative bedrock is reached, varies according to the amount and kind of evidence to be presented. Note, also, that whereas the principle of division regularly demands at least two coördinate items at each stage of an analytical sentence outline for exposition,* no theoretical objection forbids a single supporting argument anywhere in a brief. (See, as examples, "I-A-1-a-(1)-(a)" and "I-A-4-a" in the model.)

Pattern. A brief—or, more precisely, the main section or so-called body—has this general pattern:

Proposition: .... is (not) true [*or:* should (not) be done], for
 I. ...., for
  A. ...., for
   1. ...., for
    a. ...., for
     (1)........................., for
       (a). ....
     (2). ....
     (3). ....
    b. ....
   2. ...., for
    a. ....
    b. ....
   3. ....
   4. ...., for
    a. ...., for
     (1). ....
     (2). ....
  B. ...., for
    [Subtopics similar to those under "A."]
 II. ...., for
    [Subtopics similar to those under "I."]
 III. ...., for
    [Subtopics similar to those under "I" and "II."]

(2. COMPOSITION)

The brief need not be slavishly followed. Even more than other kinds of outlining, the brief tends to be too rigorous in method to be followed with exactness in the final composition. It furnishes a rational pattern of the structure of contention, thus reflecting almost solely an intellectual design. Argumentation has also a rhetorical

---

* Treated in Section A of Chapter VI; see Rule 7, page 135.

side. Devices ranging from transition to transposition can breathe life and fullness into the dry bones of a brief; even radical changes in technique of proof, provided they do not cause logical distortions, are at times justifiable for the sake of effective presentation. In particular, evidence often is better given before the point it supports instead of after (as always in the outline). Obviously, however, departures from the outline should not be made without motive.

Introduction and conclusion. As employed by lawyers and advanced students of debate, briefs are considerably expanded with introductory and concluding sections devoted to such matters as definition of terms, admissions and concessions, formulation of issues, and recapitulation of arguments. Introductions and (in the rhetorical sense) conclusions ordinarily are not stressed in technical composition. (They are, as has been mentioned already and will be taken up again in Chapter XI, more necessary in speaking than in writing.) In argumentation, nevertheless, at least the question under discussion has to be clarified in the introduction, which sometimes goes into its history, current status, and the like. Definitions may be given either formally in the introduction, or incidentally, at the first occurrence of various terms, in the body. A conclusion, usually in the form of a summary, is optional but generally advisable.

Issues. The issues are the essential points of controversy. If, for instance, the installation of a gas or a coal furnace were in question, the issues would perhaps be relative convenience of installation and operation, availability of fuel, and over-all cost. Always state very positively to yourself the issues of any argument in which you may be concerned, and keep steadily aware of them. Normally, they determine the principal entries of the body of the brief (numbered "I," "II," etc.), and the corresponding main topics of the argumentative composition itself. The issues may also be announced formally in the introduction and summarized in the conclusion.

Paragraphing. Written technical argumentation is generally easy to paragraph. Every major point, with its supporting evidence, forms a natural unit. If the extensiveness or complexity of the proof would make such a paragraph unwieldy, the material can be split into smaller paragraphs composed either of single pieces of evidence, together with the subordinate data upon which each in turn rests, or of closely related groups of such material. Usually the introduction and conclusion constitute at least one paragraph apiece, and in the body of the composition separate transitional or summarizing paragraphs often are desirable to link different issues.

CHAPTER VIII

LETTER WRITING FOR TECHNICAL STUDENTS

The business letter is an essential skill. Business, including the business phases of the profession of engineering, is largely transacted by correspondence, and many technical reports are accompanied by or actually written as letters. Everyone is obliged to write numerous letters in addition to purely personal correspondence. The business letter is, in fact, one of the basic skills for living in the modern world.

A. FORM

Learn the standard forms. Despite the very wide range of topics and considerable stylistic variation of business correspondence, the mechanics and format are rather narrowly prescribed. The suggestions, directions, and models given below, while allowing for certain alternative practices, conservatively follow the recognized customs. From them you will learn to write correct business letters. You may receive, see, or in certain employments be required to draft letters using different forms, in many particulars; however, radical deviations from the norm lack general authority and sometimes are offensive to correspondents accustomed to a standard manner.

(1) MECHANICS

Typewriting. Nowadays, almost the first rule of correspondence in business houses is use of the typewriter. Letters of application for employment sometimes are expected to be in the applicants' own handwriting, and longhand continues to be much used for transactions of individuals. Nevertheless, all directions here given will assume that a typewriter is available. They can be adapted to handwritten letters without any great difficulty, but every student would do well to secure access to a typewriter and learn to operate it.

Stationery. Heavy white paper, of smooth or glossy finish and of the standard "business size" (8½ by 11 inches, or slightly smaller —but not larger), is essential. The envelope should have dimensions of about 3⅝ by 6½ inches or (especially for a bulky letter or one containing enclosures) 4⅛ by 9½ inches. Occasionally an envelope large enough to hold the sheets without folding is used for several letters to the same addressee, or for a single letter consisting of many pages or accompanied by numerous enclosures.

Note 1: Letters in longhand, unlike most other types of handwritten compositions, should never be drafted on ruled paper. The same kind of stationery should be employed as for a typewritten letter.

Note 2: A letterhead is correct only as the first sheet of a letter. Plain paper must be used for subsequent pages.

Folding. The proper methods of folding letters for the standard short and long business envelopes, of the dimensions mentioned above, are more easily learned by imitation than from a written explanation. Observe someone you are sure knows how (not everyone does), and follow him with a blank sheet of paper. For the short envelope, a letter is folded in half upward, and then across from right to left in thirds; for the long envelope, only upward in thirds. In both styles, the letters are inserted so that the free leaves (*not* the folded edges) are near the flap of the envelope. (The reason for this habit is that the sheet is then in less danger of being cut through with a penknife or letter-opener.)

(2) GENERAL PRINCIPLES OF FORM

(1. POSITION)

First page. The first page should be so balanced as to appear to be framed on the sheet. Margins at the left, right, and top should all be made very nearly equal. Because, however, of the great amount of open space around the heading and inside address at the top, the lower margin must be somewhat greater than that at the top (and sides) if the letter is to appear centered. Let your eye be your guide: if the letter *looks* well balanced, it is optically even though not geometrically centered. A letterhead page must be balanced with due regard to the effect of the mass of printing, engraving, or lithographing at the top, in conjunction with the typewritten parts.

One-page letters. A letter cannot, obviously, be less than one page in length, but it may fill from practically all down to very little of the total space of a sheet. For the purpose of centering, four techniques are used in combination: (1) setting the margins relatively far in for a short letter and relatively far out for a long letter, (2) leaving proportionately much or little space blank at the top and bottom of the sheet, (3) varying the amount of space skipped between elements of the letter, (4) choosing between single- and double-spacing (see below).

Long letters. When a letter runs to two pages, only the first is centered; correct margins are about one inch or slightly more (the largest margin, as usual, being at the bottom). The second sheet should have the same left and right margins as the first, and a heading (to be explained later) about the same distance (i.e., approximately an inch) from the top, with no effort at vertical centering. Be sure to arrange the first page so that a substantial part of the letter is carried over to the second—never a bare couple of lines or, worst yet, merely the complimentary close and signature. If the letter has three or more pages, the second and all succeeding pages except the last are both vertically and laterally balanced (that is, written to within approximately one inch of all edges of the sheet); the last is then treated like the second sheet of a two-page letter, as just discussed.

(2. SINGLE-SPACING AND DOUBLE-SPACING)

Body. Most letters are single-spaced. However, the body, or message, if very short may well be double-spaced to help fill out the page. In a letter, as in any other composition, when generally single-spacing always double-space between paragraphs; but when double-spacing do not skip an extra space (i.e., do not triple-space) between paragraphs.

Other elements. Even if the body of a letter is double-spaced, better appearance results from single-spacing the heading and inside address, because double-spacing these elements tends to throw the middle, or balance point, of the message too far down on the page. The typed portion of the signature (below the handwritten name) also is preferably single-spaced when it consists of more than one line. The return address (on the envelope) always is single-spaced, but the outside address (also on the envelope) is double-spaced unless it is over three lines in length.

(*3. BLOCK AND INDENTED STYLES*)

Consistency among five elements. Throughout five elements of the letter (all to be described below under LAYOUT)—namely, the HEADING, the INSIDE ADDRESS, the OUTSIDE ADDRESS, the RETURN ADDRESS, and the (COMPLETE) SIGNATURE—either the block or the indented style should be consistently employed at the left edges of the entries. In the **block** style all lines begin even with the first. In the **indented,** or **echelon,** style the second line is indented a number of spaces (three, four, or five), the third twice this basic number of spaces, the fourth (if there is a fourth line) three times the same number, etc., so that the successive lines form a slant, or echelon, downward and to the right.

Note 1: As regards choice between the block and indented styles, the complimentary close is arbitrarily considered to form a unit with the complete signature (including the written and typed parts). See Plate II (page 199) for illustrations.

Note 2: Use of the block style in the heading, in the inside, outside, and return addresses, and in the signature does *not* demand block paragraphing (i.e., writing of the opening lines of paragraphs flush with the left margin) in the body of the letter. (See the two *Notes* to the discussion of "Body" on pages 195–196, below.)

(*4. OPEN AND CLOSED TERMINAL PUNCTUATION*)

Consistency among five elements. Throughout the same five elements named in Topic 3 (*Block and Indented Styles*), either the open or the closed style of punctuation should be consistently employed at the right edges of the entries. **Open** terminal punctuation means that no mark of punctuation is placed at the *end* of any line— with the exception, of course, of a period if an abbreviation occurs there. **Closed** terminal punctuation consists of commas at the close of all lines other than the last, with a period closing the final line. (For minor exceptions, see the *Note* at the end of the discussion of "Signature," page 198.)

Note: The block style joined with open punctuation is the simplest, easiest, and most favored combination for typewritten letters. Persons who write business correspondence in longhand may prefer to retain the older combination of left echelon and closed terminal punctuation. The two other possible arrangements (indented—open; block —closed) are not much practiced.

(5. DATA OF IDENTIFICATION)

Completeness; abbreviations. Both on the envelope and at the head and foot of the letter proper, names and addresses should be given fully. Abbreviations are permissible if they tend to equalize lengths of lines, but they should be used only in conformity with recognized standards: e.g., *Mo.* (not *Miss.*, which stands for *Mississippi*) for *Missouri; Ohio* (not *O.* or *Oh.*), correct only in the spelled-out form; *Rte.* (not *Rt.*) for *Route.* Do not leave out any information which might conceivably be useful for identification or postal delivery. Above all, avoid omitting the words *Street, Avenue, Building,* and the like. (Sometimes the same name occurs in a single city for, say, a street, a boulevard, a "terrace," and a building.) Do not write "City" for locally addressed mail; give the city and state in full, as in any other address.

(6. POSTAL DELIVERY ZONES)

Position; punctuation. In recent years the Post Office Department has requested that delivery zones be specified with addresses. The delivery zone is entered after the name of the city as an Arabic number, in parentheses or not according to the preference of the writer. The zone number is not preceded by a comma, but is followed by one if the name of the state is on the same line. When the state is named on a separate line, a comma follows the zone number only if closed terminal punctuation is being employed.

(7. AUXILIARY MATERIAL)

Types; position; reference. Almost any kind of fairly light, flat auxiliary matter may be enclosed with a letter. Usually drawings, graphs, and other such visual aids are made on separate sheets of appropriate paper, normally the same size as the written sheets. Simple sketches and diagrams may, however, be drawn (or, less desirably in letters, pasted) between lines of typing, below the signature, or elsewhere in the letter itself. Extra sheets of listed or tabulated data sometimes are included. Regardless of where such material is entered, it should be explicitly referred to in the text. If anything is being sent under separate cover, the fact should be made clear.

(3) LAYOUT

A business letter contains certain definitely required elements, and in addition may contain one or more optional elements. Plate I shows the parts diagrammatically. (See next page.)

Note 1: The word "firm" will be used in the following discussion to signify a company, partnership, corporation, association, society, or organization of any kind (e.g., a school) that might transact part of its business by correspondence.

Note 2: Refer, throughout, to the directions for single-spacing and double-spacing given on page 188.

(1. REQUIRED PARTS)

Eight elements are requisite for a business letter complete with its envelope. (See Fig. 1 of Plate I for the envelope, and Fig. 2 for the letter proper.)

(1) Outside Address

Position. The outside address is typewritten on the face of the envelope, being balanced on a point considerably off-center to the right and somewhat below the vertical middle. It consists of three or more lines, seldom exceeding five.

First line(s). The first line gives the full name of the person or firm addressed. An individual's name is prefaced by a title of respect, such as *Mr.* (plural: *Messrs.*), *Mrs.* (plural: *Mmes.*), *Miss* (note the absence of a period, since this word is not an abbreviation), *Dr., Major,* or *Professor.* The name of a firm should be in exactly the form used by the firm itself, as shown by its letterhead, catalogue, advertisements, or other direct evidence. When an individual member, official, or employee of a firm is particularly addressed, the first line gives his name together with his office or rank, if of significance, as President, Cashier, Purchasing Agent, or the like (the personal name and office being separated by a comma); the name of the firm is then given on the second line. Or if his name and that of his office together are long, they are placed on separate, successive lines, both preceding the line on which the name of the firm is given.

Middle lines. The next line (the second, third, or occasionally fourth) gives the street or building address (the street address of an office building or hotel should be entered on a separate, following line unless the location is very well known), Post Office box or drawer number, or rural route and box number. In a letter written to a firm or particular member of a firm, sometimes two lines are required for this part of the outside address, the first giving the name of the department or the departmental box number (or both), the second stating the street address. As a slight modification, the department or departmental box number may be entered in the line before, and the street address in the line after, the name of the firm.

Last line. The final line indicates the city or town (followed by the zone number, if any) and state of the addressee, with a comma

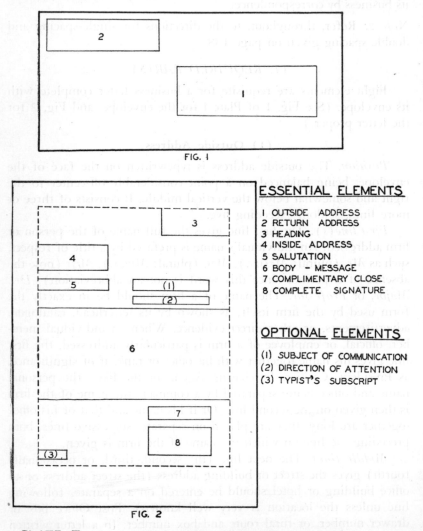

FIG. I

ESSENTIAL ELEMENTS

1 OUTSIDE ADDRESS
2 RETURN ADDRESS
3 HEADING
4 INSIDE ADDRESS
5 SALUTATION
6 BODY – MESSAGE
7 COMPLIMENTARY CLOSE
8 COMPLETE SIGNATURE

OPTIONAL ELEMENTS

(1) SUBJECT OF COMMUNICATION
(2) DIRECTION OF ATTENTION
(3) TYPIST'S SUBSCRIPT

FIG. 2

PLATE I   LAYOUT OF BUSINESS LETTER WITH ENVELOPE

preceding the name of the state. On the rare occasion when no specific local address is needed in addition to the town and state, and the rest of the outside address consists of only one other line (containing the name of the addressee), the city and state are specified on separate lines to bring the whole to the minimum length of three lines.

(2) Return Address

Position. Most firms and some individuals have envelopes printed with a return address. If a plain envelope is used, the return address is typed in the upper left of the face, with allowance of a very small upper and left margin. (Use of the back flap for this purpose is not correct business style.) The usual number of lines is three or four; an extra direction line—reading: "After _____ days return to [:]"— may be placed at the head, but is unnecessary in first-class mail.

First line. The first regular line states the name of the sender, whether an individual or a firm. An individual's name is *not* prefaced by *Mr.* or other title of respect, except that a married woman uses *Mrs.* and a married couple *Mr. and Mrs.* If the individual writes as the representative of a firm, his name may be followed (usually on the same line, with a comma for separation) by his office or rank; the next line then gives the name of the firm.

Other lines. The remainder of the return address, consisting of the sender's address, is precisely analogous to the corresponding part of the outside address, as discussed just above.

(3) Heading

Position. A heading is placed within the upper right-hand corner of the margins of the first page. The longest line of the heading should extend exactly to the right margin.

On plain paper (without letterhead). If a letterhead is not used, the heading typically consists of three lines, which give the following information in the order mentioned: (1) the local address of the sender, (2) the city or town (followed by the zone number, if any) and state, and (3) the date of the letter. By "local" is meant the street or building address (the street address of an office building or hotel should be entered on a separate, following line unless the location is very well known), Post Office box or drawer number, or rural route and box number. As many as five or six lines may be needed for the heading when the sender's place of business is given as his address: including, perhaps, lines for the department or departmental box number, the name of the firm (the order of these two entries being interchangeable), the building or street address (or both entered separately), and the city, zone, and state, together with the final line for the date.

On letterhead paper. With a letterhead containing the address of the sender, the heading consists simply of the date on one line. Some typists center the date under the letterhead, but from the standpoint of balancing the letter as a whole the regular position at the upper right probably is better.

Extra pages. Every sheet subsequent to the first properly has a heading containing the following information: the name of the addressee, the date of the letter, and the page number. Although custom has not developed any universal form, this information (the page number, most obviously of all) should not be omitted. It may be stacked in several lines at the top left, with block or indented style and open or closed terminal punctuation the same as in the heading and inside address on the first page; or it may be either closely or widely spaced across the page in a single line. This heading sets the upper and left margins of the sheet (ordinarily about one inch from each of those edges); the continuation of the letter begins two or three spaces below.

(4) Inside Address

Position; content. The inside address starts at the left margin of the first page, one or more spaces below the level of the last line of the heading. (Especially in distinctly personal correspondence, it may optionally be moved to the bottom left of the letter, beginning at the margin and below the level of the signature.) Except with respect to single-spacing and double-spacing, it is *identical with the outside address.* (See the paragraph labeled *Other elements* on page 188.)

(5) Salutation

Position; capitalization; punctuation. The salutation begins *even with the left margin.* The first word and all titles of respect are capitalized; practically, this means that the only word not capitalized is *dear* when the first word is *My.* Salutations of business letters are followed by the colon. Use of a semicolon is a blunder, and the combination of a colon with a hyphen or dash is no longer regarded as correct. In private letters to individuals for other than strictly business communications, the comma is permissible to suggest informality of tone; however, the colon is never improper. Omission of punctuation after the salutation, to accord with open punctuation in other elements, is an extreme form that has not received general favor.

Common forms. To address an individual man, *Dear Sir* is the common salutation, but the optional form of *Dear Mr. Doe* is preferred if the addressee is an acquaintance. To salute a firm composed wholly of men or of both men and women, *Gentlemen* is preferred to the older *Dear Sirs.* A firm consisting exclusively of women is addressed as *Ladies* or *Mesdames. Dear Madam* (observe the spelling, with no *e* at the end), for a married woman, corresponds to *Dear Sir;* and *Dear Mrs. Doe,* to *Dear Mr. Doe* (but is more likely to be used, even if the named addressee is known only through correspondence). The salutation of an unmarried woman, whether an acquaintance or not, must include her last name, as *Dear Miss Doe* (not simply *Dear Miss*).

Other forms. For greater warmth, the *My dear . . .* formula is available, but is not usually advisable. At the other extreme, omission of *Dear* (leaving *Sir* or *Madam* standing alone), for formality or severity in addressing an individual, is ordinarily even less desirable, but the practice is correct for writing to most high officials of government.

Skipped space. The same number of spaces (usually one or two, and practically never more than three) should be skipped both above and below the salutation, setting it off from the inside address and the message.

(6) Body

Regularity. The body of the letter, or message, though of course by far the most important part, need receive only passing mention in the present discussion of format. Structurally it is a composition like any other, almost without specific characteristics (apart from its position and surrounding elements) in consequence of being a letter. (On questions of style and content, see pages 202–206.)

Note 1: The message may be either single-spaced or double-spaced, and have the opening line of paragraphs either blocked (flush with the left margin) or indented. If, however, the block style is employed, the body *must* be generally single-spaced, with double-spacing between paragraphs, since the indication of a new paragraph is the fact that an exceptional blank space is left between successive lines of typing. (These regulations govern typewritten compositions in general.)

Note 2: As has been mentioned before, the paragraphs of the body may, with perfect propriety, be indented even though the block style is employed in the heading, inside address, etc. On the other hand, probably no typist would block the message after using the indented (echelon) style in the heading and inside address.

(7) Complimentary Close

Position. One or several lines are skipped below the body. The lateral position of the next element, the complimentary close, is determined by its own width and that of the complete signature (including typewritten parts), considered together. These two elements should form a unit whose lateral middle is approximately three inches from the right *edge* (not margin) of the sheet, provided the page has the usual one-inch margins of a fairly long letter. If wider margins are used, the lateral middle should be moved farther than three inches to the left, with an increase in the ratio of about one-half to one; thus, for margins two inches wide, the lateral middle of the complimentary close and signature would be about three and one-half inches from the right edge of the sheet.

Note 1: The foregoing specifications assume that neither element is excessively broad. Under no circumstances should any part of the complimentary close or of the complete signature encroach upon the blank right margin; sometimes, therefore, a shift still farther to the left is necessary.

Note 2: To center the complimentary close and signature in the middle of the page is definitely bad form. Some typists always arrange both elements so that the longest line exactly touches the right margin, but on the whole the position recommended gives a better appearance.

Capitalization; punctuation. Only the first word of the complimentary close is capitalized. A comma is placed at the end; omission of this comma, to accord with open punctuation elsewhere, is an extreme form that has not received general favor.

Forms. A rule of thumb for the complimentary close in business correspondence is that it regularly consists of either two or three words that include *yours* (not *your*). For the required adverb, the choice is among *truly* (virtually always correct), *sincerely* (somewhat less formal, but ordinarily in good taste), *cordially* (perhaps questionable for strictly business correspondence), *faithfully* (a bit old-fashioned, but impressive when a promise has been made or implied in the message), and *respectfully* (proper only for a letter to a person or group in some regard superior to the writer). A third word, *very,* is not used with *faithfully* or *respectfully* but is otherwise optional. Almost all possible arrangements—e.g., *Yours sincerely, Sincerely yours, Very sincerely yours, Yours very sincerely*—are correct, conveying slightly different shades of feeling. (*Truly yours* is not, however, idiomatic.) Deviation from the expected forms is in bad taste. An eccentric complimentary close, of the type of *Yours for improved sales,* tends to offend or antagonize a literate recipient of the letter.

Note 1: When in doubt among the various admissible forms, choose *Yours truly* or, for somewhat less formality, either *Very truly yours* or *Yours very truly.*

Note 2: At the close of reports written as letters, and usually, also, of letters of transmittal included with reports, *Respectfully submitted* is the customary form. *Respectfully yours* or *Yours respectfully* also may be used. Other forms—mainly *Yours truly, Very truly yours,* or *Yours very truly*—are employed if, from any consideration, the adverb *respectfully* is not felt to be appropriate. (Illiterate substitution of *respectively* or *respectably* for *respectfully,* in the complimentary close, makes a letter ridiculous.)

(8) Signature

Handwritten signature. A letter must be signed in ink by hand. The written signature should be made with a pen that feeds without scratching or splotching, and only black, blue, or blue-black ink should be used. Never neglect to sign a letter. Do not, of course, employ a rubber stamp; and, unless so directed by a superior, do not merely sign with initials. Adopt a fairly full form of your name as a regular and permanent signature, avoiding nicknames and diminutive or shortened forms. Sign in a legible hand.

Complete signature. The complete signature of a business letter consists of the handwritten signature and one or more typewritten lines. Two different forms are recognized, according to the nature of the letter: (1) the **individual signature** of a letter composed by a person either on his own account or for a firm he represents; (2) the

company signature of a letter which, although composed by the person who actually signs his own name by hand, is regarded as being legally signed by the firm itself. These forms, described just below, are illustrated in Plate II.

Individual signatures. The handwritten signature is placed far enough below the complimentary close that the two elements do not overlap. Some typists provide a continuous line (made with the shifted "6" key) to accommodate the written name. One to three (usually two) spaces lower, this name is typewritten in exactly the same form, with respect to spelling and initials, in which it will afterwards be signed. If the author of the letter writes as the representative of a firm, his office, rank, or department (e.g., President, Superintendent of Mills, Chief Engineer, Department of Soil Chemistry) is stated one line below the typed signature, and the name of the firm is given on the next line unless it already appears on a letterhead.

Note: No address—street address, building, box number, or city and state—is included here. When the name of a firm is mentioned, it is given as part of the signature, not as an address.

Company signatures. For a company signature, the typist double-spaces below the complimentary close and typewrites the name of the firm in FULL CAPITALS (every letter capitalized). Far enough below this company name to admit the written signature without crowding, a space is left for the handwritten signature, sometimes marked by a continuous line (made with the shifted "6" key). One to three spaces (usually two) below this level, the name of the signer is typed (*not* in full capitals) in the same form, with respect to spelling and initials, in which it will afterwards be written by hand. The office, rank, or department of this individual is stated on the next line; or, as a common variant in company signatures, on the same line, separated from the name by a comma. Since the name of the firm already has been given (in capital letters, above the personal signature of the writer of the letter), it is not repeated.

Note: In the open style of terminal punctuation, as previously explained, no mark (other than a period for an abbreviation) would be placed at the end of any line of the complete signature. Even in the closed style, no commas are used after the typed, fully capitalized firm name in a company signature and after the handwritten name in either a company or an individual signature.

Individual Signatures	Company Signatures
I.	**I.**
Yours truly,	Yours truly,
John Q. Doe	THE DOE COMPANY
John Q. Doe	*John Q. Doe*
General Manager	John Q. Doe
The Doe Company	General Manager
II.	**II.**
Yours truly,	Yours truly,
John Q. Doe	THE DOE COMPANY
John Q. Doe,	*John Q. Doe*
General Manager,	John Q. Doe,
The Doe Company.	General Manager.
III.	**III.**
Yours truly,	Yours truly,
John Q. Doe	THE DOE COMPANY
John Q. Doe	*John Q. Doe*
General Manager	John Q. Doe
The Doe Company	General Manager
IV.	**IV.**
Yours truly,	Yours truly,
John Q. Doe	THE DOE COMPANY
John Q. Doe,	*John Q. Doe*
General Manager,	John Q. Doe,
The Doe Company.	General Manager.

LEGEND

I. Block—Open. III. Indented—Open.
II. Indented—Closed. IV. Block—Closed
(seldom employed).

PLATE II
STYLES OF THE COMPLETE SIGNATURE
(WITH COMPLIMENTARY CLOSE)

(2. OPTIONAL PARTS)

Three elements are optional. None, only one, or any combination of them may be employed in a business letter.

(1) Subject of Communication

Purpose; position; form. The major data of a letter may be called to the recipient's attention in topical (i.e., phrase rather than sentence) form by means of an entry known as the subject of communication. Although usage differs, the best position is the approximate middle of the same line occupied, at the left, by the salutation. The subject of communication begins with the word *Subject* followed by a colon, and the remainder of the entry digests the pertinent information as briefly as possible. If two or more lines are needed, single-spacing is used and the additional lines begin even with the first word of the entry proper in the first line (not directly below the word *Subject*). Internal punctuation is employed if needed, but no period is placed at the end. Ordinary capitalization is sufficient, and nothing need be underlined.

Example. A typical subject of communication (with accompanying salutation) might read as follows:

Gentlemen: Subject: Windstorm loss, May 1, 19—;
                           Policy FT–46,502; Agency 397;
                           James R. Robinson, Assured

(2) Direction of Attention

Purpose; position; form. When a letter is addressed to a firm as a whole rather than to an individual member, employee, or official, the writer nevertheless may desire to indicate what department or person the message especially concerns. This purpose can be accomplished by means of a direction of attention, beginning with the word *Attention* followed by a colon. The position varies, depending partly on whether the letter also has a subject-of-communication entry. If not, the direction of attention may take the usual position of the subject of communication, on the same line with the salutation. If both entries occur in the same letter, the best place for the direction of attention is a double space below the subject of communication, the two being lined up with equal indention and arranged so that as a group they appear approximately centered on the page. Internal punctuation is employed if needed, but no period is placed at the end. Ordinary capitalization is sufficient, and nothing need be underlined. Since the firm itself is primarily addressed, the salutation is normally plural (ordinarily, *Gentlemen*).

Following are examples with and without a subject of communication:

Gentlemen: Attention: Mr. F. L. Jones, Manager

Gentlemen: Attention: Office of the Bursar

Gentlemen: Subject: Invoice no. 10,562, our order
                          no. M–428, July 16, 19—

                Attention: Billing Department

Note: The direction of attention is repeated at the lower left of the envelope.

(3) Subscript

Initials. The typist of a letter composed by another person places at the left margin, a double space below the level of the last typed line of the complete signature, the capitalized initials of the intended signer and the typist's own initials (in either capital or small letters), without periods or spacing, as RPL:MJD (*or:* RPL/mjd).

Enclosures. In addition to the initials, another entry may show that the same envelope is to contain one or more enclosures: for example, checks, specification sheets, or leaflets. This part also is flush with the left margin, immediately or a double space below the initials. In form, it specifies one enclosure by either the full word *Enclosure* (or: *Inclosure*) or the abbreviation *Encl.* (or: *Incl.*). Two or more enclosures are variously indicated: Enclosure (2), Enclosure (3); Inclosure (2), Inclosure (3); 2 Encl., 3 Encl.; 2 Incl., 3 Incl.; Encl. (2), Encl. (3); Incl. (2), Incl. (3).

Copies. Names of persons or departments receiving copies of the letter may also be given, in a form such as the following: Copy to Mr. R. B. Casten (*or:* Copies to Dean and Registrar). This entry is placed immediately or a double space below the enclosure statement, or, if there are no enclosures, below the initials. Unless obvious from the letter, the addresses of those getting copies are included below their names or titles. The abbreviation *cc* or *c.c.* (meaning, in both forms, either "carbon copy" or "carbon copies") commonly is used instead of the words *Copy to* and *Copies to*. Substitution of *bc* or *b.c.* shows that the notation has not been typed on the original letter, but only on the copies themselves or perhaps on the file copy alone.

B. STYLE

(1) NORMALITY

Accepted standards of grammar, language, and punctuation govern correspondence equally with other forms of writing. The business letter should be carefully organized; it should be properly paragraphed, punctuated, and spelled; and it should employ the same grammar, diction, and idioms as would be appropriate to another type of composition on the same topic for the same reader. Use of a special style for letter writing does not conform to the best current practice, and at its worst may be a mark of vulgarity or illiteracy.

Styles to avoid. In particular, two styles are to be shunned by anyone trying to learn good methods of modern correspondence:

(1) *"Telegraphic" style.* Rigorously avoid any tincture of the "telegraphic" or "breezy" manner in which pronouns, articles, auxiliary verbs, and other structural elements are omitted: e.g., "Yours received. Will say in reply shipment went out promptly on order." Intelligent, educated people do not write letters in this way. (Actual telegrams and cables, of course, are cut to a bare minimum of words, for obvious reasons; even code may be employed to reduce segments of meaning to a few letters.)

(2) *Old-fashioned style.* The set epistolary phrasing typified by "your favor," "we beg to advise," "the sixteenth ult.," "I thank you in advance," and the like has become outmoded, and although still practiced by some older people, should not be adopted by young men and women now in school or entering a career. One of its most characteristic forms is a short final paragraph of the message consisting of a participial or prepositional phrase, a comma, some such expression as "I am," or "we remain," and another comma (not a period, since the sentence is logically and grammatically completed by the immediately following complimentary close). In present style, no such formal rounding-off of a letter is expected.*

(2) PECULIARITIES

Only two peculiarities of style set the message of a well-written business or professional letter apart from any other composition on

---

* Even the complimentary close is omitted in military and naval correspondence, as also in standardized forms of interdepartmental communications established by many business firms.

a similar subject. Both, as will be seen, are merely relative, and neither constitutes a violation of general good usage.

(*1. RELATIVE PERSONALITY*)

Comparison with articles and reports. A letter usually tends to be more personal than, say, a periodical article or a report covering the same ground. Letters (especially reports in letter form) sometimes are drafted in the impersonal third person of the passive voice, but most commonly the first person (singular or plural) is employed. In fact, of many formal reports the only element cast in the first person is the preliminary letter of transmittal, which may contain distinctly personal allusions to relations between the writer and the receiver of the report.

(*2. RELATIVE TERSENESS*)

Phrasing. The average letter is a composition in miniature, for business communications are intended to be as short as possible and very much to the point. Since compression is expected, terseness of phrasing amounting almost to bluntness (not quite the same thing as curtness) seldom will give offense.

Paragraphing. Likewise, paragraphs of letters ordinarily are much shorter than those composed in essay style. While habitually "choppy" paragraphs of only a sentence or two each are not desirable, individual ones often need be no longer than that to cover adequately their portions of the whole topic.

Note: Upon most readers of any except routine correspondence, a letter of at least two paragraphs makes a better instantaneous impression than one consisting of a single paragraph. Obviously, some very brief letters cannot reasonably have more than one.

(3) TONE

The letter speaks for the writer. A letter bears a kind of personality—sometimes highly individualized, sometimes more or less formalized and generalized as representing a company, committee, or other group. This character is important. It is perceived "between the lines" as well as in direct, positive statements. You will not learn to give your letters a good tone by memorizing a set of rules, but one thing that you can do will greatly help: by reading what you have written from the point of view of the intended recipient, observe and criticize yourself as author. What would you think of the person who seems to have written the letter? Does he sound as if he would faithfully keep a promise? (Never mind whether, in point of fact, he has made a promise in the letter; the question is, whether you feel you could trust his word.) Is he small-minded or bull-headed? Would you expect him to quarrel over trifles? Analyze him carefully; to do so is well worth while. Remember that you are estimating your personality as revealed in correspondence, the only manner in which you will ever show yourself to a great many people.

Courtesy. Above all else, do you find the writer (yourself) courteous? A slight, particularly if unintended, can be smoothed over in face-to-face conversation; but a mistake of that kind in a letter is all but irretrievable. Letters of complaint should be letters of restraint; a great deal depends on what is not said—sometimes on what is never put into the mails, if written in haste.

The "big 'I.' " Look down the line of paragraphs in the first draft of your next two or three letters. Whatever the subjects, you probably will discover that very nearly every paragraph begins with the word *I.* The reader may not be consciously aware of his feeling, but just the same he would prefer not to have this selfish "big *I*" thrust at him. By a little recasting of the opening sentences, you can easily place some of the *I's* and *we's* in less prominent positions; however, do not develop a phobia that would cause you to write unnaturally rather than put first-person pronouns at the beginning of any paragraphs at all.

C. CONTENT

Importance of redrafting. Business letters are important documents, which, like reports, undoubtedly will be a principal form of your professional writing. You would not think of submitting the first draft of a formal report, and for exactly the same reasons you should not expect the original draft of a business letter to be adequate. With time and occasion, you may later learn to dictate correspondence, leaving to a secretary or stenographer the care of minor revisions and of all problems of mechanics and layout. For the present, presumably you actually do (or at least directly oversee) the typing of your letters, and you must resign yourself to the simple fact that the first draft is the place to make mistakes—not the copy to be mailed or submitted to an instructor for grading. The time of correction and redrafting is well spent, even though for a while several intermediate versions of the same letter may have to precede the final copy. Successive revisions should improve in technique, approaching nearer and nearer to correct layout, mechanics, and "framing" (balance on the page) of the whole letter as treated in Section A. Content of the message also should be brought under severe criticism, with application of general principles of logic and effective composition to the individual letter.

(1) UNITY

A rigid requirement. If you have worked in the commercial world, you have noticed that on the same day an official may send several or many letters to another official, perhaps placing them all in the same envelope. A primary rule of the business letter is that it concern *only one topic;* no form of composition is more stringent in the demand of unity. Two matters of correspondence, unless so closely interrelated that they could not possibly be considered apart, require separate letters, even though both topics may be small enough to be easily contained on the same page. One important reason for this requirement is that business and professional people keep files of their correspondence. The fact that two letters are sent to the same person on the same day does not imply that the originals will be filed in the same place by the recipient, or the carbon copies in the same place by the sender.

(2) REFERENCE

The aim: immediate clarity. A letter should make explicit reference, normally in the first paragraph, to any previous correspondence on the subject, and in particular should refer by date to the addressee's last communication to the writer. It also should make clear at once (through a subject-of-communication entry, or the opening one or two paragraphs of the text, or both) the topic and purpose of the present letter, instead of leaving these matters to be gradually learned as the reader proceeds to the end. Just as some expository paragraphs and papers unfold an idea summarily stated near the beginning in a topic sentence or early paragraph, so practically all business letters develop a thought or request presented at the outset. With almost no exceptions, the reader should know from the beginning exactly what the writer plans to discuss.

(3) COMPLETENESS

Take the reader's point of view. A successful letter tells the recipient everything he needs to know regarding the subject treated. Again, a technique already recommended, of reading the letter from his imagined point of view, is useful. Then ask yourself whether the writer has left any questions unanswered. Has he said merely "shipped" without naming the carrier? Has he said "recently" instead of giving a date? Has he made an order without arranging a method of payment, or without specifying the manner of delivery? Worse yet, has he failed to indicate quantities, prices, sizes, and catalogue numbers (or the like) in clear, orderly—preferably tabular—form? Has he alluded to other persons involved in a transaction but not given their names and addresses? Has he referred vaguely to "Mr. Jones" rather than specifically to "Mr. John P. Jones, Chief Stationary Engineer of this company"? If you were the addressee, what else would you need or wish to know? The answer to that question is a measure of the incompleteness of the draft you have just composed.

(4) ACCURACY

Errors are not excused. Accuracy cannot be absolutely distinguished from completeness, for the two are complementary. Vagueness, which may be regarded as a violation of both, is bad enough. Positive mistatement is unforgivable in correspondence, and may entail unfortunate legal consequences. Verify what you say in a letter. Do not be timid about asking questions of a superior, if you have one; use tables, directories, catalogues, and other appropriate reference material; avoid all guesswork. Carefully proofread the final draft for typographical errors or other slips. Bear in mind that you are responsible for everything sent out over your name.

D. MODELS

Limitations. The several accompanying letters obviously are not intended as a "complete handy letter writer" for all possible subjects. For one thing, consideration is not given to social notes or purely personal correspondence, although in fact some of the models are friendly letters cast in business form.* Second, an assumption is made throughout that the users will be students preparing themselves for careers in various technical fields. It hardly need be said that, like any other models, those given below are to be taken as a source of aid and suggestion, not to be copied with slight modification as substitutes for original work.

Selection of subjects. Experience shows the desirability that the practice correspondence of the student be largely—if possible, wholly—related to his actual interests and activities. Writing on topics of his own choice, within limitations set by an assignment of general type and content, he can learn all the essentials of good business correspondence. In addition, he has favorable opportunity to put character or personality into what he writes—an end to which no means are effectual other than sincerity, first-hand knowledge, and genuine feeling. If some of his class letters really are intended for mailing, so much the better. Later, he will find little difficulty in applying the mastered fundamentals of form and style to the special problems of his professional correspondence. The examples, for the most part adapted from letters submitted by students of technical English,† show various possibilities of subject and method of treatment.‡

* The term *"business" letter* does not, of course, imply that a letter is necessarily commercial in subject matter. The type is standard for civilian correspondence in general, excluding cables and telegrams, formal social notes, intimate letters, and special forms sometimes prescribed by business houses or other organizations for certain purposes such as memoranda and interoffice communications.

† Personal names and geographical data have been changed.

‡ However, the models are largely normalized in form. In particular, the block-open styles are employed (except for indented paragraphs in the body of most of the examples), since this combination is now favored in typewritten letters. Concerning these and other optionally correct forms, see under GENERAL PRINCIPLES OF FORM, pages 187 ff.

(1) APPLICATION FOR EMPLOYMENT

                                        1205 Stayton Road
                                        Paris 5, Missiana
                                        November 23, 19—

The Jacobi Electric Company
901 Jarney Street
Springfield 2, Ohio

Gentlemen: Subject: Application for employment

    Early next June I shall obtain the degree of
Bachelor of Science in Electrical Engineering from
the University of Missiana. My chief interest is
in wind-driven electrical equipment. As the Jacobi
Electric Company is the leading manufacturer of such
equipment, I have decided to ask you for a position in
your company after my graduation.

    I am twenty-one years of age and single, and am
without physical defects except for an old leg injury,
received playing football in junior high school, which
keeps me out of the armed services but does not cause a
limp or interfere with normal bodily activity. My
faith is Presbyterian. I was the salutatorian of the
class of 19— at the Athens Technical School (Athens,
Missiana); I am now in the upper scholastic quarter of
my class at the University of Missiana, and am a member
of the Tau Beta Pi Association and the American Institute of Electrical Engineers. These men have permitted me to name them as references:

        (1). Mr. J. T. Wright
            Superintendent of Schools
            Athens, Missiana

        (2). Mr. S. H. Vanders
            Department of Electrical Engineering
            The University of Missiana
            Paris 1, Missiana

The Jacobi Electric Company—11/23/**—p. 2

   Having been born and reared on a farm near Athens,
I early became interested in finding a way to supply
rural homes with electricity generated by wind-driven
dynamos. This interest caused me to decide to take
the course in electrical engineering at the University; now I am more interested in wind equipment
than before, because I am convinced by my studies that
it has enormous possibilities. That is why I am
asking for work with the Jacobi Electric Company.

   The things being done by your company are what I
most want to do, and I know that I can succeed if given
an opportunity. I am willing to start wherever you
may be able to place me, if only there is a reasonable
chance of advancement through hard work and aptitude.
I shall gladly send any further information that you
might desire.

                    Yours truly,

                    Clarence J. Simons

                    Clarence J. Simons

(2) REQUEST FOR TECHNICAL INFORMATION

722 West Eleventh Street
Paris 3, Missiana
March 17, 19—

Mr. John Van Partrand
Associate Editor
<u>Aerodyne</u>
722 Marsdon Lane
New York 15, N. Y.

Dear Sir:

May I, as a subscriber to <u>Aerodyne,</u> thank you
for the article, "The Gyroscopic Aircraft Horizon,"
which you contributed to the current March issue? The
subject interests me very much, for several reasons,
and I believe many other readers must be glad to have
this information.

One question remains unanswered in my mind, and
I should greatly appreciate your taking the trouble
to enlighten me. I have heard of "caging the gyro" on
military aircraft. You do not use any such expression
in your article, and I wonder whether it is slang for
something you explain under another name. Does it
have anything to do with the safety stops (shown as
"F" in Figure 4) that are intended to prevent excessive displacement of the horizon bar during aerial
maneuver? Or is it perhaps related to some other instrument altogether?

You may be assured of my gratefulness for any
answer you can give to my query. For your convenience, I enclose a self-addressed and stamped envelope.

Yours sincerely,

Philip Roy Wilton

Philip Roy Wilton

(3) REPLY TO INQUIRIES

(*1. CONCERNING A SCIENTIFIC PRINCIPLE*)

103 North Hall
The University of Missiana
Paris 1, Missiana
April 3, 19—

Miss Molly Peyton
1296 North Deaver Street
Tulsa 6, Oklahoma

My dear Miss Peyton:

My sister has just written to me about the monthly report you are preparing on "The Principle of Electronic Filtering of Air" for your class in physics. She suggested that you would be glad if I gave you a basic explanation of the theory, and I am very happy to do so. Of course, I am assuming that your teacher permits you to obtain outside aid for such problems, as we used to be allowed to do when I took the course three years ago.

Perhaps you have seen small pieces of paper picked up by attraction to a pocket comb given a small electric charge through friction. You can try that experiment for yourself by tearing some scraps of paper no larger than a fourth inch square and placing them on a table or a piece of glass. If you will run a comb through your hair several times and lower the comb toward the scraps, they will jump up to it.

All matter is composed of very minute particles, called atoms, which in turn contain several different types of still smaller particles, including electrons. The electrons, which are electric charges conventionally termed negative, have a certain amount of freedom to move around from one atom to another. Particles with their normal number of electrons present are said to be neutral; those with an excess of electrons, negative; and those with fewer than the normal number of electrons, positive.

Miss Molly Peyton—4/3/**—p. 2

The comb picks up some electrons from your hair, acquiring a negative charge. When it is brought near the neutral scraps of paper, which are positive with respect to the comb, they are attracted to it. You undoubtedly know the basic law that unlike electric charges attract each other.

In an electrostatic filter, ordinary alternating current is transformed and rectified to direct current of high voltage, with which the dust and smoke entering the unit are given a positive charge at a screen before being passed among negatively electrified plates. The positively charged particles cling to the plates by electrical attraction, while the now almost pure air passes on.

I am enclosing some pictures clipped from a booklet, which I happened to have, on a commercially manufactured filter of this nature. Perhaps you would like to study the whole article, since naturally it presents many more details than I could give in a letter. If you want it, just drop me a card; however, I shall have to ask you to return the booklet after you have delivered your report.

Faithfully yours,

J. DeMott Wallace

J. DeMott Wallace

(2. CONCERNING TECHNICAL DIRECTIONS)

4711 Carson Avenue
Paris 8, Missiana
March 9, 19—

Mr. W. H. Tomlin
R.F.D. Route 2, Box 106
Summit, Idaho

Dear Mr. Tomlin:

In reply to your letter of March 3, requesting directions for regulating your Delco-Remy automobile generator to increase the amount of current supplied to the battery, I will try to make clear how you can easily make the adjustment.

Around one end of the generator case is an inch-wide metal strip held by a spring catch. This catch must be dislodged and the metal strip removed. Underneath are two brushes, fairly close to each other, at the top of the generator. All regulating is done by means of these brushes.

On one end of the generator case you will find a screw that passes through the case and is fastened in one of the brushes. Loosen this screw a few turns, but do not remove it. Then move the brush to which the screw is fastened toward the other brush, to increase the amount of current supplied by the generator.

The distance through which the brush is moved should be small. Each time you slightly change its position, start and moderately race the car motor, watching the ammeter on the dashboard; in this manner, you can determine the right setting. Ordinarily, a current of around ten or twelve amperes is sufficient to keep the battery charged.

When the brushes are in correct adjustment, tighten the screw on the end of the generator case. Finally, replace the metal strip around the case.

Very truly yours,

George G. Jebbson, Jr.

George G. Jebbson, Jr.

(3. CONCERNING A TECHNICAL EXPLANATION)

221 North Hall
The University of Missiana
Paris 1, Missiana
June 2, 19—

Mr. Ray M. Blakely
201 West Rand Street
Thebes, Missiana

Dear Sir:

My superintendent at the Graystone Rubber Company, 702 Milestone Cutoff, where I am employed as a night service attendant, has asked me to answer your letter of May 30, 19—. Do not think of your request for information as in any way an imposition, which you seemed to feel it might be. We are pleased whenever we can be of help, in any way, to our customers and other friends of the company.

The problem you raise, of why small tires often are rated for more air than large ones, is easily solved. Just remember that there is no direct correlation between the weight and pressure of air contained in a tire. The common expression, "Put in thirty pounds," really means to increase the pressure to thirty pounds per square inch, or until the air that is forced into the tube exerts a push of thirty pounds upon each square inch of the casing. At most, the total weight of the compressed air, depending partly on the volume of the tire, probably would not exceed a few ounces. The significant figure, however, is not quantity but pressure.

The air pressure multiplied by the number of square inches of the tire resting on the ground equals the pounds of load carried by the wheel. Thus, if a four-wheeled automobile weighs one ton, the average load of each tire will be five hundred pounds. If, now, the tires contain a pressure of thirty pounds per square inch, on the average there will be five hundred divided by thirty, or sixteen and two-thirds square

Mr. Ray M. Blakely—6/2/**—p. 2

inches, of each tire in contact with the ground.
Again, if a bicycle with its rider weighs two hundred pounds, the average load on each tire will be one
hundred pounds. If, now, the tires contain a pressure of eighty pounds per square inch, on the average
there will be one hundred divided by eighty, or only
one and one-fourth square inches, of each tire in
contact with the ground.

    I think that by this time you clearly understand
why, for a given load, a balloon tire can carry a
smaller pressure than one of relatively small cross-
sectional area, which at the same low pressure might
actually let the wheel down flat on the ground. Manufacturers' tables, which are carefully worked out,
make safe allowance for uneven distribution of weight,
overloading, normal loss of air, slightly inaccurate
gauges, variations of temperature, and rough roads.
I do not have to tell you that extreme underinflation
and overinflation are harmful both to the tires themselves and to the mechanism of the vehicle.

                    Yours very truly,

                    John Scott Talley III

                    John Scott Talley III

(4) INVITATION TO MEMBERSHIP
OR ATTENDANCE

Rooms 102-3 Rally Building
The University of Missiana
Paris 1, Missiana
September 20, 19—

Mr. Ralph Barton Carter
155 North Hall
The University of Missiana
Paris 1, Missiana

Dear Mr. Carter:

The current registration sheets show that you have entered the University of Missiana as a freshman student of civil engineering. Although I do not yet have the pleasure of knowing you personally, I hope you will allow me to direct your attention to Theodolite, a campus organization to which all civil engineers of the faculty and student body are eligible. We meet one evening a month, usually at the Rally Building, for discussions and other programs; we occasionally also have social entertainments of different kinds, ranging from picnics to dances. There are no regular dues, and assessments are limited to the apportioned cost of the activities attended by any member.

We civil engineers are a very cohesive group, you will find, and we want you to make yourself a member of Theodolite as soon as possible. Please try to find time to come out to our first meeting next Thursday night, September 26, in the assembly rooms at the head of the stairway in the Rally Building (Rooms 102-3). Ask someone to point me out, and let me introduce you around. We are counting on you, and shall be disappointed if you cannot be with us.

Very cordially yours,

Charles O'B. Mimms

Charles O'B. Mimms
Secretary and Treasurer
Theodolite

(5) ADVICE TO YOUNGER STUDENTS

(*1. CONCERNING COURSES IN HIGH SCHOOL*)

                                    1409 Masset Blvd.
                                    Paris 4, Missiana
                                    February 20, 19——

Mr. Arnold David Sewall
47 Blanton Road, S.E.
Washington 19, D.C.

Dear Arnold:

   I was pleasantly excited to receive your letter
this morning. It bore on a subject about which I have
some rather definite thoughts, and I feel flattered
that your father should have referred you to me for
advice on arranging your last three years of high
school. I myself neglected to obtain counsel from
older students, but I now realize how valuable it
might have been.

   Yet may I begin by partially contradicting what I
have just said? I am not at all sure that such advice
is valuable until you have made up your mind exactly
what you intend to study in college, and I do not know
whether at your present age such a decision is possible or even desirable. However, if—as I gather
from your letter—you feel that you have a technical
bent of mind, there are certain courses which would
be of value in preparation for any scientific study.

   Maybe I shall discourage you when I say that
secondary-school courses at best are rather poor
preparation for serious university study, and that
personally I found their deficiency to be greatest in
the field of natural science. But I must tell you
this at the outset so that you will not be shocked if
I recommend to you as most important, not the science
courses themselves, but the more general subjects.

   I am going to urge on you first of all the study
of languages. If you take all the foreign languages
offered (with the exception of Spanish, unless you
plan to enter certain branches of commercial life), I
believe you will find them invaluable in any later
scientific career. Latin is the basis of much of the

Mr. Arnold David Sewall—2/20/**—p. 2

special terminology of science; so also is Greek, but
it is not offered in many public schools. In addition, a great part of scientific literature is in
modern foreign tongues, and is seldom translated.
Learning languages in high school will leave more room
on your university schedule for important science
courses.

Next I should like to advise you to elect all the
available mathematics. Thorough grounding in algebra
and trigonometry is an essential prerequisite for any
scientific study; mathematics has been called, with
justice, the language of science. Then you will certainly want as much history and English literature as
your schedule will allow (although I am afraid I have
pretty well filled it already), for a cultural background is necessary to any full and balanced life,
regardless of what some specialists may say.

Finally, if you can find room for them, take the
sciences: physics, chemistry, and biology. I have
placed them last because they will be repeated in the
university and will be presented much better there.
Of course, however, you must make sure to take at least
the minimum requirements in these—as well as other—
subjects for both graduation from high school and
admission to the college or professional school of
your choice.

I trust that some of my suggestions may be of use
to you. I hope, also, that you will obtain others to
compare with them, for any one person's opinions are
necessarily formed from his own relatively narrow experience, and consequently they should not be accepted
without criticism.

Cordially yours,

Martin McElray

Martin McElray

(2. CONCERNING CHOICE OF TECHNICAL CURRICULUM)

608½ Eckel Avenue
Paris 7, Missiana
December 8, 19—

Mr. James R. Spellman
210 Mayfield Court
Bestmar 5, Missiana

Dear James,

What a coincidence that you are deciding between the same two courses of study from which I, also, had to choose several years ago! No doubt your brother Wilson mentioned this fact when he suggested your letter of last Sunday.

The problem of electing either a course in chemical engineering or one in pure chemistry is very difficult to settle. Many factors must be considered.

Of primary importance is the question of whether you are personally talented in, or have a liking for, engineering. Contrary to popular belief, the chemical engineering curriculum does not consist solely of pure and engineering chemistry. All branches of engineering are studied: civil, electrical, and mechanical, as well as chemical. If you are good at chemistry yet have no knack for engineering in general, my advice is that you follow me in taking your degree as a chemistry major. On the other hand, if you like both chemistry and engineering techniques, then probably you had better enroll for chemical engineering.

Both programs have their merits. The study of engineering will prepare you for a greater variety of employment than courses in chemistry alone, whereas the latter will give you a much fuller knowledge of the pure science. Let me emphasize another point: that chemical engineers can secure positions much more easily than chemists, but that the latter can

Mr. James R. Spellman—12/8/**—p. 2

eventually find situations which, in my estimation,
are at least as desirable.

Were I in your place again, I should give this
question a great amount of thought. Let me suggest
that you see me later this month when I am in Bestmar
between Christmas and New Year's, in order that we
may discuss the matter at some length. Come over any
time to the house on Holloway Street where Wilson and I
used to have our "laboratory" in the attic.

Very sincerely yours,

Max Mitchell Gorson

Max Mitchell Gorson

(6) COMPLAINT AND RECOMMENDATION

(*1. DEMAND FOR CORRECTION*)

Division of Architecture
The University of Missiana
Paris 1, Missiana
October 10, 19—

Messrs. J. L. Coke and R. B. Burton
Associate Architects
Suite 37, Professional Bldg.
Paris 2, Missiana

Gentlemen: Subject: Garage building under construction at 3267 Ring Avenue,
Case Addition

Attention: Mr. Burton, Supervising
Architect

Both as a student of architectural engineering
and as a prospective tenant, I have been an interested
observer of progress on the garage, with attached
living quarters, being erected behind the planned site
of the house which you are now designing for my uncle,
Mr. Barnes N. Bryson. Without authority other than
the knowledge and consent of the owner, late this
afternoon I ordered the plaster-base applicators to
cease work on the interior walls of the combination
room next to the garage. I am writing immediately to
explain my action.

Paragraph 6 under the heading "Masonry and Carpentry" in your printed specifications, which are part
of the contract for this construction, states: "All
sills on concrete beams shall be creosoted and firmly
bolted to the foundation." When the concrete was
poured, for some reason the boltheads were set too low.
On the following day I called this fault to the attention of the contractors' superintendent; he replied
that either the holes in the sills would be counter-
sunk to receive the nuts, or else a special flanged
collar would be machined to rest flat on the sills
while engaging the bolts within the holes by means of
internal threads. Nevertheless, framing and sheathing
proceeded without apparent attention to his promise.

Messrs. J. L. Coke and R. B. Burton—10/10/**—p. 2

In this region, with its bad insurance record for cyclone losses, the necessity for bolting the sills to the foundation is dictated by more than the ordinary principles of sound construction. If the workmen had continued to attach panels of gypsum board to the studding as they were doing today, and if the plasterer had followed them as he was planning to do tomorrow, the contracting firm would have incurred an unnecessary later expense in tearing out these interior walls to expose the sills. For that reason, I felt justified in stopping the work.

Mr. B. N. Bryson, as owner, authorizes me to request that you inspect the building immediately, with a view to advising LaBranche Bros. concerning prompt measures for fulfilling the contract in this particular.

Yours truly,

C. L. R. Bryson

C. L. R. Bryson

cc: LaBranche Bros.
    General Contractors
    953 Riskin Way
    Paris 3, Missiana

(*2. CONSTRUCTIVE CRITICISM*)

                                    409 South Fifth Street
                                    Paris 2, Missiana
                                    October 25, 19—

Bramson Instruments, Inc.
P. O. Box 6048
St. Louis, Missouri

Gentlemen: Attention: Department of Instrument
                        Design

The purpose of this letter is to suggest a desirable improvement in the design of anemometers similar to your Model R-5.

In one of the engineering laboratories of the University of Missiana, where I am a student assistant, I have during the past month been monitor of some experiments concerning the flow of air through ducts and pipes. Measurement of changing rates of flow of the air was vital to the experiments, and various instruments were employed. One method utilized your Model R-5 anemometer in conjunction with a stop watch. The anemometer was placed at the end of the air duct, where it was held in position with one hand. For each measurement it was necessary to trip, simultaneously, the release of the anemometer and that of the stop watch. This could not be done with the free hand of the man holding the anemometer; therefore a second man was needed in the relatively simple test.

Timed operations of this general nature are, I have no doubt, frequently performed with an anemometer; and, unless the instrument can be rigidly attached to the duct under test, the wasteful use of two men's time is likely to be required. Moreover, errors can be introduced into calculations as a consequence of starting the anemometer and the stop watch at slightly different instants.

Bramson Instruments, Inc.—10/25/**—p. 2

Undoubtedly it would be possible to design a combined anemometer and stop watch, to be fabricated as a single unit with a common trigger. For some industrial uses of the instrument, a saving in labor costs conceivably might be effected; certainly, at least, the increased accuracy of timing would be a valuable improvement. I can see no reason why such a combination need be priced at more than an anemometer and a stop watch sold separately.

This suggestion I submit freely for your consideration and possible action. I believe my idea is practical, and I hope that you will sometime put on the market a single-unit instrument of the kind I have described briefly in this letter.

Sincerely yours,

George Sellinger

George Sellinger

(7) PURCHASE AND SALE

(*1. ORDER*)

1517 Pine Terrace
Paris 3, Missiana
May 2, 19—

Brown, Garton, and Company
Forty-fifth and Clement Streets
Carthage 4, Missiana

Gentlemen:

Enclosed is my personal check for $2.63, in payment for the following order of water pipe and fittings from your current (February, 19—) General Catalogue, page 452. Please ship by Railway Express, carriage charges collect.

Cat. no.	Quant.	Article	Length	Size	List	Cost
75W3457	2	Galvanized pipe	4'	½"	8¢ ft	$ .64
75W3457	2	Galvanized pipe	5'	½"	8¢ ft	.80
75W3457A	8	Pipe ends threaded (extra charge)			5¢ each	.40
75W3463	3	Galvanized elbow joints		½"	10¢ each	.30
75W3469	1	Reducer		⅜"x½"		.12
75W3470	1	Street elbow		½"		.12
75W3481	1	Arno Joint Compound		1 lb		.25
TOTAL						$2.63

Yours truly,

Benson R. Trent

Benson R. Trent

(*2. OFFER TO SELL*)

325 North Hall
The University of Missiana
Paris 1, Missiana
May 30, 19——

Box 3D-628
Care of the Paris <u>News</u>
Classified Ad Dept.
Paris 2, Missiana

Dear Sir or Madam:

Your classified advertisement in this morning's
<u>News,</u> under "Cars Wanted," almost exactly describes
an automobile I have for sale. It meets your two requirements of cheapness and suitability for local
driving by an elderly couple.

My car is a black 1937 Carliss standard coupé. I
offer this automobile, as it is, for only seventy-five
dollars cash. My reason for wishing to sell it is that
I am leaving the University early next month for a
traveling position in which I shall need a newer car.

Please do not suppose, from the low price, that
something is wrong with the mechanism. I invite you
to inspect and drive the car, or to have it checked at
any shop. I have always done my own mechanical work,
and so I confidently assure you, from personal knowledge, that you will be told it is all right for your
purpose. The only defect is that the oil pump delivers a pressure of only about ten gauge pounds, but
for driving around town at ordinary speeds, and for
occasional trips of a few hundred miles, this condition is not harmful. You will find that I have replaced much of the auxiliary equipment, such as the
carburetor and the distributor, with new parts; however, I have not been able to obtain an oil pump. The
engine and brakes are in good working order. Finish

Box 3D-628—5/30/**—p. 2

and upholstery are in fair condition; the four mounted
tires are good, and the spare is serviceable.

You are not likely to find an automobile priced
under a hundred dollars that will suit your needs so
well, and I hope you will accept a demonstration of my
car, of course without obligation. Instead of coming to the campus to see it, kindly let me have your
name and address so that I may drive it to you. To
reach me by telephone any night and all day Sunday,
call Jasper 6849 and ask for Extension 6.

Yours sincerely,

Johnson L. Swift

Johnson L. Swift

(8) THE REPORT *

(*1. LETTER OF TRANSMITTAL*)

202 North Hall
The University of Missiana
Paris 1, Missiana
May 5, 19—

Mr. James B. Kline
Department of English
The University of Missiana
Paris 1, Missiana

Dear Sir:

 The attached report, entitled "An Experiment on the Hydraulic Ram," is submitted to fulfill the assignment in English 27B of a formal report on a technical subject.

 The experiment was performed by a group of five students during March, 19—, with the hydraulic ram in the civil engineering laboratory of the University of Missiana. The purpose was to ascertain the effect of a variable discharge head on operating characteristics and efficiency. Data taken from test runs were plotted graphically and interpreted.

 As I am a physics major (not a student of engineering), I participated in the experiment, on my own time, by special permission of the laboratory instructor and the four regular members of the group. I served as recorder, and also prepared the graphs, copies of which are included. The text of my report is original, but much of the technical information was obtained from sources acknowledged in the footnotes.

Yours respectfully,

Curtes Manley Jones

Curtes Manley Jones

---

 * Report writing is fully treated in Chapter X. Concerning the letter in relation to the report, see pages 269, 273, and 274–275.

(2. REPORT IN LETTER FORM)

School of Engineering
The University of Missiana
Paris 1, Missiana
January 16, 19—

Morley Shaw and Sons
403 East Neville Street
Chicago 5, Illinois

Gentlemen: Subject: Report on overheating of exhaust
valves, Morley Shaw Engine 763

By your letter of October 20, 19—, the Department of
Mechanical Engineering of the University of Missiana
was requested to investigate overheating in the exhaust valves of the Morley Shaw Diesel Engine, Model
763, rated 220 horsepower. This engine is fitted with
valves of hollow-stem construction, permitting entrance of the cooling water into the valve stem. A
number of installations had failed during the preceding eighteen months because of valves warped by
overheating.

Procedure

Study of records supplied by Morley Shaw and Sons,
supplemented by three inspections on location, showed
that all failures had occurred in installations where
the water used for cooling was liable to contamination
with lint or sediment. Such impurities can easily
restrict circulation of the coolant, and in several
instances the resulting overheating of exhaust valves
entailed periodic shutdowns for replacements, together
with considerable unfavorable criticism of the engine
and its manufacturers.

A possible solution of the problem, involving relatively small expense for conversion, suggested itself.
The stems of the exhaust valves of the engine are cast
with holes of $\frac{1}{8}$-inch diameter for the flow of the
coolant. The valves were removed from the three
engines actually inspected in local (Wessex County,
Missiana) installations, and bored to a diameter of
$\frac{3}{8}$ inch. They were then reseated, and the engines were
put into daily service for a period of three months.

Morley Shaw and Sons—1/16/**—p. 2

At the end of that time the valves were removed and
examined. No measurable distortion of the valves had
been caused by the reduction in thickness of the stem
wall, nor could any evidence of overheating be
observed.

Thermal theory would indicate some decrease in operating temperature from the direct increase in volume
of the flush, without regard to any other factor.
More important, however, is the fact that the enlarged
bore of the valve stem permits easier passage of the
dregs which formerly obstructed the flow of coolant.

The most remarkable success achieved was at the
Wheaton Cotton Gin of this city. There the cooling
water is contaminated by lint, and previously the
Diesel could not be made to run for longer periods
than two to four weeks without replacement of exhaust
valves. With no attempt to improve the quality of the
coolant, the engine was operated continuously for
ninety days under capacity load without perceptible
deterioration of the valves.

Recommendations

It is therefore recommended that future engines of
this model be equipped with exhaust valves of the same
size and alloy as at present, but that the stem bore
be increased to ⅜-inch diameter. It is further suggested that so far as possible all replacement valves now
in the hands of jobbers, dealers, or owners be recalled.

Respectfully submitted,

DEPARTMENT OF MECHANICAL ENGINEERING

Patrick Caldwell Cassar

Patrick Caldwell Cassar
Fellow in Engineering

PCC:DLT

CHAPTER IX

LIBRARY RESEARCH

Importance. All knowledge grows by research. Every student of science and technology learns that research involves, among other procedures, careful *search* of "the literature." A report, article, or speech may require extensive investigation of material in libraries, or wherever else it can be found. Hours spent in that way are not wasted, but are saved many times over, for to neglect what already has been learned and published about a subject would be almost as inefficient as trying to build a tower from the top downward.

Qualities of the research composition. Some compositions are grounded wholly on personal experience, with research (if any) only of a practical nature—e.g., in a laboratory. Others are based, to a greater or less degree, on printed matter (and, occasionally, manuscripts and other documents) of various kinds; the term "research paper" customarily refers to a writing of this type, and will be so used in the following discussion. However, scientific research, unlike literary or historical, seldom relies wholly on the study of texts. The characteristics indicated just below are equally important in papers reflecting investigation of library sources, direct observation and experiment, theoretical study, or combinations of these various kinds of research. Largely, indeed, they are simply qualities of good composition in general.

(1) *Limited subject.* Students nearly always want to do too much: they propose to write on "Electric Power," "Modern Architecture," "The History of Glass," "Commercial Photography," "Industrial Management," "The Chemistry of Foods," "Television," "The Petroleum Industry," and the like. These are all proper subjects for books or, at the very least, extremely long articles; none could be more than skimmed in a paper of a few pages. The experienced re-

searcher knows that unless he has years or a lifetime to give to a problem, he must not expect to discover much in one investigation. Do not confuse encyclopedia articles, which attempt to tell a little about every phase of a large topic, and other writings for the general public, with research papers. A scholar may publish in both popular magazines and professional journals, but he does not make the mistake of interchanging the manuscripts.

(2) *Completeness.* The reason for sharply limiting the subject is that *whatever is done must be thoroughly done.* A researcher sets out to answer a question; his work is finished only when that question is completely answered. Sometimes an investigation that has been planned for a month may run on into years; but if a definite time limit has been set (as for a term report), the subject may have to be further limited, modified, or even abandoned for a more manageable substitute. "That's all I could find" is a wholly unacceptable excuse for incompleteness.*

(3) *Creativeness.* A true research paper is more than an assemblage of reference material; it is a contribution, great or slight, to knowledge. However much it quotes or summarizes other writings, it does something in addition. To boil down an article or report to a shorter paper may have value for learning to make a précis, but is not research in any legitimate sense of the word. Even in an investigation that does not pretend to do more than digest and reproduce information taken from various textual sources (a type of study usually, if loosely, called "library research"), the least contribution expected of the author would be originality of arrangement and presentation.

(4) *Accuracy.* If, as has been mentioned, "That's all I could find" is a bad excuse for incompleteness of a research, "That's what it says in the book" is an even worse apology for inaccuracy. In announcing a topic a writer makes himself—not his sources—fully responsible. If he is confronted by rival opinions or theories, or by inconsistent statements of supposed fact, his duty is to apply his intelligence to all the available evidence; and, besides announcing his conclusions, to show

* Occasionally, but seldom in student work, definite proof that a problem is insoluble may creditably terminate a research.

exactly the reasoning by which they were reached. He must carefully distinguish certainties from probabilities, facts from hypotheses. What he asserts as true must be the unequivocal truth. Remember the watchword of science and research scholarship: *verification*.

(5) *Economy*. The saying, "The least number of words is the right number," while not true of speeches (in which repetition often is of great value), comes very close to being valid for written compositions. Any long-windedness that appears in the early drafts should be suppressed in the revisions. A summary, however, is a useful form of redundancy commonly practiced in scientific papers; also, brief repetitions of main points may be a good method of transition between topics or sections.

(6) *Clarity*. Did you ever say of a teacher: "He seems to know his subject, but he can't make it clear to a class"? If the remark was a justified criticism and not an excuse for your own inattentiveness, it should serve as an indirect warning against presuming that conscientious research, of itself, yields successful composition. The author must have a sincere desire to communicate and a skill in clear expression. Economy of words should not be achieved at the expense of meaning. Another kind of economy—of the writer's time—is much more likely to interfere with the reader's comprehension. Hastily throwing together the results of many hours or days of research is a very poor saving of minutes, for what goes on paper is the only test by which the previous work will afterward be judged.

(7) *Formal correctness*. The formal aspects of correct composition have at least two values: (i) They contribute to meaning, as can be instantly realized by imagining a page written without paragraphing, punctuation, or any thought to grammar. (ii) They are a code of good manners—like all social forms, mainly unnoticed when rightly performed but shocking in absence or violation. Besides general formal agreement with other classes of writing, the research paper has a special technique of documentation, which will be explained in Section D.

A. PRELIMINARIES

(1) CHOICE OF TOPIC

The importance of selecting a limited subject, capable of being treated fully, already has been discussed. Usually the choice will lie within a range or field announced by the instructor; the individual student must then find a phase or topic suited to his own interests and background. Often the precise choice will be made only gradually, as various possibilities are first explored and the subject tentatively selected is then narrowed or adapted. Rapid reading of articles in journals, encyclopedias, and other reference publications can be of help in suggesting available problems for research.

(2) CONFERENCES

Not only in the selection of a topic, but in the preliminary and often, too, in the later stages of a research, interviews or conferences with instructors, local engineers, or other specialists may be of great value. Occasionally, another student who has done similar work is able to furnish expert advice.

Know what you want to ask. Almost everyone is happy to give information to students. However, the persons most likely to be sought out are very busy; the inquirer, therefore, has the obligation of conserving their time. Make an engagement by telephone, and be prompt; or approach an instructor or public official at a regular conference hour. Do not go to the interview in a vague state of mind. Know what your problem is, and as definitely as possible what kind of information or advice you want. At the last moment, look over any notes you have previously acquired, and perhaps take the more important ones with you. Be sure you have equipment for writing notes at the conference; you certainly will give an impression of inefficiency if you have to search for your pen or pencil, as though you were unaccustomed to using one, or if you are obliged to "borrow" a piece of paper. Speak up, clearly and to the point, guiding the conversation except at those points where your informant shows that he wishes to do so. Continue to ask questions until you get a full answer; after all, that is the understood purpose of your visit.

Bibliographical guidance. One of the main reasons for consulting a specialist in any field of research is that he usually is well acquainted with the reference materials of that branch of knowledge. (Reference librarians willingly help researchers with any problem, but they are not expected to have intimate knowledge of every minute subject.) Because assembling a bibliography is a slow process, the trained expert may be able in two minutes to save you two days—or two weeks—of drudgery. He will not, probably, guide you straight to the principal writings bearing on your narrowly limited topic; however, through similar researches of his own, he will know the reference tools and procedures for discovering such writings. Try to draw out this information by tactful questioning, if it is not spontaneously offered. Ask particularly about indexes, abstracts, and special encyclopedias covering the field of investigation, for they are apt to be of the highest value. (Cf. pages 239 ff.)

(3) THE CARD CATALOGUE

Importance. The key that unlocks each public and university library in the United States is its card catalogue. Library research is, literally, impossible for anyone unfamiliar with the use of card catalogues.

Arrangement. All cards are arranged *alphabetically in a continuous series,* extending through many drawers of a series of cabinets. A branch or departmental library may have its own separate card catalogue, but the general catalogue covers the whole system, including the main library and all branches. Usually at least three cards are entered for each book or other publication: (1) an **author card,** according to the last name of the author (or, representing a collaborated work, cards for each of the authors); (2) a **title card,** according to the title (a preliminary *A, An,* or *The* being recorded but ignored in alphabetization); (3) one or several **subject cards,** according to the division or divisions of knowledge treated by the publication.

Use. In consequence of the foregoing plan of the card catalogue, any holding of the library can be found by looking up, alphabetically, the author, the title, or the subject. Author cards are useful when a writer is known to have worked and published in a certain field; title cards, chiefly when a book has somewhere been mentioned without clear indication of authorship (possibly, but not necessarily, because it is anonymous). Obviously, for purposes of research the subject cards are of the greatest value. An investigator must learn to look under various subject classifications: for instance, not under "Radar" alone (if he is studying that topic) but also under "Electronics," "Radio," and perhaps "Electricity" or even "Physics" as well. Most card catalogues liberally provide cross references, inserting, under various entries, extra cards reading: "See ———" or "See also ———"; these directions should never be neglected.

Information obtained. From any card, regardless of whether it is found as an author, subject, or title card, a great amount of information can be obtained. Certain entries, being useful only or chiefly to librarians, can be ignored. So far as the student or ordinary research worker is concerned, the main data are the authorship, the exact title (in full), the facts of publication (place, publisher, and date), and above all the call number.

Call number. The call number generally is entered at the upper left of the card. Depending on the system of classification employed by the library, it consists of a combination of figures or of both letters and figures. This symbol shows the precise location of the book on the open shelves or in the stacks; therefore it must be copied in exact detail. It belongs to a systematic code, which you will gradually learn (if you do not already understand it) as you watch the library attendants find the books or are shown how to find them for yourself. Whenever permitted to do so, you should actually go to the shelves or stacks, because side by side with the book you want at the moment are others closely related to it in subject. Every researcher has the experience of discovering in this way material that he might never have unearthed through indexes and bibliographies.

(4) GENERAL REFERENCE WORKS

Some reference works are designed to cover all, or virtually all, fields of knowledge. Together with the card catalogue (which is, in effect, a general bibliography), they are the normal starting point in most library research.

Note: Here and throughout all ensuing discussions of library resources in this chapter, only reference works in English will be considered. Actually, of course, graduate students and other mature researchers usually find a working knowledge of more than one language essential. (A chemist is quoted as saying, "Any chemical engineer unable to read German is not a chemical engineer.") English, German, and French are the principal languages of the modern scientific and scholarly world, in much the same way as Latin formerly was the universal tongue of Western learning. For certain branches of science, several other languages also have some importance.

(*1. ENCYCLOPEDIAS*)

Three great general encyclopedias written in the English language are available in most libraries. (Smaller, cheaper general encyclo-pedias chiefly sold for home use cannot be recommended for re search.) The major three are:

The Encyclopaedia Britannica. Twenty-four vols., supple-mented by the *Britannica Book of the Year.**
The New International Encyclopaedia. Twenty-three vols., supplemented by *The New International Year Book.*
The Encyclopedia Americana. Thirty vols., supplemented by *The Americana Annual.*

Note: Observe the spellings, especially of *Britannica* and of the variant forms of *Encyclop(a)edia* in the names of different works.

Use; bibliographical value. All three are worth consulting for general and background information on almost any topic. The last volume of the *Americana* and of the *Britannica* contains an index to the whole encyclopedia; the index is especially important in the latter work, which has relatively long articles that generally cover a wide range of subtopics. The usefulness of an encyclopedia for research is often not in the articles proper so much as in the bibliographies appended to many of them. There, ready-made, are discriminatingly selected lists of scholarly or scientific publications related to every class of knowledge.

(*2. INDEXES TO PERIODICALS*)

Without indexes the great accumulations of periodical articles would be very nearly inaccessible to research. Some periodicals have an individual index, published annually or at longer intervals. Many, however, do not; for that reason, and also for convenience, general indexes (as well as special lists †) must be consulted. The actual location on library shelves of the publications indexed must, of course, be found through card catalogues in the usual manner. (The val-uable *Union List of Serials in Libraries of the United States and*

---

* Both the eleventh and the fourteenth (latest) edition of *The Encyclopaedia Britannica* should, if possible, be used; the fourteenth is more nearly up-to-date, but sometimes the articles in the eleventh (twenty-nine vols.) are better. Shelved with the eleventh edition should also be found the two series of three-volume supple-ments issued, respectively, in 1922 and 1926 to form the twelfth and thirteenth editions.

† See LIMITED INDEXES, LIMITED BIBLIOGRAPHIES, and ABSTRACTS on pages 241–244.

Canada shows what magazines and journals are on file in every important American library.) The most useful general indexes are:

>*Poole's Index to Periodical Literature,* covering the period 1802–1906.
>
>*Readers' Guide to Periodical Literature,* since 1900.
>
>*International Index to Periodicals* (originally *Readers' Guide to Periodical Literature Supplement*), since 1907.
>
>*Annual Magazine Subject Index,* since 1907.
>
>*Subject Index to Periodicals,* since 1915.
>
>*The New York Times Index,* since 1913. By furnishing the date on which practically all news events are reported, this index is serviceable for any other newspaper, besides, specifically, the New York *Times.*

Arrangement; use. All indexes follow an alphabetical principle, but their arrangement varies considerably and can be learned only by actual employment of each, with close attention to the prefatory explanations or key to symbols. For the most part they are wholly or chiefly subject directories; a few also include author, and to a limited extent title, entries; numerous cross references are a helpful feature of some. Each item specifies in compressed form the authorship, title, and place of publication of an article, usually including volume, date, and page or pages, as well as the name (often shortened) of the periodical. This information should be taken down accurately and in full.

Note: The *Essay and General Literature Index,* with its supplements, is a similar guide to articles published in composite books since 1900.

(3. BIBLIOGRAPHIES)

General bibliographies. Several efforts have been made to assemble a subject bibliography of writings on universal knowledge, but the possibility of success diminishes in proportion to the expansion of science and learning. None of the three works listed below would exactly qualify as a universal bibliography; however, they are about the only ones of this general character likely to prove of value in researches on recent subjects:

>W. S. Sonnenschein, *The Best Books.* Six vols.
>
>British Museum, Department of Printed Books, *Subject Index of the Modern Books Acquired by the British Museum,* covering (with the continuing supplements) acquisitions to this enormous library since 1881. (See also, for earlier works,

R. A. Peddie, *Subject Index of Books Published up to and Including 1880.* Three vols.)

The United States Catalog, since 1899; supplemented by *The Cumulative Book Index.* Books published in America and (since 1929) elsewhere in English are catalogued in an alphabetical arrangement of authors, titles, and subjects, analogous to the arrangement of card catalogues. (This is a very important reference work for many purposes.)

Bibliographies of bibliographies. A special class of general bibliography, cataloguing **bibliographies** on all topics, has more chance of being successful than the type, mentioned just above, that attempts to list treatises of subject matter. Most helpful among works of this kind are:

W. P. Courtney, *Register of National Bibliography.* Three vols. ("National" means English; however, the work is not limited to British publications.)

The Bibliographic Index; a Cumulative Bibliography of Bibliographies, since 1938.

Theodore Besterman, *A World Bibliography of Bibliographies.* Two vols.

B. SPECIAL REFERENCE WORKS

Card catalogues and the reference works so far treated are unlimited, or extremely broad, in scope. They have utility, yet in a narrowed research it is only general and usually only preliminary. More specialized investigative tools evidently are essential, and students should learn the use of those pertaining to their own fields of interest. The following lists—especially under (1) and (3)—are selective, not exhaustive, besides being restricted to technical and related studies. Many kinds of material (e.g., manuals and textbooks), too numerous for even partial inclusion, must be found through bibliographies, the card catalogue, or inquiry.

(1) LIMITED ENCYCLOPEDIAS AND DICTIONARIES

ARCHITECTURE:

Dora Ware and Betty Beatty, *A Short Dictionary of Architecture.*

Russell Sturgis (and others), *Dictionary of Architecture and Building.* Three vols. Date (1901) precludes value for recent subjects.

AVIATION:

C. G. Burge, *Encyclopaedia of Aviation.*

BIOGRAPHY:

Dictionary of National Biography [British]. Twenty-one vols., plus several supplements.

Dictionary of American Biography. Twenty vols., plus index vol. and supplement.

Who's Who [chiefly British], since 1848.

Who's Who in America, biennial since 1899–1900.

The International Who's Who, since 1935.

American Men of Science; a Biographical Directory.

Who's Who in Engineering.

BUSINESS:

Crowell's Dictionary of Business and Finance.

G. G. Munn, *Encyclopaedia of Banking and Finance.*

ENGINEERING AND TECHNOLOGY:

N. M. Cooke and John Markus, *Electronics Dictionary.*

Hutchinson's Technical & Scientific Encyclopaedia. Four vols.

[T.] E. Thorpe, *A Dictionary of Applied Chemistry.* Seven vols., plus three-vol. supplement. New edition in progress.

Richard Glazebrook, *A Dictionary of Applied Physics.* Five vols.

A. B. Searle, *An Encyclopaedia of the Ceramic Industries.* Three vols.

ETHNOLOGY:

U. S. Immigration Commission, *Dictionary of Races or Peoples.*

GENERAL SCIENCE:

Elsevier's Encyclopaedia of Organic Chemistry. Four series, plus indexes. In progress.

I. F. and W. D. Henderson, *A Dictionary of Scientific Terms.*

Hackh's Chemical Dictionary.

Hutchinson's Technical & Scientific Encyclopaedia. Four vols.

LAW:

Corpus Juris. Seventy-two vols., plus *Annotations.* An immense encyclopedia of "the body of the law," touching technical questions at many points. New edition in progress.

MATHEMATICS:

Charles Davies and W. G. Peck, *Mathematical Dictionary and Cyclopedia of Mathematical Science.* Very old (1855).

A. K. Kurtz and H. A. Edgerton, *Statistical Dictionary of Terms and Symbols.*

MECHANICS:

Machinery's Encyclopedia. Seven vols. Not recent (1917).

Dyke's Automobile and Gasoline Engine Encyclopedia. Kept up to date by frequent revisions.

MEDICINE:

The American Illustrated Medical Dictionary. Frequently revised.

PHOTOGRAPHY:

Wall's Dictionary of Photography and Reference Book for Amateur and Professional Photographers. Frequently revised.

PSYCHOLOGY:

H. B. English, *A Student's Dictionary of Psychological Terms.*

H. C. Warren, *Dictionary of Psychology.*

RADIO:

Drake's Cyclopedia of Radio and Electronics.

SOCIAL SCIENCES:

Encyclopaedia of the Social Sciences. Fifteen vols.

H. N. Rivlin and Herbert Schueler, *Encyclopedia of Modern Education.*

Paul Monroe, *A Cyclopedia of Education.* Five vols. Not recent (1911–1913). (Later reprints, five vols. bound as three.)

(2) LIMITED INDEXES

Note: Indexes limited to special subjects or fields commonly cite books, pamphlets, bulletins, and various composite works besides periodicals.

AGRICULTURE:

The Agricultural Index, since 1916.

ARCHITECTURE:

The Art Index, since 1929.

ENGINEERING AND TECHNOLOGY:

The Electronic Engineering Master Index, since 1925.

The Engineering Index, since 1884.

The Industrial Arts Index, since 1912.

GENERAL SCIENCE:

See *International Catalogue of Scientific Literature* entry under GENERAL SCIENCE in (3) LIMITED BIBLIOGRAPHIES, below.

GOVERNMENT DOCUMENTS:

U. S. Superintendent of Documents, *Monthly Catalog of U. S. Government Publications,* since 1895. Indexed monthly and annually. For biennial periods see the *Catalog of the Public Documents,* entered in (3) LIMITED BIBLIOGRAPHIES, below.

LAW:

An Index to Legal Periodicals, since 1908.

U. S. Library of Congress, *State Law Index,* biennial since 1925–26.

MEDICINE:

Index Medicus, 1879–1899, 1903–1927.

Quarterly Cumulative Index Medicus, since 1927.

PSYCHOLOGY:

The Psychological Index, covering the period 1894–1935. For the period since 1935 consult *Psychological Abstracts,* entered in (4) ABSTRACTS, below.

SOCIAL SCIENCES:

The Education Index, since 1929.

(3) LIMITED BIBLIOGRAPHIES

ARCHITECTURE:

Boston Public Library, *Catalogue of the Books Relating to Architecture, Construction, and Decoration.* Last edition not recent (1914).

BUSINESS:

Newark (N. J.) Free Public Library, *2400 Business Books and Guide to Business Literature.* Lists titles to 1920. Supplemented by *Business Books: 1920–1926.*

ENGINEERING AND TECHNOLOGY:

A. D. Roberts, *Guide to Technical Literature.*

John Crerar Library, *A List of Books on the History of Industry and Industrial Arts.* Not recent (1915). Consult also New York Public Library, *New Technical Books,* since 1915.

GENERAL SCIENCE:

Royal Society of London, *Catalogue of Scientific Papers, 1800–1900.* Nineteen vols. *Subject Index* for some fields also issued.

International Catalogue of Scientific Literature, covering the period 1901–1914.

John Crerar Library, *A List of Books on the History of Science*. Also *Supplements*, and companion *List* on history of industrial arts.

GOVERNMENT DOCUMENTS:

U. S. Superintendent of Documents, *Catalog of the Public Documents*. Volume published for each Congressional period since 1893. Supplemented by the *Monthly Catalog of U. S. Government Publications*, entered in (2) LIMITED INDEXES, above.

MATHEMATICS:

See Royal Society of London and *International Catalogue of Scientific Literature* entries under GENERAL SCIENCE, above.

MECHANICS:

See Royal Society of London and *International Catalogue of Scientific Literature* entries under GENERAL SCIENCE, above.

MEDICINE:

Index-Catalogue of the Library of the Surgeon General's Office. Four series. Extensive and useful; shows holdings of the medical library of the United States Army; not limited to medical literature in a narrow sense; alphabetical by authors and subjects.

SOCIAL SCIENCES:

London Bibliography of the Social Sciences. Four vols., plus supplements.

(4) ABSTRACTS

ENGINEERING AND TECHNOLOGY:

Engineering Abstracts, since 1919.
Science Abstracts, since 1898.

GENERAL SCIENCE:

Biological Abstracts, since 1926.
Botanical Abstracts, 1918–1926.
British Chemical and Physiological Abstracts, since 1926.
Chemical Abstracts, since 1907.
Mineralogical Abstracts, since 1920.
Physiological Abstracts, 1916–1937.
Science Abstracts, since 1898.

MATHEMATICS:

Mathematical Reviews, since 1940.

PHOTOGRAPHY:

Photographic Abstracts, since 1921.

PSYCHOLOGY:
Psychological Abstracts, since 1927.

SOCIAL SCIENCES:
Educational Abstracts, since 1935.
Social Science Abstracts, 1929–1932.

(5) LIMITED YEARBOOKS

AGRICULTURE:
U. S. Department of Agriculture, *Yearbook of Agriculture,* since 1894. (Title varies.)

ARCHITECTURE:
Architects' Year Book, since 1945.

AVIATION:
Aircraft Yearbook, since 1919.
Aviation Annual, since 1944.

ENGINEERING AND TECHNOLOGY:
Engineers' Year Book, since 1894.

GENERAL SCIENCE:
Chemists' Year Book, since 1915.

PHOTOGRAPHY:
American Annual of Photography, since 1887.

PSYCHOLOGY:
Yearbook of Psychoanalysis, since 1945.

RADIO:
Radio Annual, 1938–1942.

SOCIAL SCIENCES:
Social Work Year Book, biennial since 1929–30.

C. NOTE TAKING

Cards. Before commencing a research, always provide yourself with a liberal supply of oblong cards, either ruled or unruled. (Most scholars prefer the latter, to permit adjusting the size of handwriting to the amount of notation.) The most common sizes of note cards are three by five and four by six inches. Slips of paper in the same or similar dimensions can be purchased in pads or cut from sheets, but they are not much cheaper than cards and tend to curl or wad during continued handling.

One card—one note. Never attempt to take research notes on large-sized sheets of paper. The indispensability of small cards consists in the fact that information is not found in the same order as that of its final position in the composition. On each card is put only *one note*, defined as a single fact, statement, or other item expected to be kept intact and used, if at all, as a whole. When in the slightest doubt whether a piece of information is single or multiple, break it into parts entered on different cards. Anything written together will be almost impossible to manipulate later as separate notes, to be employed in more than one section of the final paper. Miscellaneous notes jotted all over a leaf of theme, notebook, or typewriter paper would prove an almost insurmountable obstacle to organization. A tentative bibliography of writings *not yet consulted* may be assembled (from conferences, catalogues, indexes, and the like) on one large sheet or in a notebook; however, even for this purpose, cards are better.

Bibliography cards. In consulting a book, article, or other writing, first determine by examination and rapid reading whether it contains information on your topic. If it does, at once make a bibliography card, which for ease of recognition should be labeled with a circled capital *B* or some other distinctive symbol. On this card place all the data required for entering the document in the bibliography of the paper (see Section D, including models), preferably in the same form that will be followed there. Any other information that might later be useful, e.g., the call number of a book in the library, also may be included.

Note cards. Next take *all* the notes you will possibly want from that document, each on a separate card, and then return it to the shelves or to the library attendant. Remember that others use the library, too. If you rove from one book or article to another and then back to the first in taking notes, you often will find that one you had in your hands a few minutes or a day before has been checked out or is otherwise unavailable. If you try to surround yourself with all your sources, you will needlessly withhold them from others; also, you probably will give inadequate attention to the individual reference.

Heading. At the top of *every* note card should be entered (in the same order and position on each card): (1) the **textual source** of the note, (2) the **topic** treated, and (3) the **page(s)** from which material is taken. The source normally is reduced to the author's (or authors') last name(s) and a shortened form of the title. (Guard

against ambiguities, by expanding this information to any extent necessary. Substitution of arbitrary symbols, such as stars and crosses,
duplicated from a bibliography card to every note card derived from
the same source, is inadvisable. In the end, usually, confusion and
waste of time are the consequences.) The topic should be briefly but
clearly specified, with enough blank space left for revision of phrasing as the organization of the paper, revealing the exact position and
bearing of each note, grows increasingly clear. The page number is
very important; under no circumstances may it be omitted. If a fact
or quotation extends over more than one page of the source, some
mark should be made at the margin of the card to show at what point
matter from a different page begins, for despite the initial presumption that the note is an indissoluble unity, part of it may later be
omitted. Use the reverse of the card, if it is required for completion
of the note, without an extra heading; but if more than one card
positively has to be employed for a single note (as should happen
very rarely), label the first above or beside the heading as "Card 1,"
and repeat the full heading with a similar label ("Card 2," "Card 3,"
etc.) on the others.

Note: The *leaves* of an unpaginated pamphlet should be counted and
indicated in the heading as "leaf 1 recto" (equivalent to page 1),
"leaf 1 verso" (i.e., page 2), "leaf 2 recto" (i.e., page 3), etc.
These same designations, in lieu of the absent page numbers, are
afterwards to be used in footnotes. (The abbreviation of "recto" is
"r" or "ro."; of "verso," "v" or "vo.")

Form of notes: quoted. Quotations must be enclosed in quotation
marks and copied verbatim; no changes may be made in spelling,
punctuation, or any other particular whatsoever. Even a misprint or
other evident error should be transcribed, followed in square brackets by the underlined (italicized) word [*sic*], Latin for "so" or
"thus in the original."

Exception: An omission is permissible within a quotation, provided
the purport of what remains is not falsified. Three dots (. . .),
called marks of ellipsis, must be substituted for the missing portion.
Normally, omissions at the beginning or end are not so indicated
unless part of a sentence is dropped (again, without falsification of
the sense of the remainder).

Note: The foregoing paragraph, including the *Exception,* of course
applies even more especially to the paper ultimately based on the
notes. Whatever is quoted must be repeated literally and designated

by quotation marks. On the other hand, material not quoted must be carried out of the phraseology of the original author and into that of the writer of the research paper. Merely changing, omitting, or adding a few words here and there in an almost-quoted passage is not an honorable practice, even though a footnote shows that some kind of borrowing has taken place. Unless (in addition to the footnote) quotation marks are used to acknowledge a forthright copying of language, the *style* should be original.

Form of notes: informational. Most notes, particularly on nonliterary subjects, are not taken as direct quotations, since style usually is of insignificant importance compared with content. Any abbreviations, symbols, elliptical constructions, or other shortcuts *that the writer can infallibly interpret after a lapse of time* are permissible for speed in taking the informational notes. Overcompression can lead to ambiguities and doubts, and so to the necessity of repeating parts of a library investigation. By experiment, most researchers fall into the habit of putting down notes in a telescoped sentence form, with omission of the less important words. (Shorthand becomes "cold" too quickly to be advisable.) No matter what system you develop for note taking, be sure always to spell out unfamiliar or key words (proper names, most especially), and to transcribe figures and technical symbols accurately.

Arrangement: bibliography cards. From time to time as an investigation proceeds, filled-out cards are removed from the holder (which may be a wooden or pasteboard case, an envelope, or simply a string or rubber band) in which they are taken to and from the library, and stacked or filed. One group consists of all bibliography cards. These may be left until the end in haphazard order and then alphabetized like the items of the ultimate bibliography (see model at close of chapter), or they may be arranged in that alphabetical order every time several are extracted from among the note cards and added to those bibliography cards already filed. In any event, the main thing is to keep this class of cards in a separate drawer or pigeonhole.

Arrangement: note cards. The basic division of the notes should accord with the main topics of the outline of the paper, which will be taking at least tentative shape as the research proceeds. Within each of the, say, three main divisions, every one of the large subtopics is, again, a category for the further distribution of cards; within this subdivision, each smaller subtopic constitutes a subcategory; and so on down to the most minute subtopics of the paper. In the end, if the paper has three main topics, all the note cards will be in three large piles, or kept in three boxes, pigeonholes, or drawers; but in each of these stacks or containers they will be internally separated into two or more groups, and probably the cards of each of these groups will be further sorted into small packs kept apart from one another in some physical manner. This system forces a decision, in advance of composition, as to the precise bearing of each note upon the subject under treatment, and thus contributes immeasurably to sound organization. It has the further advantage of revealing, at any stage of the investigation, which parts or subtopics are thus far inadequately covered by notes.

Discarding. Do not expect to find use for all the notes you take, or you certainly will be disappointed. Because notes are accumulated piecemeal from many sources, some will turn out to be less reliable than others acquired later, some to be irrelevant, and some to be duplicates. A discard pile or drawer should be set aside for rejected cards, each of which should be marked in some distinctive way (e.g., "Rj" for "Rejected") but not defaced or torn. By this means, discarding can be practiced freely, without danger that a supposedly useless card that has been destroyed may, afterward, be needed for some unexpected purpose.

D. DOCUMENTATION

Definition; purpose. The scholarly technique by which the origin of matter borrowed from sources is clearly indicated is called documentation. Painstaking documentation is essential in a research paper; it serves several important purposes:

(1) *Authority.* Documentation lends authority to statements which, as bare assertions, might carry no weight of proof or conviction.

(2) *Acknowledgment.* Documentation makes a just and necessary acknowledgment of the investigator's indebtedness to the work of others before him. The source of a borrowed fact must be cited in a footnote; a direct quotation or a statement of probability, opinion, or hypothesis normally requires that the author of the source be mentioned in the text and that the remainder of the citation be given in a footnote. In any case, the footnote must not be omitted.

(3) *Bibliographical aid.* Documentation is of assistance to a reader who wishes to make additional investigation of the subject. One of the ideals of researchers is to report their work in such form that it can be easily checked and utilized as a

starting point for further research, by others as well as by themselves.

(1) FORM

Basic types of documentation. Methods of documentation fall into two basic classes: (1) the type employing a **bibliography** in addition to **footnotes**; (2) the type employing only footnotes, of an expanded kind called **bibliographical footnotes.** Generally, the first class of documentation is practiced in books and reports; the second, in periodical articles. Students usually are asked to use the first (separate footnotes and bibliography) in term papers and other research themes.

Variations. No one system of documentation has even approximately achieved universal acceptance. Scholars differ among themselves; presses and periodicals often require conformity to their set practices; many branches of knowledge—e.g., chemical engineering, biology, and law—have developed forms more or less distinct from those of other fields. Students should observe, and in their strictly professional writing follow to the very best of their understanding, the most approved models they can discover in each subject. The directions, models, and explanations below, while based on actual usages, necessarily represent a middle-of-the-road compromise. The aims of this system as a whole are simplification, consistency, and general utility for various subject matters.

Form in footnotes. In both basic methods of documentation, the footnote references are numbered consecutively throughout the entire paper (or through a chapter or other main division) by a sequence of figures: "1," "2," etc. These Arabic numerals *follow* the textual matter (including any mark or marks of punctuation *) to which they refer, and are duplicated *before* each corresponding footnote. Both in the text and at the bottom of the page, they are slightly raised above the line of writing as "superior figures"; they are *not* followed by periods. In manuscript and typescript a line is drawn wholly or partly across each page having footnotes, in order to show at a glance the division between text and footnotes. (A blank space should be left both above and below this line.) The first line of a footnote is indented the same distance as that of a regular paragraph of text; other lines start at the left margin. Columns or other arrangements

---

* If, however, the footnote applies explicitly to matter contained within parentheses, the figure *precedes* the closing parenthesis. The usage is illustrated by the asterisk (equivalent to a reference figure) in the text, above, directing attention to the present footnote.

of short footnotes may, however, be spread across the page. Footnotes are internally single-spaced but are blocked off from one another by double-spacing. Each is closed with a period (except in rare instances when a question mark or exclamation point occurs at the end).

Note 1: Since footnotes obviously cannot be alphabetized, authors' names are written in normal order beginning with the first name or initials. In bibliographies, however, the last name of the author (or, for the entry of a collaborated writing, that of the author mentioned first on the title page or at the head or end of the article) is transposed to the initial position for the purpose of alphabetization. Observe the different models shown later.

Note 2: Besides footnotes indicating publications as sources of borrowed material, some may give miscellaneous information (perhaps including acknowledgment of privately received help of various kinds) that is felt to be unsuitable for the body of the text. These are entered in regular physical and numerical order among the other footnotes of the page, being attached in the usual way (by duplicated Arabic figures) to related textual matter. If such an informational footnote itself has a source, the data identifying the source are specified at the end (usually not beginning on a separate line) in the same form that would be employed for an ordinary footnote.

Note 3: All footnotes pertaining to a page must appear on that page. The last footnote on any page, if it is lengthy, may be *continued* at the head of the footnotes (or, if there are none, by itself) at the bottom of the next page, but it must at least start on its own page. The style of interlineating each footnote directly below the line of text to which it refers, very generally practiced in manuscripts prepared for the press, is not very satisfactory for other purposes, as it is unpleasing to the eye and somewhat confusing to the reader, especially if he prefers to skip many of the notes.

Reduced footnotes. Only the first footnote that refers to any textual source is written out in full form. All other references to the same document are radically reduced by application of the following directions:

(1) Use *ibid.* (for Latin *ibidem*, "in the same place"; note the *italics*—shown in manuscript or typescript by underscoring —and the period for the abbreviation) when the citation is the same as that of the immediately preceding footnote. If no page number is specified, the page is understood to be unchanged; if one is given, it replaces the page number shown

in the preceding citation. Note that *ibid.* is not, of itself, a capitalized expression; however, nearly always it is the first (more precisely, the only) word of a footnote and, as such, is then written with an initial capital.

(2) To indicate a book or other "work" cited previously but not in the directly preceding footnote, give the author's (or authors') last name(s) and *op. cit.* (for Latin *opere citato,* "in the work cited"; note the *italics*—shown in manuscript or typescript by underscoring—and the two periods for the abbreviations). The entry *op. cit.,* unlike *ibid.,* must be followed by a page number, since "in the work cited" standing alone would not imply that the page is the same as in the last reference to the same work. Without an author's name, *op. cit.* would be meaningless: most research papers cite several or many works by various authors. Note that *op. cit.* is not a capitalized expression.

(3) To indicate an article (or other document that would not be called a "work") cited previously but not in the directly preceding footnote, give the author's (or authors') last name(s) and *loc. cit.* (for Latin *loco citato,* "in the place cited"; note the *italics*—shown in manuscript or typescript by underscoring—and the two periods for the abbreviations). The entry *loc. cit.* (like *op. cit.* but unlike *ibid.*) must be followed by a page number, since "in the place cited" is not construed to include the page number of the previous citation. Without an author's name, *loc. cit.* would be meaningless: most research papers cite several or many articles by various authors. Observe that *loc. cit.* is not a capitalized expression.

(4) If works are cited in the paper by two or more authors having the same last name, give the initials or first name as well as the last, to prevent *op. cit.* from being ambiguous. Similarly, if articles are cited by two or more authors having the same last name, give the initials or first name as well as the last, to prevent *loc. cit.* from being ambiguous.

(5) If two or more works of identical authorship are cited in the paper, *op. cit.* would be ambiguous and so cannot be used. Give the author's (or authors') last name(s), a *shortened but distinctive* form of the title (underlined for italics), and the page number. Similarly, if two or more articles of the same authorship are cited in the paper, *loc. cit.* would be ambiguous and so cannot be used. Give the author's (or

authors') last name(s), a *shortened but distinctive* form of
the article title (enclosed in quotation marks), and the page
number.

(6) If a source is anonymous, *op. cit.* or *loc. cit.* would be
ambiguous and so cannot be used. Give a *shortened but distinctive* form of the title (underlined for italics to cite a work;
enclosed in quotation marks to cite an article) and the page
number.

(7) If the authorship of a source is mentioned in the text of
the paper, the name (or names) need not be repeated in the
footnote. When footnotes thus begin with *Op. cit.* or *Loc.
cit.*, the first member (only) of the entry is written with an
initial capital.

How many footnotes? A separate footnote must be given for:
(1) every direct **quotation,** (2) every **idea** or **opinion,** and (3) every
fact taken from other writings. Each of these kinds of borrowed
material could be, in length, anything from part of a sentence to
several consecutive sentences or even paragraphs. Wherever the specific extract ends—whether in the middle or at the end of a sentence,
whether within or at the close of a paragraph—a footnote reference
should immediately be supplied. Remember that *several successive
borrowings from the same source require individual footnotes,* all
except the first reduced to *ibid.* with or without a page number, as
was explained on page 250. Get rid of any false notion you may have
that only quotations are acknowledged by footnotes; you cannot acquire original title to a piece of information by changing the mode
of phrasing.

Note 1: Since in a well-written paper all sequences of material consist of closely related thoughts, some practical difficulty may be encountered in discriminating between two or more facts or ideas (de-
manding, if borrowed, two or more footnotes) and one fact or idea
having several phases. Use common sense; if doubt still remains, give
a series of footnotes instead of only one.

Note 2: Information of common knowledge, even if verified from
reference works, need not be accompanied by footnotes. (Dictionaries, for example, though freely consulted during composition, are
not cited unless *support* is wanted for some contention regarding etymology, meaning, or a similar point.) Do not, however, construe
"common knowledge" broadly as a dodge to escape the obligations
of documentation.

Form in bibliography. The bibliography provided in conjunction with regular (i.e., nonbibliographical) footnotes is placed at the end of the composition being documented. Items in a bibliography are listed in "overhanging paragraphs": that is, in paragraphs having the second and subsequent lines indented from the margin but *not* the first, which contains the word used for alphabetizing. (Note that their form is contrary to that of footnotes, which have the shape of ordinary paragraphs.) Bibliographical items are internally single-spaced but are blocked off from one another by double-spacing. Each is closed with a period. The whole bibliography (especially if short) may be organized in one alphabetical list, or (especially if long) it may be divided into separate alphabetical lists under classifying headings (such as *Books, Periodicals, Miscellaneous;* or *Primary Sources, Secondary Sources;* or *Direct Citations, General Bibliography;* or *Printed Reports, Unpublished Reports;* or *Official Documents, Other Sources*). Alphabetizing starts at the first word of every bibliographical item exclusive of *A, An,* or *The;* usually the "catchword" is an author's last name, but in anonymous writings it is the first word (other than *A, An, The*) of the title.

Content of bibliography. A bibliography records, not necessarily all writings consulted since an investigation began, but all those found to be of value for the research. Except, of course, when bibliographical footnotes are employed, any writings mentioned as sources in either the text or the footnotes must be included in the bibliography. Others, also, even though not referred to for specific facts and statements, often are of sufficient general importance to be added, sometimes in a separately headed and alphabetized section of the bibliography.

(2) MODELS

Note 1: Be extremely careful to discriminate the three classes of models, given below in the fixed order: (A) BIBLIOGRAPHY, (B) REGULAR FOOTNOTES (i.e., nonbibliographical), and (C) BIBLIOGRAPHICAL FOOTNOTES. Review the paragraph labeled *Basic types of documentation* on page 249.

Note 2: In both (B) and (C) the models serve *only* for the first citation of a source. Concerning later references, see the paragraph labeled *Reduced footnotes,* with its seven subparagraphs, pages 250 ff.

Note 3: Names of authors are omitted in the following situations: usually from (B) and (C) when the authorship is mentioned in the text; optionally from (A), replaced by an elongated dash, when an entry repeats the authorship of the one just above in the same alphabetical list; from (A) when a book collects the writings of various authors (but the editorship, if specified on the title page, is entered); from (A), (B), and (C) when a writing is published anonymously.* (Generally avoid the designation *Anonymous* or *Anon.,* which would force alphabetization of certain items at an essentially irrational position in the bibliography.) Titles (except the kind inseparably part of a name) and academic degrees of authors usually are omitted, but professional degrees sometimes are retained.

Note 4: Page numbers that are not in Arabic figures (e.g., small Roman numerals used for introductory matter of a book or formal report), or that have some symbol or letter in addition to the numeral, are entered as they appear in the source. See also the *Note* to the paragraph labeled *Heading,* page 246. Observe from the models that in (A), as contrasted with (B) and (C), page numbers are not entered for books and government documents.

Note 5: Regular use of the following abbreviations before numerals, and (as illustrated in the models) general omission of the abbreviations, are optional styles in documentation: *p.* (*page*), *pp.* (*pages*), *vol.* (*volume*), *vols.* (*volumes*). In either style, however, when an Arabic figure † *not in parentheses* is directly followed by another Arabic numeral indicating a page number, the abbreviation must be included with the latter to prevent fusion of the figures (e.g., ". . . 1935, p. 345"; *not:* ". . . 1935, 345").

Note 6: Two or more sources may be cited for a given fact or idea by a series of references, separated by semicolons, in the same footnote.

(1. BOOKS)

(A) BIBLIOGRAPHY:
Dull, Raymond W., *Mathematics for Engineers,* New York, McGraw-Hill Book Company, Inc., 1941. (Second ed.)
Bell, H. S., *American Petroleum Refining,* New York, D. Van Nostrand Company, Inc. (ᶜ1930).
Stephen, Leslie, *History of English Thought in the Eighteenth Century,* London, Smith, Elder, & Co., 1902. Two vols.

---

* If the identity of authorship can be discovered from some external source, as a library card catalogue, the name or names may be entered at the regular position but in square brackets.
† Usually indicating a date.

Cooper, F. J., *Textile Chemistry: an Introduction to the Chemistry of the Cotton Industry,* London, Methuen & Co. Ltd., n.d.

Toward Civilization, ed. Charles A. Beard, London, Longmans, Green and Co., 1930.

Planck, Max, *Treatise on Thermodynamics,* tr. Alexander Ogg, London, Longmans, Green and Co., Ltd., 1927. (Third ed., tr. from seventh German ed.)

Welte, Herbert D., *A Psychological Analysis of Plane Geometry,* Iowa City, Ia., College of Education, University of Iowa, 1926. ("University of Iowa Monographs in Education," ser. 1, no. 1.)

Delaware River Bridge and Tunnel Commission, *Report . . . to the Governor and General Assembly of the Commonwealth of Pennsylvania,* 1919.

Peterson, William H., John T. Skinner, and Frank M. Strong, *Elements of Food Biochemistry,* New York, Prentice-Hall, Inc., 1943.

(B) REGULAR FOOTNOTES:

[6] Raymond W. Dull, *Mathematics for Engineers,* 81.

[11] H. S. Bell, *American Petroleum Refining,* 162.

[34] Leslie Stephen, *History of English Thought in the Eighteenth Century,* I, 42.

[1] F. J. Cooper, *Textile Chemistry,* 108–110.

[23] L. W. Wallace, "Engineering in Government," in *Toward Civilization,* 179.

[16] Max Planck, *Treatise on Thermodynamics,* viii-ix.

[2] Herbert D. Welte, *A Psychological Analysis of Plane Geometry,* 44.

[50] Delaware River Bridge and Tunnel Commission, *Report . . . to the Governor and General Assembly of the Commonwealth of Pennsylvania,* 6.

[15] William H. Peterson, John T. Skinner, and Frank M. Strong, *Elements of Food Biochemistry,* 316.

(C) BIBLIOGRAPHICAL FOOTNOTES:

[6] Raymond W. Dull, *Mathematics for Engineers,* New York, McGraw-Hill Book Company, Inc., 1941, p. 81. (Second ed.)

[11] H. S. Bell, *American Petroleum Refining,* New York, D. Van Nostrand Company, Inc. (c1930), 162.

[34] Leslie Stephen, *History of English Thought in the Eighteenth Century,* London, Smith, Elder, & Co., 1902, I, 42.

[1] F. J. Cooper, *Textile Chemistry: an Introduction to the Chemis-*

try of the Cotton Industry, London, Methuen & Co. Ltd., n.d., 108–110.

[23] L. W. Wallace, "Engineering in Government," in *Toward Civilization,* ed. Charles A. Beard, London, Longmans, Green and Co., 1930, p. 179.

[16] Max Planck, *Treatise on Thermodynamics,* tr. Alexander Ogg, London, Longmans, Green and Co., Ltd., 1927, viii-ix. (Third ed., tr. from seventh German ed.)

[2] Herbert D. Welte, *A Psychological Analysis of Plane Geometry,* Iowa City, Ia., College of Education, University of Iowa, 1926, p. 44. ("University of Iowa Monographs in Education," ser. 1, no. 1.)

[50] Delaware River Bridge and Tunnel Commission, *Report . . . to the Governor and General Assembly of the Commonwealth of Pennsylvania,* 1919, p. 6.

[15] William H. Peterson, John T. Skinner, and Frank M. Strong, *Elements of Food Biochemistry,* New York, Prentice-Hall, Inc., 1943.

EXPLANATIONS:

(1) Names of books, authors, and publishers * should be accurately copied from title pages. The forms may differ somewhat in various publications and editions. Sometimes it is necessary to supply punctuation within a title, to correspond to a sort of punctuation which the printer achieves on the title page by type of varied sizes placed on different lines. Subtitles may be omitted in (B). Street addresses of publishers are dropped; and if several cities of publication are given, ordinarily only the first is transcribed from the title page. (If two cities are given, commonly "New York and London" or vice versa, both or only the first may be transcribed.)

(2) If the date of publication does not appear on the title page, in (A) and (C) the latest date of copyright (usually shown on the reverse of the same leaf) is entered in parentheses. Before this date a superior (raised) *c,* not followed by a period, is good bibliographic style but is not mandatory. Observe that no comma precedes the opening parenthesis. The abbreviation *n.d.* means that no date of publication or copyright can be found. A conjectural date of publication (not illustrated in any of the foregoing models), inferred from a dated preface or the like, would be followed by a question mark in

---

* *Macmillan* is very frequently misspelled by students. Observe closely the details (and differences) in such firm names as *Charles Scribner's Sons, Henry Holt and Company, Rinehart & Company, Inc.,* and *McGraw-Hill Book Company, Inc.*

parentheses. An externally obtained date of publication (also not illustrated), known with certainty though not given by the book itself, would be entered in square brackets. No comma would precede the first bracket.

(3) The abbreviation *ed.* signifies either "edition" or "edited by"; the abbreviation *tr.*, either "translated" or "translated by." Like the facts of publication (place, publisher, date), editions, editors, and translators of books usually are not specified in (B). Occasionally, however, such information is necessary to avoid ambiguity (e.g., when two editions of the same work are listed in the bibliography), and that needed is then included in the same form as in (C).

(4) "Two [*or:* three, etc.] vols." in (A) means that the book consists of two (or three, etc.) volumes and that both (or all) have been used for the research. If only the first has been employed, the notation would be "Vol. I." The entry "Vols. I and II" would indicate that there are more than two volumes, of which only the first two have been used. Whenever the volumes of a book are of different years, those consulted should be dated separately in (A): e.g., "Vol. I, 1897; vols. II and III, 1898; vol. IV, 1900." In (C), also, the date would appear after instead of before the number of the volume mentioned, to indicate that all volumes of the whole book are not of the same year.

(5) Notice the absence of page numbers in (A). More important still, be sure to observe the invariable inclusion in (B) and (C) of a page number (or, occasionally, hyphenated numbers indicating a sequence of pages) to show the *precise* origin of a borrowed fact, idea, or quotation. (If the borrowed material is taken from two or more pages that are not consecutive, the numbers would be separated by a comma or commas instead of by a hyphen: e.g., "33, 45, 452" or "pp. 33, 45, 452.")

(6) Reports and pamphlets are treated, in general, as books. At times, modifications and inventions of form, in keeping with the system of documentation, have to be introduced for a source displaying marked peculiarities. (See also the models and explanations of entries for government documents, beginning at page 261.)

(*2. PERIODICAL ARTICLES*)

(A) BIBLIOGRAPHY:

Dellinger, J. H., "The Role of the Ionosphere in Radio Wave Propagation," *Transactions of the American Institute of Electrical Engineers,* LVIII (1939), 803–822.

Lasch, Robert, "Why an MVA?" *Atlantic Monthly,* CLXXV (May, 1945), 72–76.

Kahlenberg, Louis, and George J. Ritter, "On the Catalytic Hydrogenation of Cottonseed Oil," *Journal of Physical Chemistry,* XXV (1921), 89–114.

Federer, Charles A., Jr., "Scientists Get Ready for Sun's Eclipse," New York *Times,* July 8, 1945, pp. 1+.

(B) REGULAR FOOTNOTES:

[22] J. H. Dellinger, "The Role of the Ionosphere in Radio Wave Propagation," *Transactions of the American Institute of Electrical Engineers,* LVIII (1939), 807.

[3] Robert Lasch, "Why an MVA?" *Atlantic Monthly,* CLXXV (May, 1945), 74.

[5] Louis Kahlenberg and George J. Ritter, "On the Catalytic Hydrogenation of Cottonseed Oil," *Journal of Physical Chemistry,* XXV (1921), 89–90.

[14] Charles A. Federer Jr., "Scientists Get Ready for Sun's Eclipse," New York *Times,* July 8, 1945, p. 1.

(C) BIBLIOGRAPHICAL FOOTNOTES:

Identical with REGULAR FOOTNOTES, directly above.

EXPLANATIONS:

(1) Be sure to observe that (A) shows the *inclusive* pages of the whole article, whereas (B) and (C) show the *precise* page (or, occasionally, sequence of pages) from which the borrowing of a fact, idea, or quotation is being acknowledged.

(2) When an article is continued from the page or group of pages on which it begins to a page or series of pages not consecutive with the former, this fact may be indicated in (A) either by a plus sign (+) or by actual listing of the pages: e.g., "21–22+" or "21–22, 45, 47–48, 50." Note that commas (as opposed to hyphens) signify that continuations are not consecutive.

(3) Use of italic or boldface Arabic figures, instead of Roman numerals, for volume numbers is optional and has good standing in the documentation of technical research. One method or another should be consistently employed throughout a research paper.

(4) The number of the issue (within a volume) ordinarily is omitted. If the volume number is accompanied by any other special designation (in particular, *new series,* which is abbreviated to *n.s.* in documentation), this notation must be included.

(5) For periodicals that number their pages only through the individual issue instead of through all issues of the whole volume, the *exact* date must be specified, including the month, and of a weekly or daily the numerical date of the month, as well as the year. Observe that no comma precedes the first of the pair of parentheses enclosing a date after a volume number.

(6) *The* commonly is dropped at the beginning of the name of a periodical, but not at the beginning of the title of an article.

(7) The place of publication of a periodical is not specified unless it normally precedes the name (as with most newspapers), or unless the periodical either is little known or is one of two or more issued under the same name. If the place must be specially entered, it is shown in parentheses after the name of the periodical. The publisher practically never is mentioned except as part of the italicized name of certain periodicals issued by societies and similar groups.

(8) The name of a city may or may not be regarded as strictly part of the name of a newspaper, and is italicized (i.e., underlined) or not italicized accordingly. Some writers always italicize the name of the city.

(9) When a newspaper is divided into separately paginated sections, the number, letter, or other sectional designation must be included with the page number. (The same principle of course holds for any other periodical, if a special department, a supplement, or the like happens to be separately paginated.) Volume numbers are not entered for newspapers. Column numbers, while helpful, are optional rather than mandatory.)

(3. ENCYCLOPEDIA ARTICLES)

(A) BIBLIOGRAPHY:

Callendar, Hugh Longbourne, "Calorimetry," *The Encyclopaedia Britannica,* ed. 14 (1929), V, 621–628.

Callendar, Hugh Longbourne, "Heat," *The Encyclopaedia Britannica,* supplementary vols. of ed. 12 (1922), II, 352–361.

Rosanoff, Martin A., "Thermochemistry," *The New International Encyclopaedia,* ed. 2, XXII (1916), 194–197.

"Diathermancy," *The New International Encyclopaedia,* ed. 2, VI (1914), 772–773.

"Diathermancy," *The Encyclopedia Americana,* 1944 ed., IX, 73.

Waddel, Ramond C., "Radio Developments in 1940," *The Americana Annual* (1941), 602–605.

(B) REGULAR FOOTNOTES:

⁹ Hugh Longbourne Callendar, "Calorimetry," *The Encyclopaedia Britannica,* ed. 14 (1929), V, 623.

⁴⁵ Hugh Longbourne Callendar, "Heat," *The Encyclopaedia Britannica,* supplementary vols. of ed. 12 (1922), II, 361.

⁶ Martin A. Rosanoff, "Thermochemistry," *The New International Encyclopaedia,* ed. 2, XXII (1916), 196–197.

²⁰ "Diathermancy," *The New International Encyclopaedia,* ed. 2, VI (1914), 772; "Diathermancy," *The Encyclopedia Americana,* 1944 ed., IX, 73.

³⁶ Ramond C. Waddel, "Radio Developments in 1940," *The Americana Annual* (1941), 603.

(C) BIBLIOGRAPHICAL FOOTNOTES:

Identical with REGULAR FOOTNOTES, directly above.

EXPLANATIONS:

(1) Although many of the articles published in encyclopedias are anonymous, important articles often are signed either with names or with initials, a key to the latter being provided in the front of the volume. Sometimes a table in the front of the volume shows the authorship of important articles, even though no names or initials are actually given as signatures.

(2) Be sure to observe that (A) shows the *inclusive* pages of the whole article, whereas (B) and (C) show the *precise* page (or, occasionally, sequence of pages) from which the borrowing of a fact, idea, or quotation is being acknowledged.

(3) Notice in the models that the date (given in parentheses, with no comma preceding the opening parenthesis) follows an edition number when all volumes appeared in the same year, but follows the volume number when the edition appeared over a period of more than one year. If editions are numbered by the year of issue, no further indication of date is necessary. If an encyclopedia that has had only one edition (not illustrated in any of the models) is in a single volume, the entry would be in the same form as that of a yearbook (see the last model of each group); if it is in more than one volume, the date (in parentheses) would follow either the name of the encyclopedia or the volume number to show whether, respectively, all volumes appeared in the same year or over a period of more than one year.

(4) The place of publication and the publisher's name are

omitted unless the encyclopedia is not well known. When given, this information is entered in parentheses after the name of the encyclopedia. If a date is to be entered at the same position—see (3), immediately above—only one set of parentheses is used, containing in sequence the place of publication, the publisher's name, and the date.

(4. GOVERNMENT DOCUMENTS)

(A) BIBLIOGRAPHY:

Hill, A. C., "Schools for Adults in Prisons, 1923," Bureau of Education, *Bulletin,* 1924, no. 19.

U. S. Bureau of Education, "A Manual of Educational Legislation for the Guidance of Committees on Education in the State Legislatures," *Bulletin,* 1924, no. 36.

U. S. Public Health Service, *Malaria in Eastern Texas: Prevalence and Geographic Distribution,* Washington, Government Printing Office, 1917.

U. S. Department of Agriculture, *Atlas of American Agriculture,* Washington, United States Government Printing Office, 1936. Six vols. in one.

(B) REGULAR FOOTNOTES:

[37] A. C. Hill, "Schools for Adults in Prisons, 1923," Bureau of Education, *Bulletin,* 1924, no. 19, p. 26.

[19] U. S. Bureau of Education, "A Manual of Educational Legislation for the Guidance of Committees on Education in the State Legislatures," *Bulletin,* 1924, no. 36, p. 15.

[4] U. S. Public Health Service, *Malaria in Eastern Texas: Prevalence and Geographic Distribution,* 6.

[31] U. S. Department of Agriculture, *Atlas of American Agriculture,* I (*Land Relief,* by F. J. Marshner), 14–15.

(C) BIBLIOGRAPHICAL FOOTNOTES:

[37] A. C. Hill, "Schools for Adults in Prisons, 1923," Bureau of Education, *Bulletin,* 1924, no. 19, p. 26.

[19] Bureau of Education, "A Manual of Educational Legislation for the Guidance of Committees on Education in the State Legislatures," *Bulletin,* 1924, no. 36, p. 15.

[4] United States Public Health Service, *Malaria in Eastern Texas: Prevalence and Geographic Distribution,* Washington, Government Printing Office, 1917, p. 6.

[31] United States Department of Agriculture, *Atlas of American Agriculture,* Washington, United States Government Printing Office, 1936, I (*Land Relief,* by F. J. Marshner), 14–15.

EXPLANATIONS:

(1) If personal authorship is assigned in a document, the name(s) of the author(s) should be entered as in the first model of each group. If no personal authorship is assigned but the document is ascribed to a bureau or other semi-independent agency, the bureau or agency should be entered as in the second and third models of each group. If no personal authorship is assigned and the document is not ascribed to a bureau or other semi-independent agency, the department or independent agency (e.g., the Library of Congress) should be entered as in the last model of each group.

(2) Irrespective of whether "United States" appears on the title page, in (A) and (B) "U. S." may be included with the name of a department, bureau, or other agency entered in the author position (i.e., first). This practice keeps United States documents (except, of course, those of personal authorship) alphabetically together in (A), with conformity of (B) to (A). In (C), where the individual items have no alphabetical relationship, the exact form given by the document should be copied.

(3) The notation "Washington, Government [*or:* United States Government] Printing Office" often is omitted; it seldom is entered for serial bulletins.

(4) The identifying numbers and dates of *documents issued periodically or serially* are specified in (B) as well as in (A) and (C). The identifying date, being that of the subject matter of annual reports, yearbooks, and some lists and bulletins, may be prior to the actual year of publication.

(5) Adaptations and expansions of the models given above will be found necessary for some of the many kinds of documents published by the various branches and instrumentalities of the United States government. Common sense, exercised with careful inspection of the individual document, usually is a safe guide.

(5. SPECIMEN PAGE)

(Adapted from a student research paper employing "regular" footnotes in conjunction with a bibliography.)

---

to be in the order of ten ions per second per cubic centimeter without lead screening,[8] but to be in the order of two ions per second per cubic centimeter of air in a shielded vessel.[9]

Local radioactivity does not give rise to real coincidences, since radioactive beta particles generally do not penetrate more than one Geiger-Müller counter; however, casual as opposed to causal (real) coincidences may result from random entrance of particles into all the counters within the resolving time. This disturbing effect can be controlled, for an increase of the number of counters results in a very large decrease of the phenomenon,[10] as naturally would be expected.

The Geiger-controlled cloud chamber makes possible the photographing of the tracks of ionization left by an individual particle or by "showers" of rays.[11] The gas in the chamber contains vapor, usually of water or alcohol, which becomes supersaturated as the result of cooling by a sudden expansion and condenses as droplets on the ions as nuclei.[12] When a particle passes through the chamber, the ions spread; the relay system and chamber conditions are timed for measurement of curvature of a narrow track or for counting of droplets in a more diffuse track.[13] Blackett has found that the

---

[8]Swann, loc. cit., 220.

[9]Braddick, op. cit., 1.   [10]Ibid., 7.

[11]P. M. S. Blackett, Cosmic Rays, 7.

[12]Braddick, op. cit., 8, 10.

[13]Ibid., 9-10; Blackett, op. cit., 7.

(6. SPECIMEN BIBLIOGRAPHY)

(Adapted to the limits of one page from the bibliography of a student research paper.)

BIBLIOGRAPHY

(Books and Pamphlets)

Auden, Harold A., Sulphur and Sulphur Derivatives, London, Sir Isaac Pitman & Sons, Ltd., 1921(?).

Haynes, William, The Stone That Burns; the Story of the American Sulphur Industry, New York, D. Van Nostrand Company, Inc., 1942.

Preston, Stanley W., Sulphur in Louisiana, Baton Rouge, La., Bureau of Business Research, College of Commerce, Louisiana State University, 1937. ("Louisiana Business Bulletin," vol. I, no. 1.)

Sulphur, an Essential to Industry and Agriculture, New York, Texas Gulf Sulphur Company (Incorporated), 1942.

(Articles)

Butterworth, C. E., "Water Problems in Sulfur Mining," Industrial and Engineering Chemistry, XXVII (1935), 548-555.

———— and J. W. Schwab, "Sulfur Mining as a Processing Industry," Industrial and Engineering Chemistry, XXX (1938), 746-751.

Chapman, Cloyd M., "Compressed Air in Sulphur Mining," Compressed Air Magazine, XXVIII (1923), 645-646.

————, "Freeport Sulphur Company's New Plant at Hoskins Mound, Texas," Southern Engineer, XL (October, 1923), 35-43.

Kelleher, Cornelius, "Gulf Coast Sulphur Deposits," Engineering and Mining Journal, CXXII (1926), 844-847.

"New Texas Gulf Sulphur Plant Starts Operation," Engineering and Mining Journal, CXXVII (1929), 550-553.

Reid, George H., "Producing Sulphur at Newgulf," Chemical and Metallurgical Engineering, XXXVII (1930), 668-672.

Wagner, Theodore B., "Frasch, Herman," Dictionary of American Biography, VI (1931), 602-603.

CHAPTER X

THE TECHNICAL REPORT

Because report writing is the principal focal point for all the skills of composition studied in a course of technical English, close attention should be paid in this chapter to cross references citing earlier discussions.

Examples throughout and at the end of the chapter are quoted or adapted from actual instances of student writing.

A. CHARACTERISTICS

Definition. A report is **a communication concerning work done,** with or without recommendations concerning work yet to be done. It is prepared by an expert or specialist, or group of experts and specialists, and addressed to a superior official, employer, or client; to other experts and specialists; to a particular group of laymen, such as the shareholders in an enterprise; or, rarely, to the general public. Although most reports are in some sense technical, the term *technical report* has limited reference to those specifically concerned with science and technology.

Universality; special importance to the engineer. Report writing is a universal method for recording the activities of business and the professions, including all branches of science. It is especially important for technology. Training in the preparation of technical reports is regarded as a major phase of the professional education of engineers.

Range of reports. No standardized form could possibly be devised for technical reports in general, and nothing said under *Make-up* (pages 272 ff.) should be misinterpreted as implying any such fixed pattern. Indeed, the different kinds are almost as numerous as the many different purposes for which reports are used, and as the virtually unrestricted range of actions on which they are based. Reports vary in size and degree of formality from a typewritten or jotted memorandum on a blank form by an assayer, inspector, pathologist, or clerk, to governmental or industrial issues of one or more printed volumes. When a student of chemistry, physics, biology, or engineering completes an experiment or observation, he writes a report in his notebook or in whatever other manner his laboratory instructor may direct. The building of a bridge or dam, the taking of the decennial census of the United States, the investigation by a commission of the causes and effects of pellagra in a certain region—these and untold thousands of other activities call for the writing, often the publication, of one or more reports. When a United States Navy flier radioed: "SIGHTED SUB SANK SAME," he was issuing a genuine report; military and naval reports, like all other kinds, have a vast range of complexity, from the laconic plainness of Caesar's "I came, I saw, I conquered" to heavy volumes summing up campaigns in retrospect.

Broad classification of technical reports. Since a technical report concerns either (1) a constructive or experimental activity completed or in progress, or (2) an examination or inspection, two broad classes can be recognized: the WORK REPORT and the EXAMINATION REPORT. If, by name, only the first type should appear to fit the definition of the report given in the opening paragraph of this section, as "a communication concerning work done," the reader must take into account the fact that a technical inspection or examination is itself a kind of expert work.

Subclasses. Both work and examination reports fall into numerous lesser categories, partially overlapping and not all possessing distinctive names. (See also *Types of Student Reports,* pages 290 ff.) Two important subclasses are known, respectively, as the **survey** (or **preliminary**) **report,** a type of examination report; and the **periodic** (or **progress**) **report,** a type of work report. At times, of course, the former is concerned only with surveying in the specialized sense; more often, however, it deals with all the problems that must be settled before a construction can be started. During the course of large, long-continued technical undertakings, either at regular intervals of time or at the end of predetermined stages, progress reports usually are issued by one or more persons or authorities responsible for the activity or its several phases. In business, documents of this kind— exemplified by annual audits and reports of boards of directors to stockholders—ordinarily are definitely periodical. When a survey report precedes, and is in effect the opening member of, a series of

progress or periodic reports, it commonly is called a preliminary
report.

Special types. The term **inspection report** refers, usually, to that
kind of examination report, often consisting of brief notations after
a set of printed questions, based on a routine procedure. Similarly,
laboratory report tends to imply the use of well-established laboratory techniques. When inventiveness and discovery are involved, the
account is likely to be called a **research report.** Sometimes the same
name is given to a paper grounded in large part upon library materials, a class of writing more usually referred to (especially if printed
in a journal) as the research *article.* An examination report on a subject that necessitates a search for the material to be examined may be
termed an **investigation report;** among its methods are included
tabulations and interpretations of data taken from questionnaires.
The designation **recommendation** (or **advisory**) **report** embraces
almost any kind in which proposals are given distinctly more emphasis than the antecedent work or examination.

What a report tells. Despite the immense range of lengths and
types, all reports have much in common. Invariably they answer the
same three questions, either explicitly or by implication: (1) *What
was the objective?* (2) *What was done?* (3) *What was the outcome?*
In addition, many (but not all) give consideration, and some give
prominence, to one or both of two other questions: (4) *What was
discovered?* (5) *What is proposed for the future, on the basis of
that already done or discovered?* The essential task in designing and
executing a report is clear, efficient, economical presentation of the
answers to those questions.

Style: the problem of adaptation. Reports have their style determined mainly by the requirements of the persons for whom they are
prepared. Accordingly, different industrial and engineering reports are
by no means identical in tone; but none allows room for fanciful,
whimsical, quaint, grandiose, or willfully obscure presentation. The
problem is purely that of adapting language to the practical end of
communication.

Style: student reports. University students of science and technology are confronted by the question of proper adaptation of their
reports to various preprofessional and professional courses, and to
classes of technical English. Observations were made at the end of
Chapter I on three general styles—or, rather, ranges of styles—suited
to scientific, engineering, and other technological subject matter; to
them were given the names "purely technical," "popular technical,"

and "middle technical." The first mentioned is generally well suited to homogeneous classes in which the instructor and all the students are, at least to some degree, expert in the same limited subject. Some form of this purely technical style, characterized by large use of specialized diction and of formulae and other symbolical expressions, therefore normally is employed in the reports prepared for such courses. In a class devoted particularly to technical English, on the other hand, the so-called middle style ordinarily is much to be preferred, for several reasons that have been explained previously (page 7). The popular technical style occasionally may be desirable in the college classroom or club, especially for oral reports when the topic is unusually difficult and when the group addressed includes students from several academic levels or from widely separated fields of specialization.

Note: One of the problems of style in technical compositions, particularly in process papers and procedure sections of reports, is the choice between constructions in the first person with the active voice of verbs and in the passive voice without a personal subject.* The student should learn to use each of these modes of expression with facility. The latter often is required, or at any rate expected, in formal reports written by and for specialists; the former is apt to have more appeal for lay readers or, especially, listeners. The middle range of technical styles has room for both forms, but the two should not be confusingly intermingled in the same context.

Mechanics. Technical students owe it to themselves to strive for perfection in the mechanics of composition, above all as pertaining to reports. They have only to ask any executive responsible for employing and directing young engineers, to be told that skillful "paper work" will be fully as important as actual laboratory or field activities in furthering their later advancement. If in school they assume the license of preparing assigned reports in a hasty and slipshod manner, they must not hope to polish away an ingrained carelessness at the instant of taking up professional careers. Habit is of the utmost importance in all mechanical procedures. The drafting of neat, well-constructed student reports—with strict attention to every technical requirement, from the choice of writing materials to the assembly and close proofreading of the last revision—can be a starting point for professional success and self-respect.

* This question already has been discussed in Chapter VII, as a phase of the general subject of technical narration. See *Problems of narrative style* (page 165).

Separate treatment has been given in Chapter V, which should be reviewed while the present chapter is being studied, to the mechanics of written and graphic matter, including such topics as materials, format, illustration, capitalization, italics, numbers, abbreviation, and signs and symbols. A report in letter form follows the mechanics of the conventional business letters, as explained in Chapter VIII, with only slight deviations: cf. page 273. Finally, oral reports involve what may be termed the mechanics of platform delivery, to be discussed in Chapter XI.

Grammar, spelling, and punctuation. A written report is a meeting ground of all that the author knows about grammar, spelling, and punctuation. Writers of reports dare not take the chance of error in these particulars, but must accustom themselves to the highest standards of correctness. The final draft is never ready for submission until phrasing, punctuation, and spelling (including syllabic division of words split between lines) have been painstakingly checked—against the dictionary at least, and if necessary against a handbook. Some readers will regard a single lapse as unforgivable; certainly all readers, however charitably inclined, will in large measure judge the writer's authority by the general character of his expression.

Grammar and punctuation have been studied at length in Chapters II and IV, respectively, but the principles and rules contained in those chapters can be of value only as *applied* in reports and other compositions. (Many students appear to overlook this simple and obvious fact. Having passed several courses in formal English, they seem content to make the very mistakes which, theoretically, they have learned to avoid.) Spelling—with pronunciation, which in oral reports replaces spelling and punctuation—has been treated in Chapter III, among the problems of diction.

Other qualities of excellence.

(1) *Division.* One of the first principles of report writing is *division into parts*. Even a simple memorandum report commonly consists of data spaced after separate questions or under several headings; and, as will be mentioned below, a difference of letter reports from ordinary business letters is the frequent use of centered headings to indicate organization. In elaborated formal reports, presentation of material in sections and subsections is a universal practice. So far as possible, however, the chosen categories should be relatively broad and easily comprehensible, rather than minute and unusual. Common-

place headings such as "Foundation," "Walls," and "Plumbing" are much to be preferred to fancy entries that might perplex the reader or force him to consult a dictionary.

(2) *Arrangement*. Along with division into parts goes *logical arrangement*. Together, division and arrangement constitute **organization**. Throughout the report and within each component part, the writer's conscious aim should be to discover that sequence which will afford the most orderly progress from the beginning to the end of the subject matter. Every student should learn to write from outlines, for only by means of outlining can sound organization be attained in extended compositions.

The problem of planning and organizing expository, descriptive, narrative, and argumentative technical material has been given large space in Chapters VI and VII. Concerning the analytical sentence outline for exposition, see pages 129 ff. Concerning other types and uses of outlines, see pages 158 ff., 166 ff., and 183 ff. Concerning the planning and outlining of oral reports and other speeches on technical topics, see Chapter XI, pages 347 ff.

(3) *Clarity*. A complaint against young engineers often made by superiors is that their written reports are not clear. Clarity is a function partly of stylistic adjustment (see at page 267 the paragraph on *Style: the problem of adaptation*); partly of formal correctness (see the paragraphs labeled *Mechanics* and *Grammar, spelling, and punctuation* at pages 268 and 269); and partly of careful organization, which has been treated under the entries *Division* and *Arrangement* in Subparagraphs (1) and (2), just above. Clearness is a pervasive quality which no halfway, pottering measures can achieve where it is not already present; like a jerry-built house, an obscure report ought to be wholly reconstructed. All the chapters of this book have been directed, from various standpoints, toward helping technical students to acquire the difficult, but at the same time indispensable, art of clearly expressing the facts and ideas of their reports.

(4) *Accuracy*. The value of correctness in such particulars as grammar and punctuation already has been sufficiently stressed. Accuracy is another kind of correctness highly necessary in reports, as indeed in all forms of technical composition. In the first instance, accuracy rests upon intellectual

honesty; in the second, upon industry and persistence in searching out data, sifting evidence, and drawing logical inferences; in the last, upon carefully weighed statement. *An inaccurate report is worthless.*

(5) *Completeness.* Like suitable style, completeness must be tested by the demands of the contemplated reader or readers. The simple truth, easily overlooked, is that a report, as the very name reveals, *is directed to someone or to some group.* Setting aside certain kinds of printed documents, to which the appropriateness of the term *report* might be questioned, few technical reports are issued at random to an undiscriminated public. Obviously, therefore, completeness is a relative question. Reports are deficient to the extent that they omit details, background knowledge, or explanations required by the persons actually addressed, who normally are known in advance—at least as a class, if not individually.

(6) *Avoidance of redundancy.* Also opposed to completeness is superfluity, in matters of verbal expression usually called redundancy. A reader of a report is bored when he is told more than enough, just as he is puzzled when furnished less than sufficient information. Especially in descriptions of apparatus and in narrative accounts of technical procedures, unskillful writers are liable to prolixity. Once again, however, determination of the proper degree of fullness must be relative rather than absolute, depending on what the readers probably know and probably wish to know. The perfect medium is not always attainable, sometimes because those addressed are not well known to the author of the report, sometimes because they are not a closely knit group. If for any reason either incompleteness or redundancy must be elected, the latter is by far the more endurable fault: a reader can easily skip what does not interest him, whereas he hardly can be expected to supply needed particulars not stated in the text of the report.

On the form of redundancy known as tautology, in which the meaning of a word or set of words is thoughtlessly repeated within the same phrase, see Chapter III: D 20.

(7) *Relevance.* Unity is, to be sure, a standard test of successful composition, from epic poems to business letters. Nevertheless, in many kinds of writing the touchstone of unity is

somewhat lightly applied. In the technical report (as also in the business letter, including the letter report), however, the standard is practically absolute. No section, subsection, paragraph, or sentence—not even a parenthetical phrase or a casual word—can be justified if it is not essential to full presentation and explanation of the subject. A technical writer is obligated to keep strictly to the point.

B. MAKE-UP

Variation. Being a universal medium of communication in science and industry, the report is necessarily versatile and flexible enough to accommodate great diversity of subjects. Reports ranging from brief notations scribbled in the field to complex printed works of several volumes are called by the same name—and rightly so, in view of their basic identity of functions. (Cf. *What a report tells* on page 267, above.)

Importance of form. Despite the differences of reports from one another, *form is of the highest importance.* Ideally, in each report it should perfectly reflect the content; however, allowance must be made for conventional or prescribed format, to which adherence often is expected. A technical student has missed a most significant distinction if he imagines that the principle of variety, which pertains to reports as a class, authorizes either formlessness or capricious arrangement of the individual report. (See also, concerning organization, the first two subparagraphs under *Other qualities of excellence* on pages 269–270.)

Required forms. Both engineering students and technicians in industry find that to some extent, at least, they are expected to shape their reports according to a standardized or assigned pattern. Businesses, agencies of government, and other special groups or authorities, including the instructors of each department or of particular courses in technical colleges, customarily lay down rigid specifications for the reports prepared under their supervision. They do so partly to obtain consistency among related papers in groups or series, partly to assure proper adaptation of the report to the precise needs of the person or organization that will receive it.

Following directions. As the first step in acquiring the ability to write acceptable reports, *the technical student must learn to follow directions.* Having constructed for his courses in physics, chemistry, applied science, and technical English the several kinds of reports assigned in those fields of study, always adhering with exactness to the specified forms and conscientiously using correct language and mechanics, he should have no difficulty in adapting the discipline of several years' schooling to any special requirements of his later work. Even when he is not furnished more or less positive instructions respecting the format of reports, observation of good models on similar topics, together with exercise of common sense, will enable him to apply the principles of his scholastic training in report writing to professional and industrial problems.

Memorandum and letter reports. The form of two types of reports is largely determined by local practices or by general custom. Memoranda recording normal laboratory or field procedures, or exchanged for interdepartmental in intradepartmental communication in business and industry, usually are composed in a set method and order, often on printed blanks with spaces to be filled in. Reports in the form of letters also are a common practice, the value of which is recognized, for instance, by a regulation in the United States Navy that reports are written and transmitted as letters. In civilian usage, the ordinary layout of the business letter is employed, complete with heading, inside address, salutation, body (the report proper), complimentary close, and signature. The only deviations are the use of (1) centered headings, to clarify the organization; and (2) *Respectfully submitted* as the complimentary close. Of course, no title page, table of contents, or any other such part is included. Most letter reports, like all memorandum reports, are short; if more than four or five pages would be required, usually a so-called formal report (as treated below) is composed.

See Chapter VIII, throughout, on letter writing. An example of a report in letter form may be read at the end of that chapter, pages 229–230.

Formal reports. The expression *"formal" report* does not signify a limited, distinct class; but, rather, almost any report other than those written in notebooks or laboratory manuals, on blanks, or in any other casual way as memoranda, and as letters. Formal reports usually are several or many pages in length, and (unless printed) ordinarily are presented on paper of standard size (8½ by 11 inches), with the leaves bound flat inside a cover. The following discussion assumes that a fully elaborated report is in preparation. The content and make-up must, of course, be understood by the student as typical rather than universal and inflexible. In particular, the subject matter of many reports would demand a radically different division and arrangement from that suggested below under BODY. A relatively short report is likely to leave out some of the PRELIMINARIES, especially the table of contents and the foreword or letter of transmittal; if very brief, it may omit even the title page and the abstract. The ADJUNCTS, though very common in technical reports, are not invariably employed; on the other hand, elements not mentioned (as, for instance, the index of a printed book-length report) sometimes are needed.

(1) PRELIMINARIES

Pagination. The pages of preliminary matter in a report are numbered with *small* Roman numerals (*i, ii, iii, iv,* etc.), which usually are placed (sometimes in parentheses) at the bottom center of the sheets. The number is omitted on the title page, and occasionally on certain other sheets as well, but must be mentally supplied to keep the over-all numeration exact.

(*1. TITLE PAGE*)

Content and arrangement. The title page gives five pieces of information, normally in the following order: (1) the topic; (2) the authorship (individual or group); (3) the person or authority addressed (e.g., of a student paper, the instructor and course); (4) the place where the report is issued; (5) the date of submission or publication (year, month and year, or exact calendar date). These details should be neatly arranged, without crowding, on a whole sheet. By experimentation with different spacing and length of lines, capital and small letters, and underlining, a pleasing appearance can be obtained with relatively little expenditure of effort. The subject of the report usually (but not necessarily) is announced by the formula: "Report [up]on . . .," laterally centered, above the title proper, near the top of the sheet. Pictures or other purely decorative elements seldom are desirable on a title page.

(*2. LETTER OF TRANSMITTAL OR FOREWORD*)

Letter of transmittal: form and style. Just as a preface often stands at the beginning of a book, formal reports customarily open with a letter of transmittal. As the name implies, this is a letter in which the individual or group rendering the report addresses the person or collective authority by whom it was previously requested, and to whom it is now being transmitted. The letter of transmittal is a normal business letter, complete in format with all the usual parts. The length ranges from a single sentence, at one extreme, to several pages, at the other. Probably the most usual size is one page containing, in the body of the letter, about two to four paragraphs. The tone may be abstract and impersonal, or moderately—even warmly—personal, depending upon the relationship between writer and addressee. Even when the third person and passive voice are used elsewhere, a letter of transmittal in the first person (either singular or plural, to agree with the individual or company signature) is entirely proper; indeed, in many instances it is the only personal section of the report. When reports are bound or printed, this letter is placed immediately before or after the table of contents.

For the mechanics and format of letter writing in general, see Chapter VIII; in particular, see the discussions of customary forms of the complimentary close at page 196, and of individual and company signatures at page 197. (Note specimen letter on page 228.)

Letter of transmittal: functions and content. The letter of trans- • mittal is a device for courteously submitting a report to the primary recipient. The phrasing should, therefore, allude to the circumstances of authorization and imply a formal presentation of the completed document. In addition, it may say almost anything relevant to the report or its composition. The writer might wish, for instance, to speak of some aspect of the background of the undertaking, or to acknowledge help received from co-workers or others. Sometimes a short digest of the report is given, especially if an abstract (cf. pages 278 ff.) is not to follow at another point. Very commonly, even when the report includes a formal abstract, the results, conclusions, or recommendations are briefly summarized in the letter of transmittal.

Foreword. A foreword serves the same functions as a letter of transmittal, with the difference that it is not specifically addressed to any particular person or persons. In tone it is almost always impersonal; in format it omits the salutation, complimentary close, and other characteristics of the letter of transmittal. The date, if included, is placed at the left margin a double space or more below the last line of text.* Instead of using the first person (as often in a letter of transmittal), the author usually calls himself "the writer," "the tester," "the inspector," or the like, or else avoids all such references by employing the passive voice. Forewords take the physical as well as functional place of letters of transmittal; however, they are entered before more frequently than after the table of contents.

---

* In addition, the place may be given on a line or lines immediately above the date; the author's name may be signed or typewritten, in full or in the form of initials, at the right margin below the text.

Omission and inclusion in student reports. Neither a letter of transmittal nor a foreword is always necessary or desirable in reports for courses in scientific studies or technical English. Nevertheless, occasional composition of one or the other is good training for the later writing of complete professional reports. Also, letters of transmittal, addressed to the teachers for whom reports are prepared, are instructive in the general technique and style of the business letter. Beyond the classroom, in formal industrial, commercial, and engineering reports, either a foreword or letter of transmittal generally is required to orient the reader toward the subject matter.

Note: A letter of transmittal is *not* given any special heading (apart, that is, from the address and date at the upper right corner, or the date alone if a letterhead is used). Balance on the page should be practiced in accordance with directions stated at page 187 of Chapter VIII. A foreword of one page should be so arranged as to appear balanced on the midpoint of the sheet. The word FOREWORD, usually typed or printed in full capitals, is centered two or more spaces above the first line of writing. If two or several pages are occupied by the foreword, each except the last is "framed" within approximately equal margins (between one and two inches) at all four borders of the sheet. The last page retains those same margins at the top and sides, but the amount of blank space at the bottom is determined by chance.

(3. TABLE OF CONTENTS)

Centering. If the table of contents occupies only a single sheet, it is arranged by means of adjusted margins and spacing to have a balanced appearance. If, however, more than one page is required, "framing" of the material on the last is not attempted; the same margins are used as on the preceding leaf or leaves, and the remainder of the page below the final entry is left blank.

Heading and development. The heading, CONTENTS or TABLE OF CONTENTS, usually is typed or printed in full capitals. Below, entries aligned at the left indicate at least the main divisions of the report; corresponding numbers at the right show on which page each section begins. When subdivisions of the report are included in the table of contents, progressive degrees of indention and alignment call attention to their subordinate and coördinate relationships. In its most highly developed form, a table of contents is, in effect, an analytical outline of the report it accompanies.

(1)

CONTENTS

		p.
I.	The Problem	1
II.	The Theory	2
III.	The Apparatus	4
IV.	The Process	6
V.	The Results	10

(2)

TABLE OF CONTENTS

Note 1: No entries are included for the title page and for the table of contents itself. Sometimes, also, a letter of transmittal preceding the table of contents is not noted in the latter.

Note 2: Concerning the numbering of pages in reports, see the paragraphs labeled *Pagination* on pages 274 and 282.

Examples. The two sample tables of contents on page 277 illustrate minor differences in style, as well as the distinction between simple inclusion of main headings and a more analytical development. The first, incidentally, furnishes a model for the classifying and ordering of material in many student reports. The second has been adapted from a sentence outline submitted with a student paper in lieu of a conventional table of contents.

(4. ABSTRACT)

Importance in technical reports. In the formal report the abstract is a section of great practical importance; to it, in fact, a busy reader almost always turns first. Certainly he will not read further if the abstract does not convince him that he should. Word for word, it probably should receive more care in formulation than any other section of the technical report.

Content. An abstract is a summary of a longer composition, reducing to brief space material fully presented in the body of the paper. It should give emphasis to those facts or ideas which, in the judgment of the writer, are of the greatest consequence from the point of view of the reader. In the body of a report, for example, the apparatus and procedure sections may occupy large space because of the elaborateness of certain necessary technical operations, yet be of less ultimate significance than the results of the undertaking. If so, the abstract will stress conclusions and only lightly sketch the process through which they have been reached.

Length; position. No fixed ratio can be set between the sizes of a report and its abstract. In a typed report of up to fifteen or twenty pages, the abstract usually can be reduced to not over three or four paragraphs occupying a single sheet; however, much greater proportionate length frequently is advisable in industrial and governmental reports. The arrangement on the page (or pages) should be analogous to that of a foreword, with substitution of ABSTRACT as the heading. (See the *Note* on page 276, above.) An abstract normally is the last of the preliminary sections of a formal report, but occasionally is submitted, bound, or printed separately.

Examples. The following five passages illustrate the abstracting of student reports. They also suggest several classes of topics suitable for reporting in a course of technical English.

(1)

An experiment was conducted to determine the length and cross-sectional area of palmitic, stearic, and oleic acid molecules. When a small amount of such substances, dissolved in ether, is placed on the surface of water, the organic acid spreads over the surface to give a film one molecule deep. The area of the acid film was measured, and the cross-sectional area of the individual molecules calculated by dividing the total area by the number of molecules in the film. The length of the molecules in a direction perpendicular to the surface was obtained by dividing the volume (weight/density) by the number of molecules in the film to get the volume of each molecule, and then dividing the volume by the cross section.

The results were as follows:

   (a) palmitic acid
        area $= 22.75$ A^2
        length $= 21.9$ A
   (b) stearic acid
        area $= 23.7$ A^2
        length $= 23.3$ A
   (c) oleic acid
        area $= 41.01$ A^2
        length $= 13.3$ A

The only reported check on these results was the work of Adam, who had found the cross section of the stearic acid molecule to be 20.7 A^2, and the length to be 26 A. The agreement of the present findings with Adam's results, within limits of experimental error, indicates that the method used is practical, and that the values obtained for palmitic and oleic acids may be considered a close approximation of the true dimensions of those molecules.

(2)

Our group carried out a standard laboratory procedure for the effusiometric determination of the specific gravity of a gas, with the end in view of discovering any changes that might be made in the apparatus to decrease the time and increase the accuracy of the experiment.

We recommend that a reducing valve be inserted in the line

between the gas inlet and the water manometer, taking the place of the surge tank at that point. The reducing valve would smooth out irregularities in the pressure of the incoming gas, and thereby reduce the number of readings of the orifice flowmeter necessary at various differential heads to assure precision.

(3)

Object: An inspection of the XYZ Cotton Oil Company was made for the purpose of observing the industrial synthesis of shortening for bakery and home use.

Chemical Principle: Shortening is synthesized by hydrogenation of the unsaturated glycerides of vegetable oils in the presence of an activated nickel catalyst.

Materials: The raw materials, catalysts, and adsorbents used are as follows: cottonseed, peanut, soybean, and linseed oils; hydrogen and nitrogen; caustic soda; activated nickel and activated carbon; and fuller's earth and kieselguhr.

Apparatus: The principal pieces of equipment employed are as follows: a double-acting, adjustable-stroke proportioning pump; mixing, bleaching, cooling, and storage tanks; twelve Sharples super-centrifuges; a standard vacuum drier; three Heine boilers (150 hp); a hydrogenation kettle lined with steam coils; seven plate-and-frame pressure filters; a deodorization apparatus, consisting of steam coils and a Le Blanc jet condenser; a spray water-cooling unit; a flaker; and a fluffer.

Process: Manufacture of solid shortening proceeds through the following main processes: purification, decolorization, hydrogenation, and deodorization. Purification consists of adding caustic, centrifuging, washing, and vacuum drying. The oil is decolorized by fuller's earth and activated carbon. Hydrogenation is accomplished by application of hydrogen under pressure (50 psi) in the presence of heat (135 F) and activated nickel (3/10 per cent) on kieselguhr. Steam distillation with evacuation is employed in deodorization. Mechanical flaking (scraping to break up hardened fat) and fluffing (beating of nitrogen into the shortening) immediately precede packing. Soap stock, as a by-product, and salad oil are obtained by special procedures during the cycle of operation.

Comments: The plant as a whole is efficient and economical. One defect is that deodorizing is a batch process, instead of being continuous. Also, appreciable loss of oil occurs in the filters; however, measures are under consideration for recovery by extraction with solvents.

(4)

The Navy, finding in the Second World War that the conventional method of handling materials was inefficient, devised a "pallet" system, consisting in the use of movable platforms built as double-faced frames for the loading and unloading, conveying, and stacking of matériel.

A school was conducted to familiarize personnel with the new method. First, the class was shown how the pallets were constructed and loaded. Next, the special fork truck employed to shift the pallets was demonstrated. Tours and demonstrations, showing the system in operation, composed the remainder of the training period.

The advantages of the pallet system, mainly large saving in time and labor plus greater utilization of space and reduction of breakage, enormously overweighed the original cost and (theoretical) loss of storage space incurred by the extra equipment. Potential applications of the method to industry are evident.

(5)

A course of lectures and demonstrations is proposed to furnish a class or club of college students with a working knowledge of the art of developing and printing photographs.

The lectures, except No. V, follow chronologically the different processes that start with the exposed negative and end with a finished print. Each session, including the demonstrations and the practical work of the group, is from two to four hours in length. To permit close correlation of the different processes, the eight periods should be as nearly continuous as possible.

A synopsis of the entire course is outlined below:

Lecture No. I: Negative material
  A. Physical properties
  B. Hints and cautions

Lecture No. II: Developers and the theory of development
  A. The theory of development
  B. The developer solution

Lecture No. III: Rinse baths and fixing baths
  A. The acid rinse bath
  B. The fixing bath and the theory of fixation

Lecture No. IV: Negative washing and drying
  A. Negative washing
  B. Negative drying

Lecture No. V: Chemical mixing and handling
  A. The chemicals of photography
  B. Rules and precautions

Lecture No. VI: Contact printing
  A. The theory of contact printing
  B. The contact printer

Lecture No. VII: Enlarging
  A. The theory of enlarging
  B. The projection printer

Lecture No. VIII: Development and finishing of prints
  A. Developing
  B. Washing and drying

(2) BODY

Pagination. Except in letter and memorandum reports and informal or very brief reports of other kinds, normally each main section begins on a new page and has a heading—or, at least, a numeral or capital letter that can be identified from the table of contents—centered at the top of the sheet. Subsections, on the other hand, generally do not begin on separate leaves. (A system of centered and marginal captions should be devised to indicate the various degrees of subordination.) Pages should be numbered consecutively through the body of a report and the appendix or appendices (if any), except that no page number (as distinguished from the number of a plate, figure, or table) is assigned to a sheet containing *only* graphic or tabular matter. Page numbers, in the form of Arabic numerals, regularly are placed at the upper right or upper center of each sheet; however, they are centered (often in parentheses) at the bottom of those pages, always including the first page of the body, on which separate sections of the report commence. (On the use of small Roman numerals for the preliminary pages, see page 274.)

Division and arrangement. Earlier discussions in this chapter already have made clear the fact that organization varies greatly in different reports. The sections recommended below are not intended to constitute a Bed of Procrustes on which to torture and mangle subjects they might not suit. As a whole, they are less typical of examination and inspection reports than of laboratory-research and other work reports. Sometimes a simple two-part division into "The Problem" and "The Solution," or some similar arrangement, suffices.

Length: the principle of economy. State only what requires to be communicated, employing no more words than are needed for clarity, effectiveness, dignity, and correctness of expression. When that is done, the length is exactly right.

(1. PROBLEM)

Flexibility. The problem or scope obviously is the first thing to be made clear to the reader when a research, examination, or other technical activity is reported. The formula, "The object of this [*or:* the] experiment was . . . ," customarily opens routine laboratory reports written by students; ordinarily nothing more is said concerning the purpose or occasion. When the completed work has been of a more unusual or personal nature, when it fits into a larger scheme of research, or when, for any reason, the reader cannot be assumed to be well acquainted with it in advance of consulting the report, the addition of considerable background information or other explanatory matter may be in order. Statements of problem and purpose are basically expository, but may involve large elements of description, narration (especially to recount the history of a subject or undertaking), or conceivably even argumentation.*

(2. THEORY)

Role in science. Scientists and technologists, all due allowance being made for empirical knowledge and for trial-and-error processes, work mainly by applying theory to particular problems and data. (Even trial and error, consciously and rigorously directed, can become a rational principle of action.) The fundamental technique of scientific method is the application of systematic knowledge to the solution of problems.

Treatment in the technical report. In consequence of the theoretical basis of science, technical reports of more than routine actions generally contain a division on theory, principle of operation, or the equivalent. In some instances—for example, in the interpretation of data assembled by the questionnaire method or by tabulation from gauges or other instruments—the announcement of principles is no more than mention of the general plan of procedure, and may even be absorbed into the process section. Similarly, a technical operation may be largely a matter of design, perhaps merely of carpentry or machining, again requiring little theory. More commonly, however, natural and mathematical laws, which are likely to be intricately in-

---

* Concerning the mingling of different forms of discourse in the same passage, review pages 128 and 154.

volved in the solution of problems in pure or applied science, are formally laid down. Sometimes a simple statement suffices; sometimes demonstration by derivation or other methods of proof calls for elaboration.

Characteristics. Presentation should be through clear, forthright exposition carefully adjusted to the known or assumed reader's mentality and experience. (Cf. the two paragraphs labeled *Style* on pages 267–268, above.) When a scientific principle (for instance, that all substances vaporize at higher temperatures as external pressure is increased) would certainly be known to the class of reader addressed, it may be merely mentioned or, possibly, left unstated as obvious. On the other hand, when the theory is more abstruse or difficult, longer and fully analytical treatment is needed. Whenever readers are expected who will be laymen with respect to the particular field of science or technology under discussion, an abundance of illustrations and analogies from common experience should be included. Symbolical and diagrammatic representation usually is desirable, and often is imperative, but such schematic methods should be supplemented by written text to the extent necessary for clarification. Except in communications strictly between experts of the same field, verbal explanations always should accompany the technical signs and symbols peculiar to a specialized subject.

(Technical exposition is the subject of the whole of Chapter VI.)

(3. APPARATUS, EQUIPMENT, OR MATERIALS)

Treatment in the technical report. Because technical work almost always is done with physical substances and special instruments, a section headed APPARATUS, MATERIALS, EQUIPMENT, MATERIALS AND EQUIPMENT, APPARATUS AND MATERIALS, or the like is characteristic of formal technical reports. It may be wholly tabular or may consist entirely of expanded descriptions, but most frequently employs a combination of both methods. As always, the comprehension of the intended reader should be taken into account. Any materials, tools, and mechanisms with which he might be presumed to have familiarity need only be mentioned; others should be amply—if necessary, minutely—described. Reports are not expected to list, much less fully describe, all articles of equipment down to the slide rule and ordinary test tubes. Still, the safe rule is: "If in doubt, specify."

Typical plan. A plan of general serviceability is to begin this section with one or more lists, introduced by some such sentence as:

"The following instruments and other equipment were used:"; or, "In preparation for the construction of my rotating directional antenna, I assembled the materials and tools listed below." The quantity of each enumerated item should be shown, together with any significant "name-plate" specifications such as manufacturer or capacity ratings. Classifying subheadings usually suggest themselves, as *Laboratory Equipment* and *Reagents*; or *Raw Materials, Processed Materials*, and *Tools and Instruments*. Below this list or set of lists, any pieces of apparatus that require discussion may then be described as fully as necessary in regular paragraphs. In addition, drawings or photographs can be extremely helpful in the apparatus section.

(Technical description in its various phases is the subject of Section A of Chapter VII.)

(4. PROCEDURE)

Treatment in the technical report. In many reports the procedure section is the longest part, but it nearly always is among the easiest to prepare. Typically, the writer has already made clear a certain objective, the theory on which it was approached, and the apparatus arranged for the purpose; he has now to state the process in which that apparatus was employed according to those principles in the effort to attain that objective. The section should be a straightforward narrative, practically always in exactly chronological order. The proportionate length varies greatly with different subjects; in reports of constructions, tests, and examinations, a relatively long procedure section generally is justified. However, any tendency to spin out the story for its own sake must be restrained. Although results may have to be stated briefly, as essential to complete reporting of the process, analysis and discussion of them should be reserved to a later section.

(Technical narration is the subject of Section B of Chapter VII.)

(5. RESULTS, CONCLUSIONS, AND RECOMMENDATIONS)

"Conclusions," not "conclusion." The body of a report may end with a division headed RESULTS, CONCLUSIONS, or RECOMMENDATIONS, or with separate sections on two or, rarely, all three of these topics. Logically, the last phase of a technical subject often is a statement of conclusions drawn from the information set forth in preceding parts. "Conclusions" (note the plural form) should not be taken as equal to "conclusion" (singular). Technical

papers have no space for a rhetorical flourish at either the beginning or the end. When the writer of a report comes to the end of his subject, he should stop composition and start revision.

Differing functions. If separate entries are given under RESULTS and CONCLUSIONS, the latter section sometimes is relatively unimportant. In fact, when the writer has nothing to offer beyond the results and his direct explanation of them, he may prefer to include all this material in one division captioned RESULTS. In general, the heading RESULTS implies a focus of attention upon the actual operation (or inspection, investigation, etc.); CONCLUSIONS, concentration upon interpretations, often looking (at least in part) to the future. The heading RECOMMENDATIONS much more explicitly indicates concern with subsequent actions, and is especially appropriate to the class of examination reports. The same report commonly includes both RESULTS and CONCLUSIONS, or RESULTS and RECOMMENDATIONS, as separate topics; but CONCLUSIONS AND RECOMMENDATIONS is likely to appear as a combination heading, because recommendations are a special form of conclusions.

Tone. Plain logic is its own best expositor. A glowingly enthusiastic manner anywhere in a technical report—but most of all in the statement of results, conclusions, or recommendations—would be cause for suspicion of the writer's uncertainty about his facts and inferences. Every conclusion, whether in pure logic or in any form of discourse, should follow from the premises. The "premises" of a formal report (on the assumption of its division into the parts now being outlined) are set out in the earlier sections on the problem, the theory, the apparatus, and the procedure. The statement of results, conclusions, or recommendations should manifest a sincere, unbiased effort at reasoning from the data given in those several divisions.*

Content. Almost infinite variation of content is possible in this part of different reports. The undertaking being reported may have completely succeeded or completely failed, or it may have fallen anywhere between success and failure; it may be either finished or in progress at the time of reporting; its field may be mathematical, mechanical, chemical, electrical, aeronautical, commercial, sociological, biological, etc.; it may be a self-completing project or an integral part of a larger series of projects. The report itself may be written, with complete freedom of content and method, concerning a private experiment of the author; or it may be rigidly controlled by terms of

---

* On the subject of formal logic (true and false patterns of reasoning), see Chapter VII, pages 168 ff.

the letter, commission, or legislation directing the undertaking, the report upon it, or both together. These and other factors affect the inferences that can and should be drawn for the readers' information, interest, and benefit.

Suggested questions. Some of the questions which might be answered—not, of course, all in any one report, and also not to the exclusion of any other pertinent questions—are these: To what extent, and in what respects, was the undertaking a success? To what extent, and in what respects, was it a failure? (In answering either of the preceding questions, or both, the writer should make explicit reference to his prior statement of purpose or problem, normally given as the opening section of the body of the report.) What were the specific causes of success or failure, or of the partial success and partial failure? Did the principles employed in attacking the problem prove sound; was the apparatus adequate and serviceable; and was the procedure efficient and economical? What was the effect of local and remote conditions or influences? What was the effect of the materials used, or of the special abilities and limitations of the human agents? If the undertaking should be repeated, what changes in method are recommended? What is the proper place of the undertaking in a larger program? What personal benefits were achieved for the profit, enlightenment, or convenience of the writer or others? What are the implications of the results for abstract knowledge or for future planning, design, and other practical utility? What can be concluded about the efficiency of the undertaking in terms of mechanics, finance, or social value?

Note: Throughout the foregoing questions, "undertaking" should be interpreted, variously, as the activity reported upon in a work report; that studied in an examination report; or the conduct of the investigation, inspection, or examination in the latter type. Cf. *Broad classification of technical reports*, page 266.

(3) ADJUNCTS

(*1. APPENDIX OR APPENDICES*)

Function. One or more appendices may bear to a report somewhat the same relation that a warehouse holds to a display room. Not every report, of course, requires an appendix, for often all wares can be displayed to advantage on the counters of the various main departments. Many times, again, appendices serve the purpose of storing away auxiliary materials that would needlessly encumber the other parts of the report.

Form. What has just been said does not imply that an appendix, any more than a commercial warehouse, should be an unsorted heap of rubbish or scraps. It should contain nothing that is not genuinely relevant to the problem of the report or to its solution. Furthermore, everything included should be neatly and logically classified and arranged. Headings, letterings, and other devices should be provided as guides, and references invariably should be made in the body of the report at points where further information might be obtained from the appendix. Although the most important graphs, diagrams, tables of data, and other nonverbal matter can be incorporated in the appropriate divisions of the main body, bulky or more remotely related material of this type is customarily relegated to an appendix, of which it is in some instances the chief or total content. (Note the second sample table of contents given earlier in this chapter, on page 277.) The appendix, or each one of a series, should start on a new page. Two or more in the same report are captioned APPENDIX A, APPENDIX B, etc.; or APPENDIX I, APPENDIX II, etc. In addition, a meaningful subtitle may be centered below each of these main headings.

Glossary. A glossary is a type of limited dictionary, comprising an alphabetical list of specialized or otherwise difficult vocabulary occurring in the writing to which it is appended. Each item consists of a term, written or typed flush with the left margin (and commonly underlined), followed by its definition. Second and subsequent lines of the entry are indented, in order to make the alphabetized expression stand out prominently. Usually the individual definition is single-spaced on the typewriter, with double-spacing between definitions. A glossary included in a report is essentially an appendix, and often is so indicated, the word *Glossary* being given as a subtitle under the heading APPENDIX. Sometimes, however, especially if the report contains no other appendices, only the heading GLOSSARY is used. Cross references, either in parentheses or in footnotes, should direct the reader to the glossary at the first occurrence of every defined term in the main text.

(2. NONTEXTUAL MATTER)

Types; position. Apart from signs, formulae, and equations that can be embedded more or less integrally in the sentence and paragraph structure of writing, the nontextual matter of reports may be classified as: (1) pictorial (photographs and sketches); (2) symbolical (plotted curves, maps, charts, diagrams, flowsheets, hookups, and so on); (3) tabular (tables, lists, and enumerations of various kinds). As has been explained, such material often is grouped in one or more appendices; but part, if not all, is very likely to be distributed among the several sections of the main body of the report.

(On the mechanics of pictorial and other nonverbal matter, see Chapter V: M 3.)

(3. MISCELLANEOUS)

Cover. The pages of a report intended for the press need not be fastened together, but should be stacked in numerical order and sent to the printer in a Manila envelope or other heavy wrapping sufficiently large to contain them without folding. (They should not be rolled, but accompanying sheets of graphic matter too large for the same envelope may be rolled inside a pasteboard mailing cylinder.) If, as with practically all student writing, a report is to remain in manuscript or typescript, the pages should be secured within a suitable double-leaf cover. However, short reports submitted to instructors may be folded once, either lengthwise or upwards; in this arrangement, a prescribed outer endorsement takes the place of a separate cover. School laboratory reports commonly are written or inserted as interleaves in a manual that has its own binding.

(Review Chapter V: M 1 and M 5.)

Extra pages. A leaf blank except for the centered word APPENDIX, APPENDICES, or APPENDIXES (occasionally SUPPLEMENT, GLOSSARY, etc.) should be placed between the report proper and any addenda. Another extra leaf, entirely devoid of writing or lettering, should separate the last page of the report, or of the addenda, from the back cover. (If the report is not bound, this leaf becomes the outer sheet after folding and carries the endorsement.) A corresponding blank leaf is not required at the beginning of the report, but a half-title page sometimes is inserted: i.e., a sheet on which, about halfway down, the title—or a shortened version if the full form is long—is typewritten or lettered by hand. This leaf does not replace the regular title page but instead, when used, immediately precedes it.

Note: Like the title page, a half-title page does not actually bear a numeral, but it must be mentally carried as No. i in the pagination of the preliminary sections of the report. (See page 274.)

Documentation. A report based to any degree, however slight, upon written or printed sources (books, other reports, magazine or encyclopedia articles, pamphlets, etc.) requires the special technique known as documentation, to show the places and extent of borrowing. *When the exact words of an original are retained, quotation marks must be used* in addition to *a footnote, but* the footnote is obligatory regardless of whether the borrowed matter is rephrased or directly quoted. Documented reports generally include a separate bibliography as well as footnotes, whereas articles published in journals ordinarily place all the necessary information in footnotes and omit the bibliography. Failure to cite sources of information, either by bibliographical footnotes or by both footnotes and a bibliography, is a serious offense.

Cross reference: For full theoretical explanations and numerous models of both basic systems of documentation, see Chapter IX, Section D.

C. TYPES OF STUDENT REPORTS

Note on collateral reading: In school, in government service, in the laboratory, in industry, in the library, and in the field of operations, thousands upon scores of thousands of technical reports are drafted each year. No one has access to, or occasion for consulting, more than a tiny fraction of the whole output; on the other hand, students need never lack examples to read and analyze. Every student of science and technology should familiarize himself with a variety of reports within his range of growing professional interest. To this end, he would do well to adopt the complementary habits of browsing in libraries, and elsewhere, for older ones on file; and of turning over a large number of the newer ones as they appear, with close attention to a few of special relevance to his studies. Government documents issued by the departments and agencies of the United States, either without charge or at small cost, often are at once model reports and repositories of otherwise inaccessible technical information.* The states and local divisions of government also publish numerous reports.† Most large companies will gladly send to students, on request, copies of certain of their printed documents.

* *Selected United States Government Publications,* a list issued semimonthly, is supplied gratis by the Superintendent of Documents, Government Printing Office, Washington 25, D.C.
† The Library of Congress issues a *Monthly Checklist of State Publications* (indexed annually), which is sold by the Superintendent of Documents.

(1) LIBRARY INVESTIGATIONS

Phases. The whole subject of research in the library, embracing selection and limitation of topic, finding of reference sources, note taking, and documented composition, has been treated extensively in Chapter IX. That chapter should be consulted whenever a report founded on documents of any kind is in progress, whether the investigation is research in the strict sense,* or uses sources merely for background data or for compilation of existing knowledge on a subject.

Example. The report titled "The Navy's 3500-horsepower, 1500 F Experimental Gas Turbine" (pages 299 ff., below), while closely reliant on sources, exhibits (as every report of a library investigation should) a genuine understanding of subject matter by the author—not an aimless amassing of undigested, or ill-digested, "library material." Observe the inclusion of footnotes and a bibliography for documentation. (The brevity of the latter and the absence of books as sources were consequences of the recency of the topic at the time of writing.)

(2) LABORATORY EXPERIMENTS

Characteristics. Rapid writing of routine laboratory reports— usually in compressed form, with large use of tabular and graphic devices—is a weekly or daily procedure familiar to every student of every science. Occasionally a student may conduct an independent, or partially independent, experiment in the laboratory that can furnish a suitable subject for formal reporting. Care should be taken to make perfectly clear the exact nature of the problem, the principle of solution, the laboratory materials, setup, and method, and the extent of success or failure. Recommendations may follow, concerning either improvement of technique or possible applications of the solution to other theoretical or practical problems.

Examples. See abstracts of two reports concerning laboratory experiments entered as Examples (1) and (2) on pages 279–280. Below are given the concluding sections of a report on an attempted hydraulic separation of a three-component system of finely divided solid unknowns.

---

* See, on page 232, Subparagraph (3) of the paragraph labeled *Qualities of the research composition* at the beginning of Chapter IX.

RESULTS

After the sample had been screened, the portion of the material retained on 28-mesh was found to have a specific gravity of 3.45; that on 35-mesh, 2.86. The coloration of the matter on 28-mesh was predominantly red and dark brown, whereas that on 35-mesh was a very light brown. This combination of data indicated that the red and dark-brown material was the component of highest density, and that the white and gray materials were of lower density. Nevertheless, discovery of the exact colors of the three components was not possible without further data.

After calculations of the settling velocity had been made by the simplified equation given in the Theory section, the 35-mesh material was separated in the manner explained in the Procedure section, with a water velocity of 0.2 fps. The result of this separation indicated that the correct velocity had been chosen. The overheads, or particles carried over the top, were entirely one component, of density 2.3. The color of this component was light gray, a fact which had made difficult the estimation of the relationship between the color and density of components. The tailings, or particles which settled to the bottom, were formed of two components; but three colors were present: red, dark brown, and white. It became evident that the red and dark-brown particles represented only one component.

Several efforts were made to separate the two components of the 35-mesh tailings, by high and low water velocities, but no further breakdown was effected.

Calculations were made of the settling velocity, and the 28-mesh material was put into the separator, with a water velocity of 0.49 fps. The resulting overheads were of density 3.2; the tailings, of density 3.6. In addition to having this high density, the tailings appeared, even under magnification, to contain only one component, the red and dark-brown particles. The overheads, however, contained both of the other components, and attempts at further separation were ineffectual.

CONCLUSIONS

Examination of the results reveals that it was not possible to separate completely the three unknown components of the original mixture by hydraulic means. Some of the particles remained mixed in spite of all efforts to separate them, but the experiment was not without encouraging results. The lightest component, of density 2.3, was successfully removed and a reasonably pure sample of the heaviest component, of density 3.6, was obtained. Although the component of medium density could not be isolated, samples containing a far greater percentage of this middle component than did the original material were obtained.

Two principal causes account for the incomplete separation: (1) variation of particle size even in the narrow range used, and (2) presence of turbulence in the rising column of water. The difference of particle sizes in material passing a 28-mesh screen but retained on a 35-mesh screen, is surprisingly large; the individual particles vary up to 40 per cent. Since a small particle with high density falls at the same rate as a larger particle with lower density, no fine separation can be made unless the particles are of exactly the same size. Turbulence in the water column produces variations in the free-settling velocity and, in consequence, incomplete separation.

One must bear in mind that the practicability of hydraulic separation in an industrial situation might well be determined by factors not considered at all in the present experiment. If one of the three components were a valuable mineral, the recovery of which would be profitable even in small amounts, the method typified in this report might well be followed. Even for more common materials, hydraulic separation could be employed to strip out one component surely and accurately, leaving the problem of dividing the other two components greatly simplified.

(3) TESTS

Characteristics. Among the routine laboratory assignments to which allusion has been made on page 291, testing is a frequent kind of activity. Only when the problem demands more than ordinary ingenuity or precision, however, is a test or series of tests likely to occasion a report where paragraphed discourse is more prominent than tabular and graphic matter: that is to say, one well adapted to a course in technical English. Even then, data sheets, sample calculations, graphs, and diagrams (sometimes photographs) of the test setup usually must be included to supplement written explanations. The paper should emphasize, especially, the testing apparatus and the results, and should make clear any theory by which the latter are interpreted.

Example. See pages 321 ff., below: "Tests of a Brown Model-airplane Engine." That report, though no doubt more circumstantial than would be necessary for some readers, is a good example of the middle technical style mentioned near the beginning of this chapter (page 268; cf. also Chapter I, pages 6–7). Notice—among other evidences of the author's tactful instruction of a reader assumed (in accordance with the assignment) to have no expert knowledge of mechanics—how the paper, at the end of the second section, makes clear the nature and use of the Strobotac and the Jagabi tachometer. The sketch and photographs, almost always helpful adjuncts to technical description in words, well display the design and assembly of other apparatus.

(4) DIRECTIONS

Occurrence. The giving of directions is a constant obligation of the writer or speaker on technical subjects, and occupies large space (especially in procedure and conclusions sections) in many reports. Entire reports devoted to directions are not very common, but occasionally a student may wish to elucidate a technical method, in a report grounded on his own experience, for the benefit of other students by whom the technique is unknown or imperfectly understood. A topic of this kind is particularly well suited to oral reporting.

Example. Various uses of the slide rule come to mind when suggestion or assignment of a directions report is made. Whatever subject the composer may choose, he must, of course, avoid merely rehearsing procedures already obvious to his readers or audience. The following paragraph is excerpted from a paper written to instruct students who own a slide rule, but who have not yet learned the use of that instrument for quick solution of quadratic equations having large constants. (Algebraic explanations given in the preceding paragraphs are here omitted.)

Suppose this equation is to be solved:

$$x^2 + 500x - 570,000 = 0$$

By inspection, one can see that 1000×500 ($R \times r$) nearly equals 570,000 and that $1000 - 500$ ($R - r$) equals 500. Therefore, the preliminary working assumption may be that $R = 1000$. By placing the chosen value of 1000 on the "C" scale directly over the value of 570,000 on the "D" scale, one reads the quotient, 570, on the "D" scale opposite the "C" index. Since $1000 - 570$ is less than 500, the value of 1000 is too small and must be increased. After a few shifts, leaving the indicator at 570,000 on the "D" scale and moving the "C" scale to increase or decrease the assumed values, one finds that $R = 1045$ and $r = 545$. Thus, in sufficiently close approximation for most purposes, the roots (r and $-R$) can be written as 545 and -1045.

(5) TECHNICAL PHASES OF HOBBIES

Range and style. Reports on problems encountered and solved in private or group hobbies are a type popular with technical students. The range of subjects available is as wide as the countless spare-time pursuits that may engage a student's interest, for almost any hobby has its constructional and other technical phases. Because of the intimate, often unique, character of such activities, reports of this class tend to be less formal than most other types of compositions prepared for the course in technical English. Use of the first person is common, and inclusion of humorous episodes occasionally is appropriate.

Examples. Topics on which students have written reports concerning hobbies are illustrated in the following list: "The Construction of a Dual-purpose Cabinet," "Aerial Photography from a Box Kite," "Design and Installation of a Half-wave Vertical Antenna," "Adaptation of the Optical Sight to Skeet Shooting," "A Homemade Inlaid Chessboard," "Chemical Magic," and "A Tandem Built from Two Single Bicycle Frames." The problem and procedure sections of the papers first and last named, respectively, are given below. (Each of these reports contained, as an appendix, a set of line-drawn or photographed figures not here reproduced.)

(1)   OBJECTIVE

The desk and shelf space of my den had become badly overcrowded with books, a radio, and all manner of odds and ends. To alleviate the condition, I decided to build a vertical floor cabinet that would serve both as a storage container for miscellaneous objects and as a radio stand. The cabinet was to enclose three shelves at unequal levels, to have paneled sides and back together with a hinged door on the front, and to hold the radio snugly within a narrow coaming around the top.

———————

(2)   CONSTRUCTION

At the outset I found that my uncle had an old bicycle that would give me a good start, although it was in very poor condition and required much cleaning and adjusting. From a bicycle repair shop I obtained all other needed parts and material except two small pieces of discarded driving chain, which had been replaced on a home motion picture projector, and two pieces of three-sixteenths-inch welding rod for the steering mechanism.

Following a thorough cleaning of the old parts, I cut the back fork from the frame and brazed in pieces of tubing between the front seat and the back handle bars, between the latter and the rear seat, and between the pedals. Alignment was the chief problem in the entire operation, but I overcame this difficulty by tacking the joints with small welds and straightening the pieces before finishing the welding.

I had decided to synchronize the two sets of handle bars by means of a modified chain drive, consisting of two short lengths of pin-type driving chain joined by two long pieces of three-sixteenths-inch welding rod and running on small sprockets, one at the upper mounting of the front fork and one at the bottom of the rear steering post. Since only the pieces of chain were ready-made, the sprockets had to be machined from boiler plate and the steering post from a three-fourths-inch pipe. To manufacture the sprockets I bored two small pieces of boiler plate, placed them together on a mandrel, turned them to the proper diameter, and cut the teeth with a gear cutter in a milling machine. I made the steering post so that its upper part was like that of the steering column above the front fork, by welding on a shoulder to hold the bearing race and then turning, boring, and threading the pipe in a lathe. Afterwards I welded the sprockets in place.

Synchronizing the pedals necessitated use with the rear pair of a double sprocket wheel, connected by separate continuous chains to the front-pedal sprocket and to the small driving sprocket on the back wheel. This dual assembly I formed by cutting out the center of one sprocket and bolting the rim to another, with six small washers between them to allow the two chains to pass each other side by side. The crank arm of the right rear pedal had to be heated and rebent for clearance.

Because of the ease of application, I used gummed masking tape for obtaining "flash" decorations. I painted the whole tandem white; then I cut and affixed cellulose tape in the shape of desired trimmings, and repainted the frame red.

(6) INSPECTIONS

Utility. One phase of the professional training of engineers consists in conducted or individual inspections, followed by the writing or oral delivery of reports. Notes and sketches, based on direct observation and on tactful interrogation of guides, proprietors, officials, or engineers, are made at the site. Best results, however, usually are obtained when the inspection only shortly precedes the report, so that actual memories remain fresh. This type of project is excellent for the course in technical composition, provided the reports do not merely duplicate those submitted to other classes.

Plan and content. The problem of organization is solved by a spatial, chronological, or topical sequence. (Very often, in fact, because of the stepwise or unit arrangement characteristic of technical installations, the three plans are substantially the same.) In any method, a wealth of *exact and concrete details* about the specific property or system under view should be given; for a generalized account of, say, steel making is not equivalent to an inspection report. Drawings, perfected from the rough sketching done on location, ordinarily should be added to make visualization easy. In some instances, when the rules and situation of the inspected establishment permit use of a camera, photographs can be effective additions or substitutes. Besides pictorial views, schematic diagrams such as flowsheets and floor layouts are very serviceable to augment discussions of plants and processes. Tables of specifications and ratings frequently are included, sometimes in an appendix to the report. Recommendations, although generally the main purpose of examinations and inspections by consulting engineers and other experts, may be omitted or limited to a short section in students' reports.

Examples. Every community (including the college or university campus itself) abounds in suitable objects of inspection: e.g., powerhouses, telephone exchanges, theater projection booths, ice companies, air-conditioning systems, mills, garages, kilns, laboratories, hospitals, and other installations for technology and industry, for research, and for public service. An abstract of an inspection report already has been given as Example (3), page 280.

(7) EXHIBITIONS

Classes of reports. Exhibits, demonstrations, or displays are common in the experience of all students. Reports on activities of this kind fall under two heads: (1) records and (2) proposals. A mingling of types, however, can result from a study of the failure or deficiencies of a project, for the sake of discovering the corrections needed to make it successful when continued or repeated.

Examples. The reports abstracted as Examples (4) and (5) on pages 281–282, above, are instances of the two classes of reports mentioned in the preceding paragraph. The following passages are the opening and closing sections of another exhibition report of the first type.

PROBLEM

The fundamental aim in any technical exhibit is that of performing a process as nearly as possible in the manner used commercially, at the same time presenting an explanation that can be understood by the layman and the expert alike. In the exhibition of oxyacetylene cutting under water for the last Engineering Show, explanation was much simpler than operation, and so this paper will discuss only the problems of performance.

Difficulties arose, primarily, in the designing and providing of the demonstration apparatus; and, secondarily, in the actual cutting of a steel plate under water. The former was by far the more difficult phase.

Since an auxiliary device releasing compressed air was necessary to prevent the water from smothering the flame, turbulence would make public observation from above the tank impossible. Again, the steel plate to be cut had to be held in place by something that would not be affected by extremely high temperatures. Finally, a large supply of rather expensive fuel had to be obtained.

After the apparatus had been set up and the initial kinks ironed out, operational problems could be summed up as one: forcing the flame to cut the steel plate. It involved maintaining the proper location of the torch above the metal, keeping the nozzles clean, and furnishing a steady flow of gases.

.   .   .   .

CONCLUSIONS

Every difficulty was, at last, overcome by experience and ingenuity. Both the compressed-air bell for the torch and the observation window installed in the water tank proved successful in operation. Hundreds of visitors stopped to watch the process, and many were interested enough to ask questions. The local newspapers gave special commendation to this exhibit. All witnesses appeared to agree that the principle of underwater cutting was successfully demonstrated.

D. SPECIMENS OF STUDENT REPORT WRITING

In preceding sections, numerous extracts from compositions by students have exemplified various aspects of report writing. Two full-length specimens now conclude the chapter. The first is complete with title page, letter of transmittal, table of contents, abstract, figures, and bibliography, in addition to the report proper; the second includes, besides the body of the report, the figures and a tabulated appendix.

Report on:

THE NAVY'S

3500-HORSEPOWER, 1500 F

EXPERIMENTAL GAS TURBINE

By:

L. Wallace Meier

At:

The Rice Institute

Houston, Texas

For:

English 380b

On:

June 19, 1946

Residential Halls
The Rice Institute
Houston 1, Texas
June 19, 1946

Mr. J. D. Thomas
Department of English
The Rice Institute
Houston 1, Texas

Dear Mr. Thomas:

During the past few years there has been a
concentrated effort to develop the gas turbine to
the point of efficiency where it will be able to
enter the engineering field in competition with
other types of prime movers. Only within the last
twenty years have engineers developed the gas
turbine to produce enough power to operate its own
air compressor, and still more recently to permit
power to be taken off the shaft for other uses.
As this development has progressed, the fact has
become plain to designers that soon the major obstacle will be heat limitation. The metallurgist
holds the key to the future of the gas turbine:
when he offers metals that will withstand high temperatures for long periods of time, the development of the turbine will progress at a more rapid
pace.

With considerable foresight, the United
States Navy has had installed at Annapolis, Maryland, a 3500-horsepower gas turbine, designed and
built by the Allis-Chalmers Manufacturing Company to operate at a temperature of 1500 degrees

Mr. J. D. Thomas--6/19/46--p. 2

Fahrenheit. This unit is for experimental purposes only, but the testing is being done with
an eye to the possibility of using the gas turbine
for future ship propulsion. Although the turbine
was installed in 1944, the first figures have only
recently been released, because of the past need
for security of such information.

  Herewith is presented a report of the setup
used and a short résumé of expectations for the
future.

       Respectfully submitted,

       L. Wallace Meier

       L. Wallace Meier

CONTENTS

LIST OF FIGURES*

(From "U. S. Navy Operates 3500-hp Experimental
Gas Turbine at 1350 F," Power Plant Engineering,
L (May, 1946): Figure 1 = original Fig. 2 on
p. 86; Figure 2 = original Fig. 7 on p. 88.)

-(iv)-

* Redrawn and reproduced in this book by permission of *Power Plant Engineering.*

CONTENTS

LIST OF FIGURES

The Navy's 3500-horsepower, 1500 F Experimental
Gas Turbine

ABSTRACT

Problem. Gas turbines operate at higher temperatures than do steam turbines, and must therefore have considerably higher inlet temperatures.
Present indications point to a need for operating
temperatures of 1500 F for marine propulsion and
general use. Some data have been obtained from
units already in operation; because of their
limitations, however, these turbines have not
yielded enough specific information to be of much
practical value. The larger gas turbines in commercial use operate at temperatures below 1000 F,
and gas turbine airplane supercharger units made
for military use, although operating at as high
a temperature as 1600 degrees, sacrifice long turbine life for high performance. In order to obtain
some of the much-needed data, and with an eye to
the possibility of gas turbine marine propulsion
in the future, the United States Navy has installed
at the Naval Engineering Experiment Station at
Annapolis, Maryland, a 3500-horsepower, 1500-
degree experimental gas turbine power plant.

Cycle. The cycle selected for this experimental plant was the parallel regenerative cycle.
The air from the compressor is passed through a
heat exchanger, where it is heated by the exhaust
from the turbines. There are two turbines, one
to run the compressor and the other to supply the
power.

Parts. The axial-flow compressor, containing
20 stages, has a full-load efficiency of about 85
per cent. At full load, a volume of 40,000 cubic
feet of air per minute is compressed against an
operating head of 45 psig. The regenerator has an
external heating surface of 8500 square feet and
an effectiveness of approximately 60 per cent.

Each of the two combustion chambers is fired with
a single, wide-range, mechanical, atomizing oil
burner.   At full load the combustion chambers release heat at the rate of approximately 2,500,000
Btu per cubic foot per hour, greatly exceeding that
in boiler furnaces.   Each turbine has five stages,
the first two being of the impulse type, and the
last three of the reaction type.   Full turbine
speed is 5200 rpm.

Operation.   In starting the unit, a small
electric motor of less than 100 horsepower is connected to the shaft through a clutch.   When firing
speed is attained, the burners are lighted and
the turbine is brought to full speed by manual
operation of the fuel control.   As there are innumerable test setups and combinations possible
with the parallel arrangement of the Annapolis
unit, engineers of the Engineering Experiment
Station, in conjunction with those of the Bureau
of Ships, have worked out a comprehensive test
schedule.   Test plans include running of the unit
under various operating conditions for established
periods of time, and recording of data on pressures, temperatures, flows, speeds, and power at
many stations for each test condition.   Complete
disassembly and inspection follow each run.

Outlook.   Estimates based on data thus far obtained show the possibility that an over-all
thermal efficiency of 40 per cent can be achieved
at 1500 F with a modified marine plant of the
3500-hp size.   Speculation as to the type of drive
that may be employed includes the use of electric
transmission and of reversible-pitch propellers.

I. THE PROBLEM

Gas turbines operate at higher exhaust temperatures than do steam turbines, and must therefore have considerably higher inlet temperatures.
Present indications point to the need of temperatures up to 1500 F for open-cycle gas turbine application to marine and central station installations. Certain data have been obtained already
from the successful operation of the turbines used
in the Houdry refining process, and from turbine-
driven superchargers on bombing and fighting aircraft. More information is needed, however,
because of the limitations of these two applications. The turbines used in the Houdry process,
though designed for long life and built of substantial size, operate at temperatures below
1000 F. Supercharger units operate at 1600 F,
but because of the military nature of their function, long service is sacrificed for high performance. In order to improve design of long-life,
heavy-duty, multistage gas turbines, designers
need information on operation at 1500 F. An experimental 3500-hp gas turbine power plant designed
to operate at that temperature has been constructed by the Allis-Chalmers Manufacturing Company and installed at the United States Naval
Engineering Experiment Station, Annapolis, Maryland. This unit was built to supply some of the
needed data with a view to the possibilities for
marine adaptation.[1]

The operation of this experimental unit is
expected to produce much valuable information. A
recent article in Power declares that the test and
research program on the engine "will yield (1) the
first comprehensive and detailed analysis of

---

[1]"Stationary Gas Turbine Operates at 1500 Degrees F.," Product Engineering, XVII (1946), 415;
"Progress Report on Gas Turbines: Experimental
1500-F Unit at Annapolis Yields Valuable High-
temperature Data," Power, XC (1946), 290.

-2-

actual gas flows, pressures and temperatures in
all parts of the cycle (2) data on parasitic losses
and on the effects of stratification (3) practical
service experience under full-scale conditions
with new high-temperature alloys (4) information
on effectiveness and necessity for internal cooling (5) experience and data, on thermal expansions
and the mechanical provisions for them, and (6)
complete information on the operating characteristics of gas-turbine power plants."[2]

Some of the problems faced by the new unit
were entirely without precedent. For example,
thermal expansion in the combustion chambers,
piping, and turbines requires for each foot of
metal a growth of 1/8 inch in all directions when
heated to 1500 F, while remaining pressure-tight
under 45 psig. This movement must be allowed without putting any strain on the turbine casing.
Another provision that had to be made was for the
cooling of the bearing pedestals to prevent mis-
alignment during high-temperature runs.

In order to facilitate the testing operation
of the turbine, the installation was made in such
a way that the hundreds of data-taking points were
easily accessible, and that inspection covers were
conveniently located. Also, the many parts must
be frequently dismantled, and they must be within
easy reach of operating personnel. Because of
the experimental nature of this unit, thermal
efficiency was not given primary consideration.[3]

---

[2]"Progress Report," 291.
[3]Ibid., 290-291.

II.   THE CYCLE

The cycle selected for this experimental power unit was the parallel turbine regenerative cycle. (See Figure 1.) Air from the atmosphere is compressed in the axial compressor to 45 psig, and then passed through a heat exchanger, where at full load it is heated by the exhaust from the turbine from a temperature of 363 F to 750 F.   In the laboratory setup, the air from the regenerator (heat exchanger) flows downward into the two horizontal combustion chambers.   A separate combustion chamber is provided for each turbine, one supplying the gas generator turbine driving the compressor, and the other supplying the power turbine.   This arrangement provides independent control for each turbine, and permits a wide variety of test setups.   The heat exchanger and combustion units are installed some distance from the rest of the plant, but in shipboard installation they would be above the main propulsion machinery.[4]

[4]"U. S. Navy Operates 3500-hp Experimental Gas Turbine at 1350 F," Power Plant Engineering, L (May, 1946), 87.

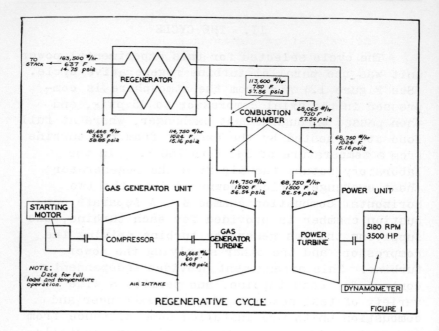

REGENERATIVE CYCLE

FIGURE I

Labels within figure:

TO STACK ← 163,500 #/hr 637 F 14.75 psia

REGENERATOR

113,600 #/hr 750 F 57.56 psia

CONBUSTION CHAMBER

68,065 #/hr 750 F 57.56 psia

181,666 #/hr 363 F 58.85 psia

114,750 #/hr 1024 F 15.16 psia

68,750 #/hr 1024 F 15.16 psia

GAS GENERATOR UNIT

114,750 #/hr 1500 F 56.54 psia

68,750 #/hr 1500 F 56.54 psia

POWER UNIT

STARTING MOTOR

COMPRESSOR

GAS GENERATOR TURBINE

POWER TURBINE

5180 RPM 3500 HP

181,665 #/hr 60 F 14.49 psia

AIR INTAKE

DYNAMOMETER

NOTE:
Data for full load and temperature operation.

III. DESCRIPTION OF PARTS

The axial-flow compressor contains 20 stages
of airfoil section. It is so designed that the air
is accelerated by the moving blades and slowed
by the stationary elements to convert part of the
velocity energy into pressure. The efficiency at
full load is about 85 per cent. Under these conditions, a volume of 40,000 cubic feet per minute
is compressed against the operating head of 45
psig.[5] The regenerator has an external heating
surface of 8500 square feet, and an effectiveness
of approximately 60 per cent with relatively low
pressure drops on the air and gas sides. It is of
the counterflow type, with the hot gases inside the
tubes and the high-pressure air on the outside to
facilitate cleaning the tubes.[6]

Each of the two combustion chambers is fired
with a single, wide-range, mechanical, atomizing
oil burner. The primary air is passed through
the central flame tube in sufficient quantity to
support complete combustion. (See Figure 2.)
Secondary air enters through the annular space
around the central flame tube, and cools the tube to
safe operating temperature. This plan eliminates
the use of refractory brickwork. Primary air
enters rotating in a counterclockwise direction,
while the secondary air passes through a series of
stationary vanes that cause it to rotate in a
clockwise direction. Upon meeting, the two streams
intermingle and pass on into the turbine.[7] At
full load the combustion chambers release heat at
the rate of approximately 2,500,000 Btu per cubic
foot per hour, greatly exceeding that in boiler
furnaces.[8] The elimination of firebrick in the
combustion chamber gives quick responses to load

[5]Ibid.
[6]Ibid., 87-88; "Progress Report," 291-292.
[7]"U. S. Navy Operates," 88.
[8]"Progress Report," 292.

-(4)-

-5-

changes, met by manual operation of two fuel
valves.[9]

The gas turbine that drives the axial-flow
compressor is substantially the same as the one
that drives the load, though the blades are a
little longer and it is equipped with an air-
operated internal by-pass valve which is opened
during starting.[10] Each turbine has five pressure
stages. The first two stages are of the impulse
type; expansion is essentially completed, and
therefore the severest temperature drop occurs, in
a fixed structure, the nozzle ring, where stress
is least likely to be harmful.[11] Of the three reaction stages, the last discharges the gas to the
turbine exhaust chamber on its way through the
regenerator to the stack. Full turbine speed is
5200 rpm.[12]

[9]"U. S. Navy Operates," 88.
[10]Ibid.
[11]"Progress Report," 292.
[12]"U. S. Navy Operates," 88-89.

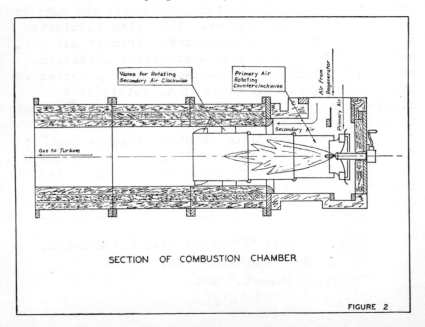

SECTION OF COMBUSTION CHAMBER

FIGURE 2

-6-

For cooling the face of the high-temperature turbine wheel, air is introduced through a system of tubes to a disk adjacent to the side of the wheel. A series of holes in the periphery of this stationary disk directs the air against the wheel. The air passes radially inward to a discharge pipe which carries it to a water-cooled heat exchanger, from which a positive-pressure blower returns it. Similarly, cooling air is introduced around the periphery of the second-stage diaphragm. This air is supplied in sufficient quantity to equal, approximately, the leakage of the diaphragm labyrinth seal.[13]

The heavy stationary parts of the turbines are made of an alloy steel of high chromium content. The blades and disks are of high-temperature Timken alloy steel (16 per cent chromium, 25 per cent nickel, 6 per cent molybdenum), which during the war was extensively used in superchargers and jet-propulsion units.[14] The two turbines and the compressor have sleeve bearings lubricated under pressure, the oil being cooled and cleaned continuously while in circulation.[15]

Large quantities of air and hot gases circulating in the 3500-hp turbine require large pipes. Even with a high velocity, the air intake has an inside diameter of 36 in., and the exhaust opening of the gas generator turbine has an inside diameter of 42 in. The piping is double-walled, and insulation of mineral block separates the inner, gas-guiding tube from the outer wall. The temperature drop across the insulation keeps outer-wall temperatures low enough to make available the full physical strength of the metal.[16]

Special expansion joints were installed in the piping to allow for expansion due to the dif-

---

[13]Ibid.

[14]Ibid.

[15]"Progress Report," 292.

[16]Ibid., 292-293.

-7-

ference in room temperature and firing temperature. The joints consist of radially placed hinges
between the flanges, allowing rotation without
stress on the turbine or compressor casings. The
piping supports, also, are so constructed as to
allow for thermal expansion.[17]

[17]Ibid., 293.

IV.   OPERATION

To start the unit, an electric motor is connected to the turbine shaft through a clutch.   This
motor is capable of rotating the turbine at from
25 to 35 per cent of full speed, with an output of
less than 100 hp.   When firing speed is attained,
the burners are lighted and the electric motor is
disengaged, and the unit is brought up to running
speed by the manual fuel control.[18]

As there are innumerable test setups and combinations possible with the parallel arrangement
of the Annapolis unit, engineers of the Engineering Experiment Station, in conjunction with those
of the Bureau of Ships, have worked out a comprehensive test schedule.   Test plans include the
running of the unit under various operating conditions for established periods of time.   Variable
functions include inlet temperatures, speeds,
pressure ratios, and rates of gas flow.   During
the tests, data are recorded on pressures, temperatures, flows, speeds, and power at many
stations for each test condition.   Fuel and
lubricating oils also are studied in performance.
Complete disassembly and inspection follow each
run.   Numerous measurements are made to determine
what changes in high-temperature parts have taken
place, including observations of the resistance
to oxidation and the development of any warps or
cracks.[19]

Difficulty was encountered in determining
combustion efficiency.   Gas turbines operate with
approximately 500 per cent excess air.   Conventional instruments, like the Orsat gas analyzer,
are capable of accurately making stack gas analysis
of boilers with 30 per cent excess air, but are
inadequate for gas turbine analysis.   The Bureau
of Standards, encountering the same difficulty in

---

[18]Ibid.
[19]Ibid.

-9-

measuring the fuel chamber efficiency of captured enemy jet engines, had developed a combustion-train method of burning out the very small percentages of unconsumed hydrocarbons, carbon monoxide, and hydrogen. This technique, in combination with other analytical methods, determines over-all combustion efficiency within a half of one per cent. The Engineering Experiment Station is using a modification of this Bureau of Standards method.[20]

The first complete test runs were made with the compressor at 40 per cent of full speed. Temperatures and speeds were raised in steps, complete tests being made at each stage, until the power turbine was run at full speed.[21] During these still continuing tests, occasional minor difficulties that have arisen have all been overcome, and the unit has satisfied expectations during over 500 hours of rigorous testing.[22]

---

[20]C. F. Kottcamp (Lt. Comdr., U.S.N.R.), "Instrumentation and Testing of the 3500-hp Navy Experimental Gas Turbine Plant," Power Plant Engineering, L (May, 1946), 89.

[21]"Progress Report," 293.

[22]Ibid.

V.   OUTLOOK FOR THE FUTURE

Estimates based on data thus far obtained
show the possibility that an over-all thermal
efficiency of 40 per cent can be achieved at 1500 F
with a modified marine plant of the 3500-hp size.[23]
In such a plant, the compressor would be in two
intercooled sections.   The turbines would be in
series, with a reheater installed between them.
Regenerator surface would be several times that of
the present unit for highest efficiency.[24]   It is
expected that turbines in future marine installations will be much lighter in weight per horsepower and more compact than either the propelling
machinery now in use or the experimental engine
at Annapolis.[25]   Speculation as to the type of
drive that may be employed includes use of electric
transmission and of reversible-pitch propellers.[26]

[23]Ibid.

[24]Ibid.

[25]Ibid.; "U. S. Navy Operates," 87.

[26]"Progress Report," 293.

BIBLIOGRAPHY

Kottcamp (Lt. Comdr., U.S.N.R.), C. F., "Instrumentation and Testing of the 3500-hp Navy Experimental Gas Turbine Plant," Power Plant Engineering, L (May, 1946), 89.

"Progress Report on Gas Turbines: Experimental 1500-F Unit at Annapolis Yields Valuable High-temperature Data," Power, XC (1946), 290-293.

"Stationary Gas Turbine Operates at 1500 Degrees F.," Product Engineering, XVII (1946), 415-416.

"U. S. Navy Operates 3500-hp Experimental Gas Turbine at 1350 F," Power Plant Engineering, L (May, 1946), 86-89.

TESTS OF A BROWN MODEL-AIRPLANE ENGINE

By E. H. Badger, Jr.

P R O B L E M

It was desired to devise and construct a dynamometer suitable for determination of the speed
and power characteristics of small internal-combustion engines and to run actual tests on a Brown
model-airplane engine. This engine has a 7/8-inch
bore and 1-inch stroke, with a displacement of
0.60 cubic inch. It is rated at 1/5 horsepower. A
12.8-inch and a 14-inch propeller were to be used
as load for two series of runs, and a curve was to
be plotted of speed versus horsepower for each
propeller, over the normal operating range of the
engine.

The dynamometer selected had to be simple to
construct and to use, while being capable of
measuring as accurately as possible the output
torque of the engine under actual operating conditions. The brake or other absorption-type
dynamometers commonly used for internal-combustion
engine tests could not be applied because of the
size and operating characteristics of the midget
engine. Therefore, a reaction-type dynamometer
was selected. It was naturally adaptable to the
requirements of the test, allowing operation of
the engine under the load of its own propeller and
providing for sensitive torque determination.

Since any loss of power to the speed-determin-
ing instrument might cause an appreciable error on
account of the small total output of the engine,
a Strobotac was selected for determination of the
speed of the engine during the tests. The use of
this instrument allowed accurate speed determination by reflected light and introduced no load

-(1)-

-2-

error to the calculations for horsepower output of
the engine.

The problem of materials for the construction
of the dynamometer, tools and equipment for construction, and instruments for tests was easily
solved, since the facilities of the university's
engineering shops were at the disposal of the test
crew.

PRINCIPLES

The output-horsepower formula for engines is:

$$\text{Horsepower} = \frac{2\pi \times T \times N}{33,000} = K \times T \times N$$

The K is a constant for all test calculations. The T represents load torque in pound-feet units. The N represents the speed of the shaft rotation in revolutions per minute. Torque and speed must be measured under varying operating conditions as a basis for calculation of data for engine-performance curves.

In this test, a reaction dynamometer was designed and built to measure the torque. The reaction principle was better, in this case, than the usual system of absorbing the output of the engine in a friction Prony brake or other output-absorption device for torque measurement. Prony brakes are not adaptable to high speeds, and all the absorption setups would have required the use of a flywheel rather than the air propeller normally used on the engine. The flywheel load was undesirable, because the engine would not have been operating under normal conditions, and also because of difficulty in properly cooling the cylinder. The reaction-type dynamometer measured the reaction torque, which, by Newton's third law, is exactly equal and opposite to the output torque of the engine.

The manner of torque determination by the dynamometer designed for this test may be explained by reference to Figure 1. The engine was fixed on a cast-iron mounting block and the whole unit was pivoted about pin bearings in the block as shown. A light torque-balance arrangement with a 20-inch balance arm and a 0.224-pound movable trimmer weight was bolted to the block so as to rotate with the engine. The system was balanced under static conditions without the adjustable

-(3)-

-4-

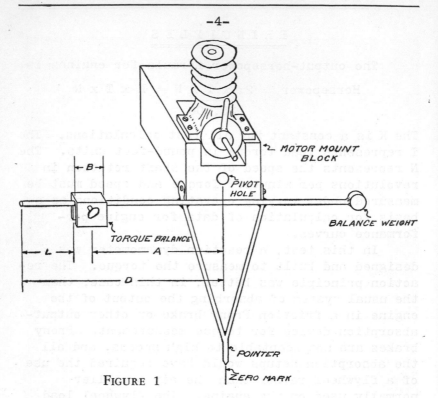

FIGURE 1

SKETCH OF REACTION DYNAMOMETER.

trimmer weight. Then, when the engine was running
at the desired speed, the torque-balance trimmer
could be run out on the arm until the pointer
stayed on the zero mark. Under these conditions
the torque being delivered to the propeller
was equal to the weight of the trimmer balance
multiplied by the distance A, or WA pound-feet.
Actually, distance L was noted in data taken during
the tests, because that length could be easily
measured with a steel rule during the tests; the
use of this system eliminated the necessity for
calibrating the balance arm directly. Then the
required distance A was computed from the equality:

$$A = (D - B/2) - L$$

The bearings about which the block rotated were

-5-

FIGURE 2

ENGINE MOUNTING.

merely 0.4-inch pin bearings made as frictionless
as possible and well oiled. The natural vibration
of the engine and block was depended on further to
reduce errors due to static friction. The motor

–6–

FIGURE 3

FULL VIEW OF DYNAMOMETER-ENGINE ASSEMBLY.

ignition wires had to be loose and were brought in
close to the rear pivot so as not to introduce
torque errors.

There is an error with this type of dyna-

–7–

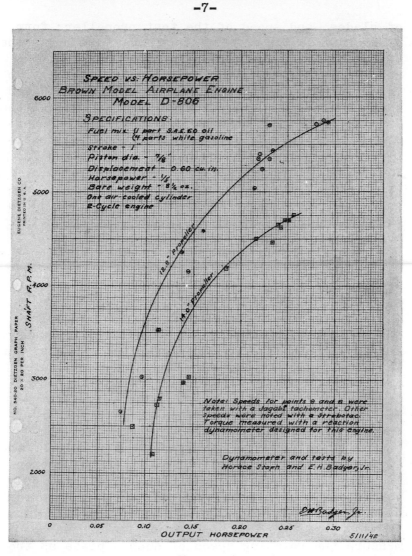

FIGURE 4

CURVES SHOWING RESULTS OF TESTS.

mometer due to the whirling slipstream caused by
the propeller, which reacts against the engine and
supporting structure, resulting in inaccurate
torque readings.   The factors involved in a correction of this error are: diameter, pitch, number

-8-

of blades, and speed of the test propeller; form
of engine; design of test stand; and size and shape
of the enclosure or nacelle in which the engine is
run.   Such a correction is obviously difficult to
determine accurately.   If the error is considered
great enough to require correction, the slipstream
is usually straightened out by inserting a honey-
comb, or grid, between the engine and the propeller, rather than by calculating a correction
factor to be applied to the horsepower formula.
As affecting the test results included in this report, the error above mentioned was considered to
be small and, because of limited time, was entirely
neglected.

The Strobotac used for speed determination
allowed measurement of speed without the imposition of any load on the engine and therefore
introduced no error in results.   The Strobotac is
an electrical instrument which is, in principle,
a neon light flashing at a controllable frequency.
A knob adjusts the frequency over the range of the
instrument, 600 to 14,500 vibrations per minute,
and the frequency at any instant is read on a dial
on the top of the instrument.   When this instrument is pointed toward a piece of rotating or
oscillating equipment and adjusted to the frequency of rotation or vibration of that piece, the
apparatus seems to stand still.   This phenomenon
is due to the fact that the piece is lighted only
when it is in one position of its cycle.   An error
of an exact multiple or fraction of the speed may
be made with this instrument when it is used to
measure the rotating speed of such a piece as the
two-bladed propeller of this test, since there
is a possibility of the propeller seeming to stand
still if the Strobotac should be emitting light
at a frequency to bring the propeller into view
at every half revolution, or at every second or
third revolution, etc.   With some experience an
operator is not likely to make such a mistake, but
a Jagabi tachometer was used to check the speed

-9-

range of the Strobotac in these tests.   The Jagabi
is a direct-reading tachometer which has a rubber
cap to be pressed onto the end of the shaft of
the engine.   When a button is pushed down on the
Jagabi, the needle moves around the dial to the
speed of the shaft and stops.   In principle, the
Jagabi is merely a timing device which allows a
needle to travel at a certain fraction of the shaft
speed for a predetermined constant time interval,
so that when it stops it is indicating shaft
rotation (in revolutions per minute) on the dial.
The Jagabi, like all other mechanical speed-
measuring devices, robs the shaft of a certain,
though small, amount of power.

A P P A R A T U S   U S E D

Brown Model D-806 midget engine with ignition system and propellers; Strobotac No. 2898, speed range 600 - 14,500 rpm; Jagabi Tachometer No. 69027, speed range 0 - 10,000 rpm.

Materials for dynamometer:

One	1½" x 2½" x 4" cast-iron block for motor mount	
One	¾" x 1½" x 1½" cast-iron block for trimmer balance	
One	¼" x ¾" x 1" boiler-plate steel for balance weight	
Two	3/16" diam rods for balance arm and pointer unit	
Two	⅛" diam rods for balance arm and pointer unit	
One	¼" x 2" x 9" boiler plate steel for motor mount base	
One	½" diam x 1" mild steel for front pivot	
One	1" diam x 3" mild steel for rear pivot bolt	
One	½" nut for pivot lock	
Four	¾" screws for mounting base on table	
Six	1/16" brass bolts for motor mount and balance unit attachment	

Tools and equipment for construction:

Cincinnati milling machine with circular-milling-saw cutter
Ram-type reciprocating shaper
Lathe with thread-cutting attachment
Oxyacetylene welding outfit with brazing rod and flux
Analytical balance scales and weights
Hammer, grinder, hacksaw, crescent wrench, screwdriver, pliers, etc.

-(10)-

P R O C E D U R E

The first step after designing the system
was the construction of the dynamometer. The base,
which was to form the cradle for the motor mount
block, was cut from a piece of mild-steel boiler
plate with a hacksaw. It was heated with an
acetylene torch and bent to shape in a vise with
a hammer. The rear vertical part of the base was
bent double and brazed together to provide for
a longer threaded hole for the mounting of the
adjustable pivot bolt. The mounting holes and
bearing-pivot holes were drilled and the rear pivot
hole was tapped for the adjusting bolt. The cast-
iron motor mount block was then made. After being
squared up, it was clamped in the milling machine and
grooved to hold the crankcase of the engine. The engine mounting holes and balance-arm bolt holes were
drilled and tapped. The piece was then chucked up in
a lathe, and the female pivot impressions were bored
in place in each end. The mild steel for the front
pivot was clamped in the lathe chuck and the pivot
turned to size. This piece was then brazed in
place in its hole in the base piece. The steel for
the rear pivot bolt was chucked up and turned to
shape. The handle was knurled and the threads were
turned as shown in Figure 2.

The welding rods from which the balance-arm
unit was made were bent to shape and brazed
together. The attaching tabs were heated, flattened
to shape with a hammer, and drilled for the attaching bolts. Then the entire setup was assembled
and screwed to a table, and a vertical line was
marked directly under the center line of the engine
as a zero mark for the pointer. A small weight
was brazed on the free arm of the balance system
and additional brazing rod melted on it until the
system was perfectly balanced. The adjustable
trimming balance weight was formed on the shaper

-(11)-

-12-

and slotted with the saw in the milling machine.
It was drilled and tapped for the clamping wing
bolt and accurately weighed with the bolt in place.

Figure 3 shows the final assembly, after the
ignition system had been attached to the engine.
The pivot bearings were oiled, and the Strobotac was
adjusted and set up in front of the propeller,
completing preparations for the test.

The engine was started and two interlaced
series of runs were made, one with each of the two
propellers. (See Appendix.) The distance L and
the shaft speed were taken for each run of each
series. During the tests Operator I read the
Strobotac and the Jagabi, Operator II adjusted the
engine and operated the balance arm, and Operator
III recorded the data. After nineteen runs had
been made, the Strobotac was removed and twelve
more runs were made with the Jagabi revolution
counter being used for speed determination.
Actually, it was found that these readings checked
very closely with those taken by the Strobotac,
though the Jagabi had been intended only to give the
approximate speed range of the Strobotac.

R E S U L T S

The results of the tests are illustrated by the graph. (See Figure 4.) The larger propeller absorbs a given horsepower at a lower speed than the smaller one. The speed curves show that the horsepower absorbed by the propeller is approximately proportional to the square of the speed for either propeller. The maximum horsepower output noted for the engine on these tests was 0.298 horsepower at a speed of 5710 rpm; this result was obtained with the 12.8-inch propeller. The largest horsepower obtained with the 14-inch propeller was 0.257 horsepower at 4750 rpm. The engine, which is rather sensitive in operation, was not working as well as it should have been during the test runs. Some ignition trouble was present, and it is believed that a greater output and speed could have been obtained by further adjustment and tests. However, the curves illustrate the normal operating range of the engine. (See graph and Appendix.)

CONCLUSIONS

Though the Strobotac, when properly adjusted and skilfully used, unquestionably gives the better speed determination, the speeds taken with the Jagabi checked very closely in this case. In fact, the points determined by the Jagabi speed runs were accurate enough to be used as some of the points determining the curves of this report. The Jagabi is the easier to use of the two instruments and probably absorbs only a very small amount of power.

Improvement in the accuracy of results might be made by installing ball or tapered roller bearings to reduce the friction in the pivots of the engine block. Another refinement could be made by the use of a grill-work to straighten the slip-stream passing the motor.

This type of dynamometer is commonly used for factory performance tests of nearly all aircraft engines, but is not ordinarily used for other types of engines.

An interesting special use of the principle is an application to aircraft engines in actual airplane installations. When so applied, the system affords an accurate indication of the actual performance of the engine at various attitudes and altitudes of flight. Such results could not be obtained by test-block methods because of the variable temperatures, air densities, and humidities and other similar conditions that an aircraft engine encounters in service. The torque indicator is incorporated as an integral part of a planetary reduction gear system between the crankshaft and the propeller, and is similar in principle to the reaction dynamometer described in this report. The annular gear surrounding the planetary gear system is anchored to two pistons which operate in oil-

-(14)-

-15-

filled cylinders. The reaction of the annular gear
is transmitted to the oil in these cylinders, and
the resulting pressure is indicated on a gage
calibrated in pound-feet torque. This gage reading,
together with the reading of the gage of the direct-
driven tachometer of the engine, gives data for
determination of the horsepower being delivered
by the engine to the propeller under any condition
of operation in flight. It is possible to design
an instrument which will utilize the oil pressure
from the torque cylinders and the tachometer speed
to give a direct horespower reading on the dial of
a gage during flight.

A P P E N D I X

C O P I E D   A N D   C A L C U L A T E D   D A T A

Strobo-tac* reading	Run no.	N rpm	L inches	A feet	Output horse-power	Pro-peller length
45	1	4500	5.6	1.125	0.216	
30.3	2	3030	5.3	1.15	0.146	
94	3	4700	4.1	1.25	0.251	
22	4	2200	5.5	1.135	0.107	
27.3	5	2730	7.5	0.965	0.112	
95	6	4750	4.0	1.26	0.256	
70.5	7	3530	10.1	0.75	0.113	
89.4	15	4470	4.4	1.225	0.234	14"
95	16	4750	3.9	1.27	0.257	
29.8	17	2980	5.9	1.10	0.140	
28	18	2800	11.4	0.950	0.113	
25	19	2500	9.3	0.815	0.087	
	20	4650	4.65	1.205	0.240	
	21	4740	4.45	1.22	0.247	
	22	4620	4.3	1.23	0.243	
	23	4190	6.7	1.035	0.185	

* Speed for runs in which no Strobotac reading is recorded was taken with the Jagabi tachometer.

-17-

Strobo-tac* reading	Run no.	N rpm	L inches	A feet	Output horse-power	Pro-peller length
107	8	5350	7.5	0.955	0.218	
115	9	5750	5.0	1.175	0.288	
114.5	10	5730	5.3	1.15	0.280	
107	11	5350	7.0	1.01	0.231	
30.2	12	3020	10.1	0.75	0.097	
26.5	13	2650	11.1	0.666	0.075	
108	14	5400	7.6	0.957	0.220	
	24	5030	7.15	0.995	0.214	12.8"
	25	5730	4.7	1.20	0.293	
	26	5710	4.35	1.23	0.298	
	27	5440	7.0	1.01	0.234	
	28	4590	9.3	0.815	0.160	
	29	5270	7.2	0.99	0.223	
	30	4360	10.2	0.74	0.138	
	31	4160	11.4	0.64	0.144	

* Speed for runs in which no Strobotac reading is recorded was taken with the Jagabi tachometer.

CHAPTER XI

THE TECHNICAL SPEECH

Value to the technologist. That technical people have real need of training in speech is confirmed by much professional experience and testimony. For example, in a survey conducted by the Society for the Promotion of Engineering Education,[*] faculty members in engineering colleges [†] ranked speech above qualitative and quantitative analysis, organic and industrial chemistry, general and engineering economics, differential equations, geology, and foreign languages for primary importance, among courses not of a strictly engineering content, to the curriculum that should be required of every engineer.[‡]

Learn to speak by speaking. Where class drill in oral reports and other types of public speaking is given in courses of technical English, as is becoming increasingly customary, participants have the great advantage of a common ground of subject matter, a friendly audience, and experienced criticism during what are for many the beginning efforts on the platform. Even though you have the opportunity for this kind of instruction and practice, you also should make it a habit to take the floor as frequently as possible in all the schoolroom classes, the professional, religious, or fraternal organizations, and the other groups in which you have membership. The more regularly you do so, the sooner you will become an accomplished public speaker.

Learn now. Age and occasion never will be more suitable than at present. If in your college days you continually tell yourself: "Oh,

[*] Now the American Society for Engineering Education.

[†] Almost all those polled were professors of technical subjects.

[‡] The figures are tabulated on page 417 (vol. I, 1930) of the *Report of the Investigation of Engineering Education, 1923–1929*, Pittsburgh, Society for the Promotion of Engineering Education, 1930–1934: Bulletin Number 9, "A Summary of Opinions Concerning Engineering Curricula."

English composition was ranked even higher than speech, yielding—by very narrow margins—only to algebra, trigonometry, solid geometry, physics, and analytical geometry. It stood above calculus and inorganic chemistry.

I don't have anything to say; surely they don't want to listen to *me*,"
you will pass by many chances for learning to speak under extraordinarily favorable conditions of a kind that almost never recur in
later life. You may not realize it, but if you are a university student
your mind is just now at its keenest, your knowledge most ready. Your
physical and psychical energies, alike, and your ability to profit by
experience, are better than they ever have been or are likely ever to be
again. Stand on your feet, open your mouth, and speak out; once in a
while, perhaps, you will be tiresome, but much more often you will
surprise both the auditors and yourself by the number of things worth
saying and hearing that emerge.

A.   METHODS OF SPEAKING

Five types of speech.   Five methods of speaking are available for
different circumstances and purposes: (1) **memorized,** (2) **manuscript,** (3) **impromptu,** (4) **extemporary,** and (5) **extemporaneous** speeches. The first two classes constitute a group, in that
they are prepared and delivered verbatim. The last three, since their
exact phrasing is shaped at the time of delivery, form a second group;
within it, however, extemporary and extemporaneous speeches are
so similar as to be a subclass sharply opposed to the impromptu talk.

Why "set" speeches generally should be avoided.   Speeches given
from memory or from a written copy have their rightful place, but it
is not a college class where elementary public speaking is being
learned. A high official of state or industry, whose every word will
be analyzed for the finest line of political or legal implication, or a
radio speaker on an exactly timed program, may of necessity use a
manuscript; and some long, formal addresses (especially if intended
for frequent repetition) are committed to memory. These two kinds
of speaking require great artistry to be effective, yet almost always
a novice imagines that one or the other is the easy and proper way
for him to make a speech. Struck with dismay at the thought of talking
without a definite text for even four or five minutes, the ill-advised
beginner either brings forth a sheaf of papers from which to mumble
at the audience, or else flounders through a memorized harangue with
false emphasis and unnatural facial and bodily expression, if not
downright lapses of memory. Undoubtedly you can recall unpleasant
instances of such speaking on the part of others; do not imagine yourself as doing better unless you already have the expertness that comes
only with long experience on the platform.

The impromptu speech. If delivered without premeditation, usually because no previous notice has been given to the speaker, a talk is impromptu. After-dinner speeches are sometimes impromptu, but most of the good ones have much solid, thoughtful preparation behind their apparent frivolity and spontaneity.

Extemporary and extemporaneous speaking. Most of your speaking, both in classroom practice and in later life, will be extemporary or extemporaneous. These two type of speech cannot be sharply distinguished, and may be regarded as essentially the same. The usual application of the term *extemporaneous* is in contests where a topic (or small choice of topics) is assigned a relatively short time, varying from five or ten minutes to perhaps at most an hour, before the talk is due. *Extemporary* is a loose expression for any other kind of speech planned in advance, even as long as months in advance, but not delivered word for word from a prepared text. The master of extemporary speaking is a master of the platform.

B. PREPARATION

Let us assume that an extemporary speech or oral report is to be delivered as part of the work of a course in technical English. The student will, of course, understand that any of the suggestions given below may be modified or superseded by the instructor's directions, which should be followed exactly.

(1) TOPIC

General assignments. If a definite topic is assigned, obviously no problem of selecting the subject can arise. Very often, however, the topic is announced in a general way rather than specifically. "A five-minute talk on a controversial issue within some field of electrical or chemical engineering, or of pure physics or chemistry, to be treated expositively rather than argumentatively" might be a typical assignment of that kind.

Sources of topics. Unless directed one way or the other by your instructor, you now have the choice of deciding on a subject within your own experience or of going to the library to discover one in technical books and journals. Of course, both reading and personal knowledge can be combined in the finding of a theme. In addition, discussion with instructors and fellow students may furnish leads.

Consider yourself. Because the choice of a topic is the most important single act in planning a speech, it is worth time and consideration. Take several days, if necessary—not, of course, for constant but for intermittent thought about the problem. What have you recently been doing in the laboratory? What now are or once were your hobbies? What have you constructed at home or in a shop? What branches of technology do you follow in your reading with keenest interest? What developments of science have lately aroused your curiosity? Bear in mind that other people, even other students of your own technical field, do not know the same things you do; they may have a smattering of all your subjects and all your hobbies, but they will welcome a clear, precise, definitive statement on almost any topic. Indeed, the fact that they already know something about the matter can prove an advantage, for a foreground of new information is the more easily sketched against a background of shared knowledge.

Consider the audience. At the same time, avoid subjects that really are obvious and trite from the standpoint of those addressed. To explain the hydraulic ram to mechanical, the Orsat apparatus to chemical, or the "mousetrap" switch to electrical engineering students, is not likely to add to their previous knowledge. At the opposite extreme, any subject must be rejected if it cannot satisfactorily be brought down to the intellectual level of the intended audience. A graduate student in physics, speaking to a mixed group of younger undergraduates, will do well to shun a topic like "Prevention of Industrial Current Interruptions by High-speed Power Switching," certainly in a brief talk not allowing room for extensive supplementary explanation and definition.

What will interest? Novelty, unusual point of view, relation to current affairs, availability for practical application by the listener, humor, human interest—these are some of the qualities that appeal to an audience. Still, potential interest resides as much in the speaker as in his theme, for even the driest kinds of abstraction and remoteness can be galvanized into life by one who, having thought out a problem with intellectual eagerness, discusses it with enthusiasm. As between two otherwise equally good subjects, choose the one holding the greater intrinsic interest; but do not reject a good topic in favor of a poor one merely on the ground that it might be dull. If your subject does not bore you, it will not bore your hearers, provided you are an effective speaker and are wise enough to stop when you have said enough.

Limiting the subject. Of paramount importance in the final selection of topic is the limitation of scope or magnitude. During a talk lasting around ten minutes (usually not much more time can be allowed each student in a class of average size), you will perhaps utter a thousand to fifteen hundred words, or about the equivalent of four or five typewritten pages. If you consider how little could be said in that amount of space on paper, you will begin to recognize that for a short speech you must choose a narrowed topic—that is, if you expect to do more than abuse the audience's courtesy by ineffectually skimming the surface.

Hearers are not readers. Moreover, you must realize that only a fraction of the ideas and facts that could be packed into the same number of written words can be set forth with clearness in a speech. Whereas a reader is able to slow down, to stop and reflect, to compare, to reread, to review your main points, or to do whatever else may be necessary to draw the last ounce of information from what you have written, the auditor of a speech hears but once, with no opportunity to revive previous statements except as you may do so for him. Since fullness and leisureliness of presentation are essential to clarity of oral discourse, only a very few points can be made in a short talk, particularly one of technical content.

"Little" vs. "big" topics. For every reason, therefore, the subject for a speech of ordinary length must be small, instead of covering some large technological activity or broad phase of scientific knowledge. A talk of a few minutes' duration on "My Design for a Combined Morning Alarm and Automatic Window-closer," "The Principle of the Gyrocompass," "Installation of an Interdepartment Communication System in the X Plant," "A Recent Solar Energy Patent," or "The Tape Recorder versus the Wire Recorder" will be more interesting, clear, and adequate than one (similarly brief, and delivered with equal skill) on "The Types of Engines," "Steel and Concrete Structures," "Methods of Prospecting for Petroleum," "Naval Strategy in the Second World War," "Smoke Control," or "The Design of Commercial Transport Aircraft."

(2) MATERIAL

Personal sources. For a technical speech grounded altogether on private knowledge, the obtaining of material is chiefly by thought and recollection, with perhaps some recourse to previously taken notes or to practical activity in order to freshen memory or enlarge experience. Conferences with experts or authorities often can provide needed additional information. University campuses afford a ready source of exact knowledge on many subjects in the departmental staffs, whose members always will give attention to serious, intelligent inquiries from any student investigating a problem in their respective fields. So, too, will most industries, although the student may have to consult the information or public-relations department rather than executives or engineers.

Reference material. Pamphlets, reports, catalogues, and other printed matter can be obtained from branches of the national and state governments, and from businesses and chambers of commerce. Libraries, needless to say, are the main repositories of reference works of most types. The methods by which the library is explored for the substance of a research paper serve also, of course, to provide reference material for speaking. (See pages 234–248 of Chapter IX.)

Originality. No matter how the information used in a speech is compiled—from direct knowledge, interviews, or library references; or from any two or all three together—an element of originality is obligatory, at the very least in the way in which facts and ideas are selected and combined. Merely to paraphrase, synopsize, or garble some article or chapter is a poor fulfillment of a speech assignment. It is, in a mild way, a swindle perpetrated upon the listener, who has a right to expect something more than what he could read in one place for himself. The speaker should keep his mind vigorously active in shaping and controlling material borrowed outside the compass of his immediate experience, as well as that based on what he himself has done or seen.

"That's what the book says." Above everything else, the speaker must fully comprehend, not halfway or nine-tenths understand, what he is talking about. The bland remark, "The author didn't make that point clear," will not excuse a person who is taking up a great amount of the collective time of an audience. He comes forward, not as an apologist for the insufficiency of some book or article, but as a bringer of clear knowledge on his announced topic. Therefore, he simply is not ready for the platform until that knowledge is crystal-clear in his own mind.

Acknowledgments. Honesty and courtesy demand that credit be given for any important help received from individuals or from printed or written sources. If this acknowledgment cannot be made unobtrusively in close connection with the facts or opinions themselves (as, actually, it very often can), a brief statement concerning the extent and origin of borrowed matter may be inserted into the introductory or concluding remarks of the speech.

(3) PLANNING AND OUTLINING

Criteria of the plan. Two apparently conflicting standards for the plan of a speech are: (1) *definiteness* and (2) *fluidity*. The seeming dilemma is best resolved by keeping the outline relatively brief and revising it frequently. Some speakers make one or more completely written drafts of the whole speech on the basis of rough preliminary plans or sketches, and then prepare a short topical outline from the best version. A less elaborate procedure is in order when only a short, semiformal talk is contemplated; in particular, writing out the speech even once is not always profitable. Every public speaker has to discover for himself the amount of outlining he requires for talks of different kinds, but ordinarily a substantial quantity of work on paper precedes actual presentation from the floor.

Three-part division. Taking gradual shape as the material is thought out, gathered, and assimilated, the outline should ultimately furnish a clear picture, on a relatively small scale, of the logical and chronological development of the projected speech. The time-proved divisions of "Introduction," "Body," and "Conclusion" nearly always are serviceable, as any address is virtually certain to have all three parts. However, it should go without saying that the middle section is by far the most important, and that the plan ought to be arranged to give this division the greatest proportion of the total speaking time.

(1. INTRODUCTION)

Orientation. The introduction orients the auditors toward both the speaker and his subject. It must be free enough in plan so that it can be adjusted, at the moment of delivery, to whatever the chairman or previous speakers may have said; very commonly, reference to such preceding statements is the most effective way to begin.

Be sure the topic is clear. A speaker must always make certain that his subject is absolutely clear. Even if the chairman announces it, repetition will do no harm. It really is remarkable how often the exact topic of amateur talks fails to emerge until somewhere near the middle, or perhaps toward the end—if, indeed, the subject ever does become clear. The effect is ruinous. (Deliberate postponement for the sake of suspense is, of course, permissible, although seldom appropriate to technical exposition.) Do not hesitate to be exceedingly detailed and plain-spoken in stating your topic; those for whom you are needlessly elementary will, if anything, be gratified to feel that they grasp the subject more quickly than other members of the audience.

Be especially sure that all key terms, proper nouns in particular, are expressed distinctly. You have noticed how often your instructors write words on the blackboard or spell them aloud, and sometimes you will find the same devices useful in a technical speech. Habitual users easily forget the strangeness, to uninitiated ears (as once to their own), of such expressions as *thermoelectrometer, Wheatstone bridge, heterogamous plants, Garand rifle, beryllium, Van de Graaff, interferometer, sphygmograph, azimuth, microfarad, Reaumur scale, cataphoresis, ionosphere, stoichiology,* or *Geiger-Müller counter.* A most distressing experience is that of listening to a speaker without knowing, literally, what he is talking about.

Synopsis. Often a desirable, if slightly mechanical, element of the introduction of a technical theme, is forthright announcement of the main points that will be taken up in the body of the speech. By this means the listeners are furnished, as it were, a program to follow mentally as the speech develops. Remember that they can know nothing of the speaker's intentions except what he himself tells them, and that as a consequence much that is clear to him from previous meditation may be obscure to them. Where he sees meaning and correlation and drift, they perceive only isolated facts and assertions unless their minds are very carefully guided. Many times, of course, the guidance can be sufficiently provided in the body of a talk that is neither long nor unusually complicated; still, to sketch the main lines in the introduction is seldom a mistake.

Miscellaneous introductory statements. To justify his claim to the floor, usually a speaker can tactfully explain or intimate his concern in or special knowledge of the topic. Even more important is to show the values it may have for his hearers: intellectual interest, solution of personal and practical problems, potential monetary profit, application to public needs, and so forth. Other matters frequently taken up in the introduction include: history of the question, definition of terms (often important), conceded or omitted points, acknowledgment of written sources or of private help in preparation, recommendation or prediction of future investigations or developments (more usual in the conclusion, however), connection of the present discussion with previous ones on the same platform or elsewhere, refutation of arguments made by opponents or expansion of those made by colleagues, and economic or political ramifications of a technical problem.* Any personal remarks, such as expression of

* Such preliminary statements are by no means necessarily elaborate or formal. Often a mere hint will sufficiently arouse the expectancy of the audience, settle a minor issue, or give impetus to a future train of thought.

pleasure in having been invited to attend and address the meeting, ordinarily come at the very outset of the introduction, but may be repeated briefly in the conclusion of the speech.

Never apologize for your topic or yourself. However strongly you may be tempted, never apologize for a speech. Audiences are normally courteous and sympathetically disposed toward a speaker who does his best to interest and inform them. But they take him pretty much at his own evaluation: if he implies that his best will be poor, they are inclined to accept the suggestion. Furthermore, a self-depreciating attitude is psychologically bad from the speaker's own point of view, for success in any art (including the art of speech) is not likely on a basis of excuses. Should he have a real fault—of enunciation, for instance—he will not improve matters by directing attention toward it. If he can invent no better opening than "Since I have to talk about something today, I suppose I may as well . . .," he had better give no reason at all for his presence in the front of the room.

(2. BODY)

Avoid excessive complexity. In planning the main part, or "body," of a speech, just as in choosing the topic in the first instance, keep steadily aware of the relatively small number of ideas that can be communicated even in a large number of spoken (as opposed to written) words. Certainly, during a class talk of five or ten minutes' duration, of which a fourth or fifth of the time will be spent on opening and closing remarks, seldom more than two or three main topics, each with a very few subtopics, can be covered satisfactorily. If you find that your total subject positively refuses to lend itself to that much simplification, the sooner you accept the fact and further reduce its scope, the better.

How oral discourse resembles written composition. Whatever you know about exposition, narration, description, and argumentation is applicable to public speaking. As has been pointed out in Chapters VI and VII, the four "forms of discourse" usually are much intermingled. Exposition or, less often, argumentation tends to preponderate in talks on technical subjects, but without excluding large use of the other forms. No essential difference in *general* lines of development divides good written and good oral composition. The fundamental principles of sound factual or persuasive prose can be carried over, with little change (mainly in the direction of avoiding complexity, so far as possible), into the planning, practicing, and final phrasing of a speech.

Logical method. Not a point of difference from well-ordered compositions on paper, yet one to be particularly stressed in oral discourse because of the fleeting nature of what is merely spoken to an audience, is the demand for systematic method. In the body of the speech, if not always quite so much in the introduction or the conclusion, a distinctly logical arrangement is an absolute necessity. Each of the few main heads must be brought into such clear relationship with the others, and also with its own subtopics, that never for a moment will a reasonably attentive listener be at a loss to know whence the discussion has come and whither it is proceeding. This objective is not attained without thoughtful advance planning, for the most intelligent audience can become confused by an address lacking—or seeming to lack—perfect harmony of parts within a unified structure. To vary the familiar figure of "not being able to see the forest for the trees," we may say that a poorly designed speech throws away a multitude of significant details by scattering them like confetti over the auditors' minds, each particle alighting with equal lack of force and the mass remaining vague in texture and shape.

The outline is important. Although the outline (at least in its final form) should be fairly short, good outlining is a major secret of successful public speaking. Anybody who hopes to address an audience skillfully must not only get his subject entirely clear in his own thoughts; he should also set down his plan on paper in schematic form, as a basis for rehearsal and for successive revisions. The final topical outline ordinarily ought not to be encumbered with many details; nevertheless, if it is hastily and loosely thrown together, it will lead to failure on the platform. Naturally, the most concentrated effort of preparation should go into the design of the body, or middle and principal section, of a speech. The corresponding part of the outline, as ultimately evolved through experiment and modification, should combine the characteristics of simplicity, succinctness, and logical clarity. Together with ordered lists of points to be mentioned in the introduction and the conclusion, it should be fully committed to memory (by no means the same procedure as memorizing the speech itself), even if it also is transcribed on note cards. (Proper and improper handling of the note cards during delivery is treated on pages 357 ff.)

Aids to clearness. Because of a speaker's temporary relation to his listeners, two standard means to clarity in written composition are even more helpful in spoken discourse, and liberal provision for both should be made when oral discussions of technical subjects are being planned. One is **repetition;** the other, **exemplification.** Furthermore, the problem of **transition** should be given deliberate attention, not left to take care of itself.

Repetition. A plain fact of experience is that making an important oral statement only once usually does not suffice. Beginning teachers are cautioned to "say you are going to say it, say it, and then say you have said it"; and, granted that teaching is not exactly speech making, the prospective speaker benefits by heeding the same advice. *Mere* repeating is not often desirable, for an audience easily becomes bored at hearing the same remark two or three times in approximately identical phrasing. Also, to some extent an emphatic delivery can direct attention to main ideas, but subtly varied repetition is still more effective in forcing them upon the consciousness of the listener.

Exemplification. Use of illustrative material of a graphic or physical nature will be discussed later (pages 358–360). Besides the display of actual exhibits, exemplification has also its verbal forms of examples (or instances) and analogies. In listening to a speech on a scientific topic, almost anyone, whether layman or specialist, will welcome concrete illustrations of general truths; a well-chosen example is seldom a waste of time. Analogy, a form of comparison between the abstruse and the commonplace (as in the old "billiard ball" atomic conception, in the likening of the variable-pitch propeller of airplanes to the variable-speed gearing of land vehicles, or in the parallel between an electric current and a flow of water) can at times quickly clarify a difficult subject.

(See the discussion of analogies, especially of their function in scientific thought, on pages 171–172 and 175–176 of Chapter VII.)

Transitions. Smooth transition is one of the hallmarks of all expert composition, both written and oral. Jerkiness between sections and topics, on the other hand, besides being awkward, may interfere seriously with communication of thought. Although transitions seldom appear in the outline itself, they should be consciously planned and practiced. Useful functions are served by transitional words (e.g., *however, also, nevertheless, fourth, likewise, thus*), phrases (e.g., *for instance, on the contrary*), clauses (e.g., *as you may recall, when we consider the second phase*), and complete sentences or, not infrequently, groups of several successive sentences. In addition, use of reference words (pronouns and pronominal adjectives: e.g., *this, that*), and repetition of important terms (usually nouns) from one passage to another, contribute greatly to transition. With a little ingenuity, almost anyone can easily and rapidly improve in manipulation of transitional devices. At the very least, the mannerism should be avoided of constantly employing a few unvarying and half-meaningless formulas, such as "next," "passing now to . . .," and "it seems that." Perhaps the worst offenders, among habitual expressions of this kind, are "so" and "well."

(3. CONCLUSION)

Conclusions must be planned. The conclusion, while best kept rather brief, needs careful attention in the planning of a speech. Perhaps nothing is more difficult about talking in public than making a graceful withdrawal from the floor. Before entering upon the platform the wise speaker knows the exact remarks which he is to make, and the order in which he is to say them, during the moments just preceding his return to his seat. The unwise speaker, lacking a planned conclusion, faces the prospect—a painful ordeal to both himself and the audience—of floundering helplessly while trying to end his address after it obviously is finished.

Summary. Repetition, as a means to clearness through emphasis, was mentioned in connection with the body of the talk. One good way to repeat is to summarize. Just as the main points to be taken up often are previewed in the introduction, similarly they can be clinched by final enumeration in the conclusion. Still, if a talk is short and the structure free of unusual complications, to use the conclusion for this purpose is not always necessary or desirable. Whether to do so must, of course, be decided in each instance by the probable needs of the audience: as soon as the speaker has driven home the principal things he has tried to say, further repetition would be an indiscretion. In any case, the stock "thus we see" formula of conclusion should be avoided, not because it is bad in itself but because it has become annoyingly hackneyed through long overuse.

Conclusions and the conclusion. In talks on controversial issues, whether expository or argumentative in tendency, the concluding section sometimes is the best place for the speaker to present his interpretation of facts or his appeal to action. However, despite the seeming implication of the word *conclusions,* it is not true that the larger relations of a subject should always, or even usually, be completely deferred until the last. Good organization requires that they be implicit, and in many discussions explicit as well, throughout the body of the speech—not mere tacked-on addenda. Whatever their position, of course, they must reasonably follow from the premises. "Thus we see" conclusions, generally displeasing for the reason of triteness noted a paragraph above, are intolerable when they propose a questionable view that the audience really cannot see from the evidence offered.

Miscellaneous concluding statements. In written compositions on factual themes, the best conclusion is very often none at all: when an author has fully clarified a technical subject, any rhetorical flourish is usually superfluous. Neither does the technical speaker wish to plan a spellbinding peroration, but of course he must say *something* to afford an exit. If a summary or statement of conclusions does not seem called for, some reference to related topics of discussion, implications not examined in the speech, anticipated future developments, practical applications available to the auditors, or the like may be proper. Very commonly a polite remark about the occasion of the talk (but not an apology for real or supposed shortcomings) is the statement leading to the speaker's closing "I thank you."

C. DELIVERY

(1) REHEARSAL

Importance of practice. No skill is acquired by wishes, nor is mastery to be attained through the assumption that achievement is easier than it truly is. Dancing or pitching a baseball curve must be learned in what popular speech significantly calls the hard way—not by being told, "Why, it's just like walking"; or, "There's nothing to it." Reading a book on "The Art of [the desired ability]" can be helpful; a good teacher aids even more; critical observation of successful and unsuccessful attainment in others also has value. In the end, however, a technique is gained by *doing,* and speaking is a technique like any other in this respect. The time you individually spend at the classroom rostrum may not total as much as a half hour during an entire semester. Nevertheless, marked increase of skill and poise is certain if—but only if—recognition that effective public speaking is not easy or automatic leads to sincere effort. Naturally, most of that effort will be expended outside class. Not only must your oral reports be carefully planned; they must be *practiced aloud as speeches.* The more often you rehearse them, on the whole the better they will be, and (what is really important) the more enduring will be the ability developed.

Space the rehearsals. Here is a caution, however. Somewhat as an amateur athlete can strain his muscles by unduly prolonged continuous exercise, you may drive yourself into an intellectual fog by rehearsing the same talk in several *successive* practices. Allow an interval—at least a few minutes, at best several hours or a day—between each two rehearsals. You will find that your mind is refreshed and that many difficulties, even seemingly hopeless problems of expression, will mysteriously have solved themselves in the meantime. (See also *The mirror and the friend* on page 363.)

(2) LANGUAGE

Audiences are critical. A speaker is judged by his language. Practically everyone is more or less lax of speech in a streetcorner discussion, and by the same token readily forgives, or probably does not notice, the minor conversational slips of others. Nevertheless, audiences (even the relatively poorly educated members) take a very critical attitude toward a formal spokesman. He comes before them as an avowed authority, not merely in his subject, but likewise in his manner of presenting it.

A speech deserves your best English. You have been studying and using the English language for many years. The platform brings to focus all you have ever learned about diction, grammar, and phrasing (as does a business letter or a written report); and, besides, about pronunciation and enunciation. The audience has a right to assume, and most certainly will assume, that what you say represents your highest ability—that you are showing yourself to the best possible advantage. Guard against the "it don't," the "most all," the "idear," the "sure will," the "cain't," the "ex-spearmintal," the unfinished sentences, the hemming and hawing, or any of the other careless mannerisms of undisciplined speech into which you may tend to lapse. If you do not, to a degree (a larger degree than you may suspect) you are sure to discredit yourself before the audience. (See also the analysis of *Vocal Faults*, pages 363–365.)

(3) POSTURE

Normal stance. Except under abnormal circumstances, a speaker takes his stand near the lateral center of the platform. The "position of a soldier," as required by the manual of arms, is very nearly the proper normal stance in public speaking. Let the body be erect but not stiff, with the chin slightly retracted, the shoulders thrown back, and the chest arched upward and out to give full room to the lungs.

Let the arms drop naturally at the side, the hands neither clenched into fists nor rigidly spread flat. Let the heels be almost but not quite together, with the toes turned out at an angle of about forty-five degrees and neither foot farther advanced than the other. Now let the weight of the body be equally distributed on both legs and evenly transmitted to the four points of contact with the floor, the balls and heels of both feet. The plane of the body should be parallel with the front edge of the platform or the first row of the audience, and the head should face full forward. No part of the body, particularly the knees, hips, and waist, should be bent or twisted; and any tendencies to jiggle, weave, or bob, and to pluck parts of the clothing or other objects with the hands, must be firmly resisted.

Freedom of movement. What has just been described was called speaker's "normal" stance, signifying the one to which he should almost always return when movements or other positions have been employed for special purposes. He should not, of course, stand like a wooden Indian in one rigid pose. Occasionally clasping the hands behind the body * or putting one in a pocket—but not pocketing both simultaneously—may relieve tenseness. Besides gestures (see below), any purposeful motion, if not awkward, is entirely suitable to speaking. A few steps to one side often mark transitions, but should not cumulate in one direction to pull the speaker far away from center. It is permissible to walk anywhere on the platform (for instance, to connect a switch for an exhibit), but when the necessary action has been performed the speaker should return to his regular place near the middle.

"Draping the furniture." A maxim among actors is not to "drape" the stage furniture. The rule applies also to public speaking: nothing should be touched except for a definite purpose. Unless an address is to be read from manuscript or physical objects are to be shown, the speaker does better without a table or reading stand. If one is provided, his best position is beside (not behind) it, far enough away so that he will not be tempted to rest his fingertips or the heels of his hands upon the edge. (A natural movement between sections of the speech is to the opposite side.) Never should he lean against furniture or incidental objects, including the classroom blackboard with its chalk well.

The eyes compel. A shy speaker soon loses his audience if he yields to the temptation to look at the ceiling, out a window, or vaguely into

* A woman, when speaking or singing, naturally clasps the hands in front, but a man should not do so.

space. The optimum basic focus of the eyes is about two thirds of the distance from the front to the rear of the room and near the lateral middle. That point is, however, merely the right position of departure and return for the glance. As the speaker delivers his address, he should repeatedly play his gaze over the whole audience, somewhat in the manner of lightly sprinkling a lawn with a garden hose. Moreover, unless the group is extremely large, he should regard not just general sections but actual individuals, looking them in the face and thus fixing and commanding their attention. When this technique is executed well, every person, even in the remotest corner of the auditorium, has a sense that the speech is being delivered immediately and personally to him, though the time in which his and the speaker's eyes are joined may not amount to more than a few seconds. Incidentally, any disturbance usually is best brought under control by looking (not sourly or even severely, but pleasantly) directly at the person or persons responsible.

(4) GESTURES

Function in the technical speech. Technical speakers, valuing dignified presentation of facts and conclusions above starry-eyed oratory, ordinarily reduce gesticulation to a minimum. Restraint can, however, be carried to a fault, for some use of gestures is almost essential to effective delivery. Besides motion with the hands and arms (the popular sense of the term), gesturing may be understood to include a shrug of the shoulders, the raising of the eyebrows, a well-timed smile, or any other movements suggestive of thought or feeling.

"Wooden" gestures. The practicing of specific gestures almost infallibly defeats its purpose. No doubt you have watched with amusement, in school oratorical contests, the mechanical step forward after the announcement of topic, the raised right fist and index finger at climactic points, the palm-upward supplication and palm-downward deprecation, and all the other baggage of set gesticulation. Just the same, the old habit of teaching stock gestures for special effects rests upon a solid psychological basis, since various kinds of emotion and thought do impel—and, in turn, can be partly communicated to an audience by—particular bodily attitudes.

How to practice gesticulation. Unless a gesture is spontaneous at the moment of speaking, it is sure to fail. You should not, therefore, deliberately plan your gestures, nor should you give them much thought when you finally come to the platform. Instead of practicing *the* gestures of a talk, you should practice *gesturing,* which is not at all the same thing. Thoroughly natural gesticulation may at first be too crude or violent, but it will at least be organic and expressive. Watch yourself in a mirror as you rehearse, or solicit the critical advice of a friend; awkwardness will decrease very rapidly. As a novice, you may have the experience in your first few speeches of "freezing up" and failing to use any gestures whatever. However, the audience will not notice this failure in a short talk. Quite to the contrary, even statuesque rigidity, undesirable as it is, will be far better received than a series of obviously "canned" movements.

(5) NOTES

Note cards. Many public speakers prefer, and sometimes students are required, to speak without carrying notes to the platform. When employed, speaking notes (as distinguished from preliminary drafts or outlines) should never be made on large sheets; but, instead, always on small rectangular cards or slips of paper. The largest size that ought ever to be used is three by five inches; dimensions of two and a half by four inches are even better, as cards or slips of the smaller size will fit into the palm of the hand almost invisibly.

Producing the notes. If the speaker brings on his notes in his hand, they are of course ready for use whenever needed. With some adroitness, however, a more clever method of obtaining the notes can be performed. The cards are carried in one of the side pockets of the coat, from which, by a casual dropping of one hand into that pocket during the introductory remarks, they can be produced in a most natural way.

Holding the notes. Correctly handled, notes do not interfere with good posture and gesticulation. If fittingly chosen for size, the cards can be held at the usual lowered position of the arm without squeezing or spreading of the grip. A right-handed speaker should hold them in the left palm; as a matter of fact, however, almost any desired motion, other than writing, can be made about as freely with the encumbered as with the free hand. While the notes are actually being consulted, the arm should be bent at the elbow with the forearm against the body and parallel to the floor; this position puts the cards themselves below the eyes at the proper reading distance. Never raise your arm to a height that even partially interposes notes between your face and the audience.

Least use best use. As a general principle, notes are used well when they serve their purpose to the speaker and yet are practically unnoticed by the audience. A hesitant speaker can destroy the listeners' initial presumption of his authority by openly consulting notes between major points, as if he does not even have in mind the main ideas and drift of his subject. If ever, in delivering a speech, you really do forget what comes next, at all cost keep talking on the present topic (repeat as though summarizing, if you can do no better), and meantime take a hasty glance at your cards while still speaking. Afterwards, come to a pause; look at the audience, *not* at your notes; then launch confidently into the next section. Open consulting of notes is seldom a good technique except for quotations, statistics, and other data that the auditors would not expect anyone to "keep in his head." On the whole, the less the visible use of notes the better.

(6) EXHIBITS AND VISUAL AIDS

Auxiliary function. Any exhibits or graphic aids useful to facilitate communication may be employed in speeches on scientific subjects. Be sure, however, that they genuinely do help. You will puzzle or offend the audience by an inscription, sketch, graph, chart, or material object that cannot be clearly seen by some or all members, that is not suited to quick visual comprehension, that is shown in an awkward manner, or that is not verbally explained and explicitly related to the spoken discussion. Keep always in mind that the exhibition is not independent, but auxiliary.

(1. FLAT SURFACES)

The blackboard. When a blackboard is available (in a classroom, for example) it is handy for displaying diagrams, graphs, and the like. There are two good ways of using the board:

(1) *The prepared figure.* One method is to make the drawing (or tabulation, etc.) in advance of the speech, preferably before the audience begins to arrive. In this way, pictorial exhibits can be prepared with care and in some detail; however, minutiae should be avoided except when absolutely essential, because of the danger of diverting attention to trivialities.

(2) *The chalk talk.* The other acceptable manner is that of the so-called chalk talk, in which the lecturer rapidly sketches on the board during brief intervals in the speech, or even while actually talking. Unless he has unusual facility in free-hand drawing, he reduces everything to highly simplified lines, dots, crosses, and curlicues that would be exceedingly

unpictorial to a stone-deaf member of the audience. The accompanying spoken words bring them to life and, by a curious exchange, are in turn vivified by the imagery thus evoked.

Charts and maps. If no blackboard is furnished, or if complicated drawings are needed that for some reason could not be made on the board earlier than the time of speaking, large charts on cloth, cardboard, or heavy paper can be prepared. Maps also fall in this class. Charts or maps should be attached to a wall or screen behind the speaker, hung from one or more standards set to the side of his normal platform position, or as a last resort propped firmly on or against a chair, reading stand, or table. (The last method is the poorest for every reason, not least being the danger that the exhibits may be accidentally knocked or kicked over.) Wherever they are put, they should confront the audience directly, never obliquely. It is best either to arrange them in advance, or else to have them placed by an assistant just before or after the chairman's announcement. The worst of all possible plans is for the speaker to bring them with him, and then have to spend several minutes in undignified stage carpentry.

Correct demonstration from flat exhibits. The duty of the speaker is to look *at* his auditors while speaking *about* material on exhibit. In oral discussion of technical subjects, a person inexperienced in the art of speech, ignorant of this obligation, may fail to dominate the attention of his audience. The most careless type stands as if his back were intended for the center of attention, meanwhile haranguing the graphic material that half the audience cannot see because of his interposed body. The correct procedure is as follows: Take a position about one pace in front of the exhibit and almost at arm's length to that side of it toward the middle of the platform. Stand squarely facing the audience. Point with the arm and hand next to the drawing (not across the body), from time to time briefly turning the head just far enough to verify that the right place is being indicated. The palm of the hand should be kept toward the audience while pointing, with all fingers except the index loosely curled under the thumb. Do not touch the board or chart; rather, keep the arm and hand in a straight line with the shoulders.* Ordinarily a pointer or yardstick

* Although actually the hand is several feet in front of what is being shown, from the viewpoint of the audience this fact is not apparent. There is no need whatever to swing the arm awkwardly back and make physical contact with the board, at the same time perhaps smudging some of the lines or producing annoying tapping sounds.

should not be used. If one is necessary for an unusually large exhibit, be sure you know where it is so that you do not have to hunt or ask for it; equally important, put it back at the earliest possible moment instead of retaining it in the hands as a plaything.

(2. SOLID EXHIBITS)

Display. Physical objects ordinarily must be placed on a table or stand, and like movable charts are preferably either arranged well in advance or else set up by an assistant just before the speech. Sometimes a very small exhibit can be kept in the pocket until needed.

Demonstration. Articles in the round are demonstrated very much like graphic material, the only important difference being that often the speaker may conveniently stand behind them instead of to one side (but never, of course, between them and the observers). As in illustrating from a blackboard or portable chart, remember while talking about the exhibit to look mainly at the audience; this principle is more vital to successful delivery than the novice generally realizes.

(3. PROJECTIONS)

Methods; functions. Teachers and professional lecturers frequently make supplementary use of slides or photographs thrown on a screen in series, and sometimes of motion pictures. The screen is treated much like any other flat surface, but a long pointer is a practical necessity. Normally, an assistant should operate the machine so that the speaker can have freedom for movement and for concentration on vocal smoothness, clarity, and emphasis.

(7) PLATFORM MANNERS

Public speaking has its accepted code of manners—partly conventional, but also partly determined by common sense and good taste—which every participant is expected to follow.

Personal appearance. First of all, the physical appearance of a speaker should be neat and correct. Neatness is a general standard, applying to both person and clothing. Correct dress is relative to the audience and the occasion, and should be ascertained, if necessary, by inquiry. Nearly always a conservative business suit is acceptable; accessories, particularly the shirt, necktie, and shoes, also ought to be conservative. Clean fingernails, face, and shirt, along with combed hair, a well-arranged tie, polished shoes, and a recently pressed suit, should go without saying. Even in a practice speech delivered as a classroom exercise, a little dressing up can do no harm, and probably will be accompanied by increase of dignity in the speaker and reciprocated by attentiveness in the audience. Perhaps you have seen a schoolboy come to the platform wearing no socks, or chewing gum; but did you ever hear anyone so bereft of pride give a first-rate speech?

Courtesy. Not often in schoolroom speaking sessions, to be sure, yet rather frequently in less artificially arranged speeches, provocation is exceedingly great to lose patience with opponents, hecklers, askers of foolish questions, late comers and early leavers, and disturbers in general. However, to descend to bitterness, discourtesy, name-calling, or bickering in dealing with an audience, or with opposing speakers on controversial issues, only lets the situation slip out of hand. Humor, pleasantry, mild irony (not verbal brutality), tacit or, if necessary, open appeal to the sense of fair play, obvious candor and fairness in remarks and behavior—these are far stronger armor than blind rage against malicious, fractious, or stupid interruptions and misconduct. Even though they were not, never-failing courtesy would be its own sufficient excuse for being.

Conventional opening. The usual manner of beginning a speech is well established by custom. The speaker, having been announced by the chairman, comes to the front center of the platform (one or two paces to the left or right of the table or reading stand, if there is one) and faces the chairman. He bows slightly, at the same time saying: "Mr. [Madam] Chairman," "Mr. [Madam] President," "Mr. Toastmaster" (at a banquet), or "Mr. [Mrs.; Miss] Doe." Then he turns toward the audience, and after a slight pause salutes the audience as "Ladies and Gentlemen," "Gentlemen," "Ladies," "Friends," "Classmates," or the like. When any persons are present whom he wishes to distinguish with special notice, they may be mentioned directly after the chairman. Typical examples might be: "Mr. Chairman, Professor Blank, Gentlemen"; "Mr. President, Guests, and Members"; or (in a debate) "Mr. Chairman, Honorable Judges, Worthy Opponents, Ladies and Gentlemen."

Forms of reference. If the chairman is mentioned in the course of a speech, he or she is designated as "the chair." Members of the audience and other speakers are either called by their names, always prefaced by "Mr.," "Mrs.," "Miss," or some other title (e.g., "Dr."), or referred to by polite expressions such as "the gentleman of the opposition," "the lady from Clifton Junior College," "the questioner," "our honored guest," or "the two gentlemen who preceded me on this floor." Judges of contests are "the honorable judge(s)."

Conventional close. When the speaker has finished what he has to say, he pauses for a moment and then, bringing his voice to a natural tempo and tone if the last several sentences have been somewhat excited or elevated, pronounces the formula "I thank you" (signifying his gratitude for the attention of the audience). These words should be spoken while he is still in the center of the platform; neither they nor the concluding remarks of the speech proper should ever be accompanied by a simultaneous movement toward an exit or toward the speaker's chair upon the stage.

(8) OVERCOMING DEFICIENCIES

(1. NERVOUSNESS)

A temporary condition. The main secret of overcoming nervousness in public speaking, like any form of stage fright, is simply to endure it as patiently as possible until it takes its departure—whether suddenly in the midst of a single speech, as often happens, or gradually during continued experience of the forum. Some comfort is had in knowing that the trouble is next to universal among speakers, if not entirely so; that agitation is infinitely less perceptible outwardly to an audience than inwardly to the victim (for instance, an odd vocal tone probably will be taken as a natural platform style, even by members of the audience familiar with the speaker's usual conversational voice); finally, and most encouraging of all, that a certain amount of tenseness is genuinely beneficial by keeping the speaker on edge, and certainly is greatly preferable to apathy.

Avoid difficult situations at the outset. Ease of speaking is contingent upon three factors: (1) smallness and (2) sympathy of the audience, and (3) a familiar topic. The hardest possible problem, one to be attempted only by a master, is a speech upon an obscure subject before a hostile mass meeting. At the opposite extreme is a talk delivered to a class or club of friends on a theme of personal interest and experience. In college courses, with ingenuity and cooperative spirit, classroom situations of varied audience response and increasing demand upon the speakers can be devised for successive rounds of talks.

Never quit. One caution about a potential consequence of nervousness is very important: *Do not quit.* By every effort, keep on speaking without interruption. Should doing so become entirely impossible, pause momentarily, look as pleasant as you can, and give your disturbed respiration and excited feelings five or ten seconds for recovery; then proceed. If you weakly abandon the platform, in all probability you will ever afterwards lack the courage to go upon another.

(2. FAULTS OF POSTURE)

Practice and criticism. Correct speaking posture already has been described (pages 354–356). Eradication of faults never occurs spontaneously, but only as a consequence of self-criticism and attention to the criticism of others. Probably your instructor will make some personal suggestions after each class talk, and you can gain much benefit from practice outside the classroom.

The mirror and the friend. In rehearsing a talk you should stand up and speak aloud with the same pose, tone, and manner you expect to use before your later audience. Both as a means of overcoming native hesitancy to speak into empty space, and also as a stern rebuke to faults of posture, you will find addressing a large mirror to be beneficial. You may regard one or two friends as more satisfactory than a mirror, but they are better only if they are intelligent, attentive, sympathetic, and *constructively* critical. Any atmosphere of scoffing or hilarity—to which members of the same family are prone—is disastrous. For the most part, the best critic at rehearsals is likely to be another student preparing an address for the same occasion as yours, with whom you are able to exchange services as listener.

(3. VOCAL FAULTS)

Anyone with sound organs of speech can develop an adequate speaking voice. The most common faults to be overcome are insufficient volume, uncontrolled pitch, bad tempo, mumbling, nasality, and harshness.

(1) Volume

Use your lungs. Speakers who do not make themselves heard are simply afraid to "open up" as they would in singing a favorite song. What they try to do, instead, is to make themselves shout by contracting the muscles of the throat; the increased tenseness produces a shriller and therefore somewhat more penetrating sound, but it is a poor substitute for true volume, which must come from depths far below the throat. Throw your shoulders back, arch your ribs, and let your whole chest heave as you in-h-h-h-hale and ex-h-h-h-hale. You will soon discover that you have been talking like Nick Bottom, Shakespeare's unskilled actor of *A Midsummer Night's Dream,* "in a monstrous little voice," instead of really using the vocal engine given you by nature.

The thunderer. Infrequently, someone overdoes loudness to the point of thundering at an audience, but this error is much more easily corrected than the opposite fault. Although any speaker's biggest voice will sometimes be in demand, volume must be adjusted to the size of the audience and to the acoustical situation. After a little experience and outside criticism, the adjustment is made almost automatically. (Public-address systems and radio broadcasting introduce special factors that are, on the whole, unfavorable to naturally loud voices and favorable to naturally soft voices.)

(2) Pitch

Discover your range. The customary speaking voice of many persons is pitched so high or so low as to be unpleasant to listeners, if not partially inaudible. Since anyone, even if entirely untrained vocally, can sing at least an octave, obviously no one "natural" pitch is permanently fixed by nature. Somewhere within your full register is to be found a note that will carry distinctly and, at the same time, please the ears of an audience. Nor is changing pitch in the least difficult; the only reason that most people never do so is that the need and feasibility of the correction are not forcefully called to their attention. Experimentation with the range of your own voice is worth trying; you will find regulation of pitch the simplest of all improvements.

(3) Tempo

Regulate tempo gradually. Perhaps you think that speed of delivery might be even easier to control than volume or pitch, but unfortunately it is not. Because in speech one sound evokes the next semi-automatically, a large voluntary increase or, especially, reduction of speed is liable to produce confused or artificial enunciation. If you know that you speak too fast or too slowly, or if competent critics tell you that you do, try to slow down or speed up gradually, not radically in a short period of correction. Of course, no one tempo is right for all topics and all personalities. The natively rapid speaker, however, must cultivate an especially clear enunciation and force upon himself distinct pauses after important statements; the naturally leisurely speaker, also, must strive to avoid monotony.

(4) Mumbling

The lips shape speech. Mumbling—that is, habitually obscured enunciation of individual or phrasally combined words—largely results from facial laziness. You are almost certainly mumbling if you have the sensation of talking chiefly in the throat and back of the mouth. Using a mirror, attentively watch your mouth during your practice speaking; unless the lips and lower jaw are constantly working with vigor and mobility, you are a mumbler. Bad enough in ordinary conversation, this weakness is intolerable at the rostrum.

(5) Nasality

Keep vowels in the mouth. Sufferers from head colds and hay fever are erroneously said to "talk through the nose," when actually the trouble is that they cannot do so and thus are incapable of articulating nasal consonants (*m, n,* and *ng*). Some people, nevertheless, really do talk through the nose by pushing vowel sounds partly into the nasal chamber and out the nostrils. No English vowel or diphthong (sound of blended vowels) is properly nasalized. You probably do not know whether you have a nasal twang or not, but your hearers most certainly do; therefore you should seek and accept outside advice on this question. The fault, which is extremely unpleasant to the ears of cultivated listeners, is not readily corrected except by direct imitation of those who do not have it.*

(6) Harshness

Correction. The word *harshness* brings attention to a miscellany of similarly displeasing voice habits. As usual, friendly but candid criticism is needed for the discovery of failings. A good conventional or magnetic record of the voice can be of considerable aid, also, but recording with amateur equipment may introduce so many distortions as to be worthless for speech correction.

Forms of harshness. Among the causes of harsh voices are flatness, monotonousness, gruffness or huskiness, sibilance (a slightly prolonged whistling accompanying the *s* sound and sometimes also related sounds, especially *z*), undue vigor of consonants (particularly *t, d,* and *p*), poor resonance of vowels, and "choppiness" of utterance (staccato articulation). Not, perhaps, exactly a type of harshness is a certain bad habit of filling out pauses by "oh-ing," "ah-ing," "uh-ing," "well-ing," "why-ing," or "er-er-ing."

---

* A quick way to determine the right quality of an individual vowel or diphthong is to pronounce it with the nose held shut, so that all possibility of nasalizing is prevented.

D. GROUP DISCUSSIONS OF SCIENTIFIC AND TECHNICAL QUESTIONS

(1) TOPICS

Abundance of themes. All technical fields abound in controversial or unsettled questions suitable for joint treatment by a group of speakers. Random examples would include:

two-stroke and four-stroke cycles for internal-combustion engines
steam, Diesel-electric, and gas-turbine locomotives
helicopter, Autogiro, and airplane
radial, air-cooled versus in-line, liquid-cooled engines for various classes of aircraft
variable-pitch and fixed-pitch propellers
different runway layouts for airports
sea power versus air power
graphic versus analytic solution of practical problems in mathematics
welding and riveting (or specialized types of either)
electricity, gas, and natural ice for household refrigeration
commercial water-softening processes
frequency and amplitude modulation
theories of the formation of salt domes and petroleum
rival methods of synthesizing nitric or sulphuric acid
the explanation of catalysis
the corpuscular and wave theories of light
the quantum theory
the nebular hypothesis
potential uses of atomic power

Audience interest. Groups studying the various sciences will readily think of numerous problems of similar character. In deciding upon a topic for discussion before an audience, however, they must take care to avoid one so highly specialized that the listeners will have difficulty in understanding it. The danger is real, for several persons having common interests are more liable than an individual to talk above the heads of an audience: perceiving one another's quick comprehension, they are less inclined to remember the need of other hearers for elementary and routine explanations. Of course, such explanations can and should be given, but it is best if the chosen subject itself is well within the range of interests or studies shared by a majority of the expected audience.

Limitation. A group can undertake a broader topic than would be suited to an individual speaker. Still, this liberty is not to be abused. Any of the sample questions proposed above could be improved by being limited to a single aspect, factor, or application; in fact, most subjects that originally suggest themselves can be narrowed, to advantage, as the planning of a joint discussion advances.

(2) TYPES

Debates. The most highly formalized type of group discussion is the debate. Always argumentative, a debate must be on a subject having an affirmative and a negative side diametrically opposed, yet as nearly as possible equally defensible. Two teams composed of the same number of speakers separately prepare conflicting "cases" on the issues of the question to be debated. Each team works in the closest internal harmony, but no consultations are held between the teams except to choose the topic, to arrange details like timing and method of delivery, and sometimes to discuss such matters as definitions of terms. On the platform they sit on opposite sides, each at a table where the respective members can write and exchange notes as the argument proceeds. Speakers take the platform in rotation, beginning with the first affirmative, followed by the first negative, and so on to the last negative. Then comes a round of rebuttal, during which one or more speakers for each side return to refute the opposing case, again in alternation but according to some arrangement that invariably gives the final speech to the affirmative. There are three or five judges, a single critic-judge, or none at all with perhaps a vote of decision from the audience. A chairman conducts the debate, and a timekeeper holds the speakers to agreed periods of, typically, eight-minute constructive speeches and four-minute rebuttals. The chairman and the timekeeper should not serve either as judges or as team members, but if necessary the same person may act as both chairman and timekeeper.

Panel discussions. Technical students often find a panel discussion better suited to their requirements than a debate. One advantage is that the panel method can be used for expository, as well as for argumentative, treatment of controversial issues. Two or more speakers present, in turn, different parts of or points of view toward a given subject, or rival devices or plans for accomplishing a certain end. They do not necessarily attempt to refute one another; indeed, each member of the panel may treat both advantages and disadvantages on his side of the topic. Sometimes a moderator, who can also serve as chairman, makes a summation and correlation of what has been said by the several speakers. Frequently included in the panel type of joint discussion, are periods in which the speakers quiz one another and submit to questioning and comment by the audience.

Round-table conferences. A round-table conference can be immensely enjoyable to participants and auditors, but without real preparation and coöperation it will either lag, after a few set remarks, or else degenerate into aimless chatter. A board of at least four or five members is needed to keep a lively conversation going; one among them must be the designated leader, not only to open and close the discussion, but to see that it is made to proceed smoothly but vigorously along predetermined lines. The group as a whole should meet at least once to plan the conference in general outline, and perhaps to do some rehearsing. At this meeting each speaker is assigned certain points or subtopics as his particular responsibility; afterwards, he should prepare himself on them (and, less fully, on the subject in its entirety) as seriously as if he were to make an individual address.

Unprepared discussions. The three methods of joint discussion just explained are alike in requiring definite preparation of a subject by several persons, who unite to present it to an audience. In everyday life, obviously, most conversations are spontaneous and the participants are their own audience. Innumerable informal talk-sessions naturally occur in homogeneous groups, the classroom included. If a serious topic is either agreed upon or furnished by an outside source, a wholly unplanned discussion can be an educational as well as entertaining and easy mode of public speaking.

Semiformal discussions. For placing a worth-while subject before a club or class interested in science and technology, one good method is to invite an authority on some matter of scientific or technical interest to speak for the first half of the period, with the understanding that in the remaining half the group will be free to ask questions or make statements related to his theme. A chairman should be appointed beforehand to introduce the visitor, to keep order during the discussion period, to advance a remark or question of his own whenever none is offered from the floor, and to end the meeting with an expression of thanks to the principal speaker.

APPENDIX A

APPENDIX

A

EXERCISES

FOR CHAPTER I

A. Read passages or chapters, as recommended by your instructor or suggested by an examination of the table of contents or index, in one or more of these books: Albert C. Baugh, *A History of the English Language*; J. B. Greenough and G. L. Kittredge, *Words and Their Ways in English Speech*; H. L. Mencken, *The American Language* and *Supplements I, II*; C. K. Ogden, *The System of Basic English*; Leonard Bloomfield, *Language*; Alfred Korzybski, *Science and Sanity* and *General Semantics*; C. K. Ogden and I. A. Richards, *The Meaning of Meaning*; Stuart Chase, *The Tyranny of Words*; Irving J. Lee, *Language Habits in Human Affairs.*

B. Plan three oral reports on the *same* topic (such as an inspection of an industrial plant, or one of your recent laboratory experiments), to be delivered before: (1) a group of instructors of advanced technical subjects; (2) a class of college students not majoring in science; (3) a club of girls in high school. Following your three outlines, write summaries employing the same style and diction you would use in actually delivering each report. Which report is, or would be, the longest? the shortest? the easiest to plan? the most difficult to plan? the easiest to deliver? the most difficult to deliver? To which of the three styles discussed at the close of the chapter does each correspond? For which of these differing styles of composition do your technical studies most directly prepare you?

C. Find in other publications besides this book short examples of "purely technical," "middle technical," and "popular technical" writings. Bring one of each to class. Be prepared to read the passages aloud and to conduct a discussion of their merits and deficiencies.

371

D. Comment on this proposition: "First and last, good technical English is good English."

*   *   *   *   *

FOR CHAPTER II

A. Explain and, in as many complete sentences as necessary (not copied or directly imitated from the examples given in the chapter), fully illustrate the following grammatical terms: (1) SUBSTANTIVE; (2) PRONOMINAL WORD; (3) FINITE VERB; (4) VERBAL; (5) CASE; (6) PERSON; (7) TENSE; (8) SUBJUNCTIVE MOOD; (9) ADJECTIVE; (10) ADVERB; (11) SPLIT INFINITIVE; (12) DANGLING CONSTRUCTION; (13) SQUINTING MODIFIER; (14) FALSE SERIES; (15) ELLIPTICAL CONSTRUCTION.

B. Correct errors in the following sentences; in every instance clearly explain, with reference to a definite rule given in the chapter, both the fault and its correction. Avoid making needless changes. Some of the sentences are entirely right.

1. Because Jess's father objected strongly to his son studying architecture, the boy elected a pre-engineering curriculum.

2. No one should attempt to write their letters and reports without having convenient access to a good dictionary.

3. In 1941 over 500,000,000 pounds of plastics was produced.

4. We would be glad to have you investigate our product.

5. Will you be required to take advanced calculus next year?

6. Costs of both labor and material tended to fluctuate due to strikes.

7. These plans are outmoded, being drawn as long ago as 1934.

8. He is one of the few civil engineers who thoroughly knows the history of surveying instruments.

9. Everybody should carefully plan his future during the years of his education.

10. He was trained like me and is just as competent as me.

11. He tests thoroughly practicable models.

12. We know who he is.

13. We know who you think he is.

14. We know who you think him to be.

15. We know who you were discussing when we arrived.

16. We know who you think will be defeated.

17. Who do you suppose is most likely to be successful?

18. I know nothing about who he may nominate or who may nominate him.

19. Sit the beaker to one side and allow the contents to set hard; meanwhile, avoid letting the glass strips lay exposed to the atmosphere.

20. Backton was too interested in ornament to pay proper attention to construction.

21. The course includes lectures on hydraulics, thermodynamics, and has numerous laboratory periods.

22. You may only find one textbook that satisfactorily treats your topic.

23. The assembly line passes quite a few stations, where quite a number of workers perform different operations.

24. Never approve an engine that does not perform good under load.

25. He not only is a skilled athlete but also an excellent student.

26. Chemurgical research is rapidly progressing both in America and Europe.

27. The blueprint shop and the mold loft are at least as important, if not more so, than the ways.

28. The Eiffel Tower was one, if not the highest, towers ever built for an exposition.

29. The jury, having reached a decision, was filing into their places in the box.

30. In a radar set is included the modulator, radio-frequency oscillator, directional antenna, receiver, and indicator.

31. Built in one cabinet is both a sender and a receiver.

32. Neither a speaker nor earphones is needed.

33. Either a network of small antennas or a "searchlight" principle is the basis of scanning.

34. A crystal detector in addition to electron tubes is used.

35. The real secret is deflections of beams in one or more cathode-ray tubes.

36. There is horizontal as well as vertical deflections.

37. Geopolitics was my most interesting social study, while mechanics had been my most beneficial course in science until I took electronics.

38. This type cell consists of dissimilar elements connected through a resistance.

39. The diamond's hardness and coal's friability are typical instances of the elements' heteromorphism.

40. If the earth was permanently barren of all vegetation, could any forms of animal life continue?

41. They expected to have been able to have removed all impurities in the form of slag.

42. The fumes smelled sourly, and soon everyone near the vent felt very badly.

43. He spoke much briefer the second time he presented his argument.

44. Most all American sulphuric acid is made from native sulphur.

45. One cannot deny but that Bavarian hops are superior to ours.

46. Einstein has made more fundamental contributions to mathematical physics than any thinker since Newton.

47. Einstein is the greatest of any other mathematical physicist since Newton.

48. After determining the specifications of the lamp, the materials were obtained.

49. Although light in armament, speed and accurate fire made that class of small tank dreaded by the enemy.

50. Wireless telephony began in 1906, and which R. A. Fessenden is believed to have been the first to achieve.

*   *   *   *   *

FOR CHAPTER III

A. Write the entire *Study List of Words for Technical Students,* given as D 24, at dictation (in two or more sessions, if necessary). Then transcribe as a personal list all the words you have misspelled, or of which you have felt uncertain even while actually writing them correctly. Set about mastering the words of this reduced list at definite intervals: one a day, one every morning and every night, five each Saturday afternoon—or by almost any other timing that suits you. The important two *R's* are *regularity* and *review.* Persist until you can make a perfect score on any set of words dictated from the master list.

B. Obtain the help of a friend whose sense of pronunciation you know to be superior. Read aloud, slowly, the entire *Study List of Words for Technical Students.* Check each pronunciation he challenges. Verify the correct sounds of the checked words by consulting a dictionary. Again, as with spelling (cf. Exercise *A,* immediately above), compile a personal study list and master it, word by word, in a *regular* program interspersed with adequate *review.*

C. Adopt the habit of carrying with you a card or envelope on which to jot down doubtful expressions that you read or hear from time to time. Indicate a question of spelling by "Sp.," one of pronunciation by "Pr.," one of definition by "Def.," or the like. At the end of the day or week, spend some time clearing up the accumulated terms with the aid of a dictionary and, if necessary, an encyclopedia or other reference works. Allow the process of association to carry you freely from one word to another, but never rest until you genuinely understand each problem of diction you investigate.

D. Study the meaning of the following words in relation to their etymology:

telephone	anthropology	digit	transit
telescope	biology	digitalis	zenith
telegraph	entomology	dexterity	nadir
telegram	etymology	gaucheness	plus
grammar	terminology	universe	minus
phonograph	vocabulary	ether	decimate
photograph	diction	earth	apparatus
seismograph	nomenclature	atom	connection
orthographic	physics	electron	complex
isometric	chemistry	neutron	metamorphosis
projection	medicine	nucleus	principal
trajectory	metallurgy	meson	principle
protractor	engineering	proton	electrolyte
antenna	technology	photon	electrocute
aerial	geology	ion	kilowatt
airplane	geometry	iron	battery
automobile	trigonometry	hydrogen	vernier
locomotive	calculus	oxygen	astonishing
euphony	logarithm	uranium	thermometer
dyspepsia	rhythm	plutonium	thermostat
cinema	genius	gas	radiate
kinetics	genuine	gauss	radar
kinematics	genetics	bisect	sonar
kinesiatrics	antigen	bicycle	loran
kinesthesia	homogenize	icicle	shoran
anesthesia	anomaly	isinglass	oscillator
ammonia	abnormal	calipers	insulation
aluminum	asymmetrical	cirrus	peninsula
vacuum	heterogeneous	cirrhosis	capillary
vaccinate	superheterodyne	brake	alcohol
derrick	dynamic	conduit	aliphatic
bunkum	dinosaur	aqueduct	oleum
buret(te)	ounce	malaria	oleomargarine
pipet(te)	inch	explode	hemorrhage

magnetism	igneous	multilateral	inflammable
trinitrotoluene	nylon	isosceles	incandescent
tularemia	rubber	isotope	fluorescent
polymerize	equation	convergence	effluvium
synthesis	equivalent	divergence	automatic
absorption	equilateral	benevolence	robot
adsorption	unilateral	malevolence	rabbet

E. Differentiate: (1) IMPROPRIETY and BARBARISM; (2) SLANG and VULGARISM; (3) REDUNDANCY and TRITENESS; (4) IDIOM and GRAMMAR.

F. Explain and, in several sentences, illustrate the distinction between *compare(d) with* (or *in comparison with*) and *compare(d) to* (or *in comparison to*). Point out other distinctions of meaning conveyed by small differences of idiom.

G. Comment on: *tudor* and *fordor* (sedans), *grease-monkey, disc-jockey, phony, buzz-bomb, bogie* (in radar), *gusher, circumambulate, brimstone, ben trovato, à la carte, quisling, to home, you all, unaccustomed as I am to public speaking, adequate enough to suffice, superficial surface decoration, end up with, somebody else's, mechanic on duty.*

H. Spell, and state the rules governing: (1) *cool* plus *ly*; (2) *full* plus *ly*; (3) *defer* plus *ment*; (4) *deter* plus *ent*; (5) *offer* plus *ed*; (6) *note* plus *able*; (7) *service* plus *able*; (8) *service* plus *ing*; (9) *advantage* plus *ous*; (10) *stone* plus *y*; (11) *colic* plus *y*; (12) *shellac* plus *er*; (13) *try* plus *s*; (14) *alloy* plus *s*; (15) *defy* plus *ance.*

* * * * *

FOR CHAPTER IV

A. Punctuate (and supply capitals for) the following paragraphs. Divide words correctly at the end of lines. Be ready to justify each mark of punctuation by reference to a definite principle.

(1)

other experiments have shown that charcoal an intermediate constituent furfural of nylon plasterboard a good grade of paper and a fair grade of linoleum can among other products all be obtained fr om cobs furthermore corn stalks yield an acceptable quality of pap er and to quote darcey corn fiber may someday be the chief raw mater ial in the paper industry since the cost of wood seems to be appro aching a prohibitive level the excellent dorner process which was devised in 1912 is still the standard method of pulping the stalks eit her for paper or for industrial board finally the united states bureau of plant industry recommends chopped or ground stalks for catt le feed

(2)

need i say that the main problem is the making of the sixty fou r squares however that problem is not so difficult as it might seem pr ovided the method i shall state is followed saw four strips of waln ut and four strips of maple 3/32 in thick 1¾ in wide and 15 in long these strips must be exactly the same width therefore cut all eight pi eces at the same setting of the ripping attachment glue the eight str ips together with alternating colors using the bar clamps at the same time the strips must be clamped between flat boards with c clamps to prevent their buckling under the bar clamp pressure when the glue h as set twenty four hours remove the eight glued up pieces from the cl amps you will then have a board measuring 14 in by 15 in

(3)

the velocity of the wind varies in different storms as well as wit hin an individual storm close to the center inside the eye of the stor m the wind is very light and the sky clear or partially covered with high thin clouds away from the eye of the storm particularly on the ri ght hand side going with the storm it is common for the winds to re ach velocities of 90 to 115 and occasionaly as high as 135 miles per hour the wind speed falls off rapidly with increase of distance from the center so wind speeds of 30 to 40 miles per hour are typical at di stances of 150 to 200 miles.

(4)

an alarm clock of the mechanical round two dollar variety was ava ilable as a timing device and a small inexpensive camera made by the eastman kodak company known as a baby brownie was obtained wh en the kite had been tested and found to fly successfully the clock and camera were installed in it they were arranged on the lower cross braces of the kite as shown in fig 2 the clock being screwed to a br ace and the camera firmly tied between two braces the alarm of the cl ock would go off at the desired time when the shaft used to wind the alarm began to turn pulling the thread slowly and finally tripping

the camera shutter by operation of the instantaneous setting the shu
tter opened and automatically reclosed as the alarm winding shaft
continued to turn it broke the thread to the camera of course only one
picture could be taken on each flight.

   B. Explain the distinctions of form and use between: (1) SEMI-
COLON and COLON; (2) DASH and HYPHEN; (3) PARENTHESES and
BRACKETS; (4) DOUBLE QUOTATION MARKS and SINGLE QUOTATION
MARKS.
   C. (1) Account for each hyphen in the following sentence:
*Certain well-known professors are up-to-date in their lectures, yet
write for a semi-illiterate public in so-called pulp magazines.* (2) Ex-
plain the absence of apostrophes in the following sentence: *I lent
them mine, and he borrowed theirs; however, no one could find yours
in its hiding place.*
   D. Define: (1) INDEPENDENT CLAUSE; (2) COÖRDINATING CON-
JUNCTION; (3) CONJUNCTIVE ADVERB; (4) FUSED SENTENCE;
(5) COMMA SPLICE.
   E. Take TESTS A and B, below; then check your answers against
the KEY. If you have missed any points, carefully review P 2b.

TEST A

Consider the following sentence:

   In the Andes, where I was studying extinct volcanoes as the
   main part of my research toward the doctorate in geology, I
   met several friends whom I had known in the United States.

Both underscored clauses are necessary to convey in full the intended
thought, but the one enclosed in commas may be assumed to be
somewhat more important to the writer's meaning than the one not
enclosed in commas. From this sentence and your general knowledge
of the restrictive and nonrestrictive relationships, which one of the
following conclusions do you reach:
   a. That the sentence is incorrectly punctuated?
   b. That the sentence is badly constructed?
   c. That restrictive clauses are always more important than
nonrestrictive clauses?
   d. That nonrestrictive clauses are always more important
than restrictive clauses?
   e. That one cannot determine whether a clause is restric-

tive or nonrestrictive by deciding whether it is more or less important than some other clause in the sentence?

TEST B

Write *T* ("true") or *F* ("false") before each number:

1. Nonrestrictive clauses should be set off by commas.
2. Nonrestrictive phrases should be set off by commas.
3. A modifier that expresses no part of the meaning of a sentence is without function, and therefore should be excluded from that sentence.
4. If a modifier that contributes some part of the meaning of a sentence were removed, the part of the total meaning expressed by that modifier would be taken away from the sentence.
5. Nonrestrictive modifiers usually contribute no meaning, and therefore should be excluded.
6. Restrictive modifiers usually contribute no meaning, and therefore should be excluded.
7. Neither a restrictive nor a nonrestrictive modifier could be removed from a correctly written sentence without subtracting part of the total meaning of that sentence.
8. Whether a modifier is restrictive or nonrestrictive is not determined by whether it contributes to the meaning of the sentence in which it occurs.
9. Whether a modifier is restrictive or nonrestrictive is not determined by whether removal of the modifier would affect the total meaning of the sentence.
10. Whether a modifier is restrictive or nonrestrictive is determined solely by its *relation to the word or words modified*.

(KEY: TEST A—ans. *e*; TEST B—ans. 1, *T*; 2, *T*; 3, *T*; 4, *T*; 5, *F*; 6, *F*; 7, *T*; 8, *T*; 9, *T*; 10, *T*.)

* * * * *

FOR CHAPTER V

A. The four paragraphs on pages 376–378, above, given as Exercise *A* for Chapter IV, also constitute an exercise in capitalization. Notice that the strange appearance and immediate unintelligibility of the texts, as printed, result almost as much from the absence of capital letters as from the omission of punctuation.

B. In textbooks, periodicals, or library reference works, find examples of the plotted CURVE, the TABLE of statistics or data, the FLOWSHEET, the CONNECTION DIAGRAM (HOOKUP), the BAR GRAPH, the PIE DIAGRAM, the SCATTERGRAM, the MAP or CHART, the FLOOR (or PLOT) PLAN or LAYOUT, the ELEVATION, the SECTION, the CUT-AWAY, the PHANTOM, the PHOTOGRAPH, and the pictorial SKETCH. Can you name or describe any other types of illustrative matter that commonly serve as adjuncts to technical compositions?

C. In your reading during a period of several weeks, pay close attention to capitalization, italics, Arabic figures and worded numbers, abbreviations, and symbols. Review the discussions of these topics in the chapter. Do you observe general consistency or inconsistency among various authors treating the same classes of topics in science or technology? Can you discover any deviations from the norm in the selections printed in this book? What conclusions do you draw regarding the desirability of a consistent practice in your own technical writing? Would it make any difference whether you were composing for laymen or for experts? whether you were drafting a paragraphed text or were lettering, say, a diagram or table?

D. If possible, procure for occasional use a copy of Richard C. Jordan and Marion J. Edwards, *Aids to Technical Writing,* Minneapolis, University of Minnesota, Bulletin No. 21 of the Engineering Experiment Station, 1944. In particular, Chapters XII ("Conversion Factors"), XIII ("Letter Symbols"), and XV ("Graphical Symbols") bring together specialized material too extensive for the present book. Other chapters contain useful directions and hints concerning many phases of the mechanics of technical writing, illustration, and publication.

* * * * *

FOR CHAPTER VI

A. SAMPLE TOPICS FOR TECHNICAL EXPOSITION:

Diesel fuel problems

sonar

chemical fire-fighting agents

equations of the Haber process

the inductive element in mathematical induction

radio ranging

causes and correction of generator sparking

the diode rectification circuit

the theory of engine knock

nonnutrient products of soybeans

corrosion in pipes

functions of a production control department

comparative utility of artificial rubbers

the purpose of a control experiment

the hydrostatic paradox
the general elastic-curve equation
new rivals of quinine
the Rh factor
contrast of jet-propelled and rocket
missiles
triangulation methods of measuring
inaccessible but visible heights
analysis of results in a tension,
shearing, abrasion, compression,
or other strength-of-materials test
principle of operation of the planim-
eter, the gyroscope, the dial telephone, the automobile differential, Fluid Drive, the transit, the
fluorescent lamp, the electron microscope, the ultracentrifuge, the
cyclotron, the photoelectric ex-
posure meter, the nonrecoil can-
non, the water-purifying deion-
izer, the electrodialysis cell, the

spectroscope, the interferometer,
the portable flame thrower, the
Comptometer, the torsion-balance
mechanism
grades of cotton, rice, tea
definition of catalyst, equilibrium,
parallax, precession, relativity,
geophysics, geodesy, cosmography,
ecology, protein, virus, stoichi-
ometry, thermodynamics, thermi-
onics, prime mover, engine, motor, machine, instrument, servo-
mechanism, "electric eye"
classification of military explo-
sives, naval surface vessels, combustion engines, branches of engineering, girders and trusses,
roadbeds, cloud formations, blood
types, sulpha drugs, bridges, du-
plication processes for graphic
matter, pyrometers, silicones

B. Construct an analytical sentence outline, comparable in scope and detail with that beginning at page 138, on one (or on a delimited aspect of one) of the subjects listed just above, or on some other acceptable expository topic. Study and follow, in every particular, the explanations and rules given on pages 134 ff.

C. Write the composition outlined as Exercise *B.*

D. After an interval of at least a week, critically re-examine the composition written as Exercise *C*: for grammar, diction, punctuation, paragraph organization, transition, general clarity and coherence, accuracy, completeness, and style or tone. Then improve it by revi-sion, and submit a clear copy for comment and grading. (You may afterwards be asked to redraft it still another time, to hand in a cor-rection sheet, or to repeat Exercises *B, C,* and *D* with another topic.)

E. Choose an expository article or selection (for instance, one of the reading selections included in this book) of five or more para-graphs. Analyze each paragraph to discover: (1) the TOPIC SEN-TENCE (pages 144–146), (2) the method or combined methods of ORGANIZATION (pages 146–147), and (3) devices of TRANSITION pages 147–148). If in any paragraph the topic sentence appears to be latent rather than expressed, attempt to phrase it for yourself. Do you find any sentences of wholly transitional function? any purely transitional paragraphs? any badly developed paragraphs? (If the answer to the last question is "yes," explain the faults and suggest desirable changes.)

F. Compile a special vocabulary grouping transitional expressions by their functions: of **addition** (e.g., *and; furthermore; also*), of **reversal** (e.g., *but; nevertheless*), of **comparison** (e.g., *on the other hand; by contrast*), of **reference** (e.g., *this; those*) of **exemplification** (e.g., *especially; to cite an example; for instance*), and of as many other functions as you are able to note. Keep adding to this list, and use it to vary and enrich the transitions in your own written and spoken discourse.

G. By consulting dictionaries, encyclopedias, and other reference texts of any kind that may prove helpful, attempt to distinguish accurately between the member terms of each of the following pairs: (1) HYPOTHESIS—THEORY; (2) LAW—PRINCIPLE; (3) FACT—TRUTH; (4) EVIDENCE—PROOF; (5) AXIOM—POSTULATE; (6) DOCTRINE—DOGMA; (7) ABSORPTION—ADSORPTION; (8) PHYSICS—CHEMISTRY; (9) SOCIOLOGY—ECONOMICS; (10) CENTRIFUGAL FORCE—CENTRIPETAL FORCE.

H. Write a **formal definition** (see page 149) of five of the twenty entries in Exercise *G,* directly above. In each, print the term (subject of definition), circle the verb, draw a wavy line under the genus, and underscore the differentia (specific difference) with a straight line.

I. Copy and criticize several definitions of scientific terms from your textbooks on technical subjects.

J. Become acquainted with the useful series of compact definitions, supplemented by cross references to regular articles containing other technical definitions, at the entries "Electrical Terms" and "Engineering Terms" in vol. X of *The Encyclopedia Americana.*

K. Formulate a classification of some group of hand tools, as wrenches, hammers and mallets, or saws.

* * * * *

FOR CHAPTER VII

A. SAMPLE TOPICS FOR TECHNICAL DESCRIPTION:

an unconventional automobile body	the essential equipment of the surveyor
calcareous formations in a cave	
the control line for a model airplane	new finishes for interior walls

a homemade photographic enlarger, archery outfit, pair of skis, set of chessmen

fogs and strati

the compartments of a torpedo

the slang of mechanical engineering, of the petroleum industry, of the armed services, of the merchant marine, of the building trades

universal joints

the lighting of a pageant

fine woods for gunstocks

a functionally designed, modern factory building

the bronchoscope

a model glider

a scale-model dam for laboratory testing

visual perceptions in color blindness

a boiler room, pattern shop, submarine pump room, blast furnace, blooming mill, transformer vault, compressor station, planing room, filter press, heat exchanger, metal lathe, wood lathe, grinder and buffer, drill press

the range of coal-tar dyes

fillet welds

a well-ordered tool cabinet

internal construction of the clinical thermometer

a laminated-wood beam

the theoretically perfect diamond

an air-conditioning system

the rural distribution system of an electric company

diffraction phenomena

the elastic properties of amorphous sulphur

underground equipment in the Frasch process

ornaments blown from glass

a traffic plan for an engineering show

B. SAMPLE TOPICS FOR TECHNICAL NARRATION (INCLUDING DIRECTIONS):

overhauling a motorcycle

the process of soap making, sugar refining, flour milling, concrete mixing and pouring, ice manufacture, bookbinding, tanning, tin smelting, paper making

a midget-racer contest

an economy test, tensile-strength test, ballistics test

first aid and resuscitation in gas poisoning, burns, electric shock

distillation of gasoline from coal

extraction of magnesium from sea water

reclaiming of lead from old storage batteries

change-over in a projection booth

disassembly, cleaning, and reassembly of a machine gun or an automatic rifle or pistol

seismographic exploration

tracking a weather balloon with radar

a portable crystal radio set made from junk

the construction of a drawing desk

operation of a private branch exchange

a surveying party

the processing of blood plasma

calibrating a gauge

the steam automobile

Morse and the telegraph, Bell and the telephone, Marconi and the radiotelegraph, De Forest and the radio tube

the life cycle of the anopheles mosquito, of the malaria parasite, of the tapeworm, of the common fly

a photographic experiment with

varied lens aperture and shutter speed

decontamination procedures in chemical warfare

conversion of a gas mask to a diving helmet

emergency repair of a leak

an improvised fuel-volatility test

building a small electric furnace

determination of the capacity of an unlabeled condenser

correct application of paints

C. SAMPLE TOPICS FOR TECHNICAL ARGUMENTATION:

control of nuclear energy

oil proration

governmental hydroelectric projects

collective bargaining in essential industries

relative nutritional values of butter and fortified margarines

the best source of artificial rubber

apprentice training under the "G.I. Bill of Rights"

the explanation of hypnotism

the practicability of solar heating

the theory of an "expanding universe"

plastics for structural members in vehicles

the German chemical industry in the postwar world

social and economic effects of mass production

advertising claims for harmful or ineffective substances

desirable length of the curricula in

engineering and architecture

theories of adhesion

the evidence against the effectiveness of vaccination, against the doctrine of evolution, against the habitability of other planets

defects of the mechanical cotton picker

the decline of celestial air navigation

chemistry vs. chemical engineering as a profession

magnetic vs. disc recording

regenerative vs. convective preheaters

reciprocating vs. centrifugal pumps

solid vs. molten transportation of sulphur

black-and-white vs. color television

crystal vs. variable-frequency oscillators

amplitude vs. frequency modulation

social responsibilities of technology

D. Collect several examples of writings containing **convincing** technical arguments. Analyze each for inductive, deductive, and analogical reasoning. (See pages 169–172.) Try to restate all the deductive arguments in the form of syllogisms (cf. pages 170, 173), and to reduce all analogies to their inductive and deductive phases (cf. page 171). Following these procedures, are you still convinced? Have you found any concealed, and originally unsuspected, flaws of logic? Explain and defend your answers in statements pretendedly addressed to the writers or to their opponents.

E. Collect several examples of writings containing **unconvincing** technical arguments. Analyze each for fallacies (see pages 172–179), and write a full rebuttal of the one you consider most illogical. Afterwards, analyze your *own* arguments for possible fallacies; or, preferably, exchange papers with another student for the benefit of mutual criticism.

F. In performing Exercises *D* and *E*, watch for arguments (in particular, deductive arguments) that may be logically **valid** and yet **untrue.** Explain the distinction (see page 172), and suggest methods of defense against this paradox.

* * * * *

FOR CHAPTER VIII

A. Specify: (1) the elements common to the heading, the inside address, and the outside address of a business letter and its envelope; (2) the elements common to the inside and outside address but not to the heading; (3) the element contained in the heading but in neither the inside nor the outside address.

B. Distinguish: (1) block and indented styles; (2) open and closed terminal punctuation; (3) individual and company signatures.

C. Explain the required harmony of: (1) the salutation and the inside address; (2) the complimentary close and the message.

D. Define: (1) subject of communication; (2) direction of attention; (3) subscript.

E. Discuss: (1) single-spacing and double-spacing of the parts of a letter; (2) "framing" of pages; (3) desirable and undesirable peculiarities of letter-writing style; (4) general qualities of the successful business letter.

F. Write and carefully revise, with attention to grammar, spelling, and punctuation as well as to content, layout, and style, the following letters or those indicated or substituted by your instructor:

(1) A letter addressed to the head of your major department in school, applying for an assistantship, gradership, or some other appointment.

(2) A letter replying to one from an acquaintance who attends a women's college of liberal arts, requesting you to furnish information about a laboratory apparatus or process used in a science course.

(3) A letter (a) to a first-year student in the high school of which you are a graduate, offering advice on the choice of subjects to be taken in preparation for the same curriculum which

you are following; *or* (b) to a senior in high school, explaining in some detail the curriculum you are following.

(4) A letter to a firm that manufactures technical equipment or supplies, tactfully suggesting an improvement in, or addition to, its products or services.

(5) A letter offering to sell the rights to a device you have invented.

(6) A letter to a superior, (a) requesting leave of absence for a cause other than illness; *or* (b) making a complaint about certain conditions of work; *or* (c) applying for a change of duties.

(7) A letter to be duplicated and widely distributed, suggesting the formation of a professional organization.

(8) (a) An unfavorable reply to Letter (7), above; *or* (b) a favorable reply, containing constructive comments.

(9) A letter of transmittal to accompany a report that you are writing for one of your technical courses.

(10) A report in letter form of an activity on which you also are writing a formal report (not in letter form) for one of your technical courses.

* * * * *

FOR CHAPTER IX

A. Closely examine and stand ready to describe, on request: (1) the card catalogue of a library; (2) the three major general encyclopedias in English, together with their annual supplements, and five of the other GENERAL REFERENCE WORKS (including the *Readers' Guide* and the *International Index*) listed beginning at page 236; (3) five of the LIMITED ENCYCLOPEDIAS AND DICTIONARIES listed beginning at page 239; (4) five of the LIMITED INDEXES listed beginning at page 241; (5) five of the LIMITED BIBLIOGRAPHIES listed beginning at page 242; (6) five of the ABSTRACTS listed beginning at page 243; and (7) two of the LIMITED YEARBOOKS listed on page 244.

B. Choose two topics concerning, respectively: (1) a phase of the early history of science, and (2) a recent technological development. Prepare for *each* a tentative bibliography giving full citations, in correct form, of not less than twenty-five items, including at least one book, at least one periodical article, at least one encyclopedia article, and at least one government document or special type of source material other than the foregoing. Turn in these bibliographies for criticism by your instructor.

C. When the tentative bibliographies submitted in Exercise B, above, have been returned, spend a week in library research on *each* topic, making a large number of bibliographical and note cards in usable, permanent, uniform style. At the beginning of the third week, in conference with your instructor, exhibit and discuss your cards, and decide which of the two subjects is the more promising for continued research. (If neither appears suitable, choose a new topic and start again.) As you continue to take and organize your notes, make a tentative topical outline (cf. pages 247–248); then, when the research has been completed, develop it into a sentence outline. (See Chapter VI, Section A, pages 129–139.) From the sentence outline and the correspondingly distributed note cards, compose the final paper, taking particular pains with accuracy of reference and form in the footnotes. Draft the bibliography from your alphabetized bibliographical cards. In the whole process of documentation, follow the directions and models presented in Section D (pages 248 ff).

D. Observe numerous examples of documented writing in various kinds of publications devoted to several fields of scientific and technical research. Are methods of documentation uniform in all types of books, reports, and articles? If not, are they uniform in each book, report, or article? in the same type of publication treating different subjects? in different types of publications treating the same subject? in different instances of the same type of publication treating the same subject? How many radically or strikingly diverse systems of documentation are you able to discover? Does the system recommended in this book strike you as easy and efficient? Whether it does or not, you may be permitted—or, under some conditions (such as composition for a journal definitely chosen in advance), even be expected—to adopt another system. Bear in mind, however, that in no circumstances is any plan of documentation worth using unless it is clear, precise in citation of references, and self-consistent.

*   *   *   *   *

FOR CHAPTER X

A. Discuss the definition of the word *report* stated on page 265. Does it adequately cover the various classes of reports mentioned on pages 266–267, those suggested for student composition on pages

290–298, and all others you have prepared or observed? If a more explicit or comprehensive definition should seem desirable, attempt to phrase it.

B. Which of the four "forms of discourse" is most likely to predominate in: (1) a section stating the problem of a report; (2) a principle-of-operation or theory section; (3) an apparatus section; (4) a process or procedure section? (See pages 283–285 of Section B, and cf. Chapters VI and VII.) Analyze several of your previous reports for passages of exposition, description, narration, and argumentation. So far as your own report writing is concerned, does the title of Chapter VI, "The Major Function of Technical Discourse: Exposition," appear to be accurate? Is any type of discourse unimportant for reports in general?

C. Discriminate, as definitely as possible, the terms *results, conclusions,* and *recommendations.* Find examples of published reports containing one or more sections so labeled. Do you notice any tendency of these terms to overlap in meaning? Which two are most sharply distinguished in usage?

D. Recommended assignment for a course in technical English: three reports averaging about five typewritten pages on subjects chosen from Types (4), (5), (6), and (7) listed in Section C (pages 294 ff.), due at intervals during a semester; *or:* two such reports, due at the middle and end of a quarter; *or:* one such report, due at the end of a short term; *or:* one long report of fifteen to twenty typewritten pages—complete with title page, table of contents, letter of transmittal, abstract, body (including graphic illustrative matter), and appendix—on a subject chosen from Types (1), (2), and (3) listed in Section C (pages 291 ff.), due at the end of a semester or quarter.

E. See, as additional assignments on the technical report, Exercise *F,* (10) for Chapter VIII on page 386, above; and Exercise *C* for Chapter XI on page 389, below. Numerous topics suitable for reports may be adopted or adapted from the lists given as Exercise *A* for Chapter VI (pages 380–381) and Exercises *A, B,* and *C* for Chapter VII (pages 382–384).

F. For further study of report writing, consult: T. R. Agg and W. L. Foster, *The Preparation of Engineering Reports;* Ray Palmer Baker and Almonte Charles Howell, *The Preparation of Reports, Scientific, Engineering, Administrative, Business;* C. G. Gaum, H. F. Graves, and L. S. S. Hoffman, *Report Writing;* J. Raleigh Nelson,

Writing the Technical Report; Alta Gwinn Saunders and Chester Reed Anderson, *Business Reports.*

* * * *

FOR CHAPTER XI

A. Choose one of the following topics for a talk of about ten to fifteen minutes: (1) a recent invention or improvement of a technical device, formula, process, or the like; (2) a comparison of two or more rival devices, formulas, processes, or the like, both or all of which serve the same technical function; (3) formal definition and expanded definitional discussion of an important term in science or technology (cf. Chapter VI, Section C, pages 149–152; and see also near the end of Exercise *A* for Chapter VI, page 381, above, a group of sample topics for definition). Obtain any necessary reference material in the library or elsewhere. Develop an outline for the introduction, body, and conclusion (cf. pages 347–353 in Chapter XI). If you plan to speak partly from notes, transcribe the essential portions of the outline, together with data or textual matter intended for itemizing or direct quotation, on not more than three cards of uniform size (cf. pages 350 and 357). Do not attempt actual delivery of the talk until you have given it at least five complete rehearsals while standing, speaking aloud, and practicing the use of gestures and good platform manners (cf. pages 353–357 and 360–361).

B. Exchange services with a friend who also is practicing public speaking. Request him to observe critically your first or second practice, with attention especially to possible deficiencies of posture and voice such as those discussed in Section C, pages 363–365. In a series of rehearsals (preferably not in immediate succession), concentrate separately on remedying each of the different faults he may have indicated. Then invite his comments as, in a final practice speech, you attempt a generally improved performance.

C. Obtain permission to deliver orally, in class, one of your assigned technical reports on a subject requiring considerable use of graphic matter or of solid exhibits. Before coming to the platform for the report, carefully prepare and arrange these materials as blackboard drawings, wall charts, or displays of other kinds. Study pages 358–360, and attempt to acquire a skillful manner of demonstrating a topic with exhibits. Remember, especially, that never should your body obstruct anyone's clear view of the part of the display toward which attention is being directed. More especially still, bear in mind that even though you are talking *about* an exhibit, you always are talking *to* the audience.

D. In different groups, plan and present: (1) a ROUND-TABLE CONFERENCE on liberal arts courses (prescribed and elective) in curricula of science and technology; (2) a DEBATE on the question, "Resolved: That a uniform registration law for engineers [*or:* for architects] should be adopted"; (3) a PANEL DISCUSSION of professional societies—regional, national; general, specialized—in the technical world.

E. Recommended textbooks for further study of speech: James A. Winans, *Public Speaking*; Wayland Maxfield Parrish, *Speaking in Public*; A. R. Thompson, *Handbook of Public Speaking*; Alan H. Monroe, *Principles and Types of Speech* and *Principles of Speech*; John Dolman, Jr., *A Handbook of Public Speaking*; William Trufant Foster, *Argumentation and Debating*; James A. Winans and William E. Utterback, *Argumentation*; Lionel Crocker, *Argumentation and Debate*; Alan Nichols, *Discussion and Debate*; A. Craig Baird, *Public Discussion and Debate*; J. M. O'Neill, *Extemporaneous Speaking*; James Thompson Baker, *The Short Speech*; C. Raymond Van Dusen, *Training the Voice for Speech*; Virgil A. Anderson, *Training the Speaking Voice*; Donald C. Bryant and Karl R. Wallace, *Oral Communication*; S. Marion Tucker, *Public Speaking for Technical Men.*

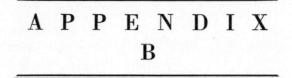

APPENDIX
B

APPENDIX

B

READINGS

THE PROFESSION OF ENGINEERING

by Clement C. Williams *

Definition of Engineering. Because of the diversity of considerations and operations included in the work of engineers, it is difficult to set the boundaries to the province of engineering through a definition. A definition that includes everything that has been labeled engineering would be so broad as to cover the entire realm of applied art, applied science, and applied economics. A definition that includes the great core of engineering and at the same time permits associated activities to fall within the fringes at the border lines may be stated: "Engineering is the scientific utilization of the forces and materials of nature in the design, construction, production, and operation of works for the benefit of man."

"Scientific utilization" involves a choice of method best suited to the desired end, requiring an expert knowledge of past experience and a creative ability to meet new situations, for in many cases the procedure is without precedent and the problem must be solved afresh. The results of scientific utilization should be reliability and economy.

The "forces" involved include those derived from heat energy from fuels through steam and internal-combustion engines, waterfalls, electricity, gravitation, wind pressure, buoyancy of water, mechanical action, radioactivity, magnetism, cohesion, etc.

The "materials" comprise iron, stone, timber, copper, water, rubber, composite materials, alloys, etc.

* Reprinted by permission from BUILDING AN ENGINEERING CAREER, 2nd Ed., by Clement C. Williams, Copyright, 1946, by the McGraw-Hill Book Company, Inc. From Part I, Chapter II. The author was a civil engineer, university professor and administrator, and consultant in engineering and industrial education.

"Construction" embraces the erection of bridges, buildings, railroads, water systems, highways, and other forms of public and private works. "Production" means principally power generation and the manufacture of goods on an organized scale. "Operation" means organizing man power, funds, and procedures in carrying on industrial and utility enterprises. "Works" includes not only public works but factories, machines, and manufactured products as well.

The "benefit of man" means essentially supplying the economic needs of men, such as housing, transportation, communication, food, clothing, entertainment, and convenience, and implies a knowledge of economic organization of society, because the economic needs of the race are supplied through highly complex organization of production and distribution.

Origin of Terms "Engine" and "Engineer." According to the "New English Dictionary on Historical Principles," the term *engine* is derived through the old French from the Latin roots *in genere,* meaning to beget or to create, being closely akin to *engender.* The words *ingenious* and *ingenuity* are from the Latin roots and have related meanings. The Latin word *ingenium,* meaning a clever device, either an implement or a plan, may be considered more directly as the ancestral form of "engine."

In the early English, the word *engine* sometimes meant ingenuity, as in Chaucer's "Canterbury Tales" (1380), "A man hath sapiences three, memorie, engin, and intellect." At that time also the word had the meaning of a mechanical contrivance, as when the monk Robert Brunne wrote (1330), "Geauntz sette them [the stones of Stonehenge] on an hil full hey with engyns fulle queyntely." The word *engine* was early used in English as a verb also, meaning to plan or to contrive, in the identical sense as the Latin word *ingeniare.* Thus Poet Gower wrote in 1400, "With fair haste and great skill, of gold gifts that they have engined together," and Barlow (1609), "The most horrible design . . . that ever was engined." To engine a device, therefore, signified to plan it with acumen, and one who engined or contrived ingenious devices was, therefore, an engineer (engine + er), just as a contriver was one who contrived. The word was sometimes spelled *enginer,* as in Shakespeare's "Hamlet," "For 'tis the sport to have the enginer hoist with his own petar," or by Ben Jonson (1600), "He is a good enginer that alone can make an instrument to get preferment," but it was more frequently spelled *engineer.*

The word is of similar form in most of the European languages, e.g., French, Dutch, . . . and German *ingenieur,* Spanish *ingeniero,* and Italian *ingegnere,* and in all of these tongues the word means ingenious designer. Those who first took the name *engineer,* in England as well as in other countries, were designers and not machine or engine operators.

The word *engineer,* therefore, means an ingenious designer or planner, and only in a recent and local sense does it signify one who operates an engine, for which vocation *engineman* is more accurate and appropriate. This latter use of the word *engineer* is confined to the United States and almost entirely to the uneducated.

The Vocation of Engineering. As a vocation, engineering is a profession and involves to a greater or lesser degree the characteristics of a science, an art, and a business.

As a *science,* engineering requires a knowledge of the physical laws of nature and an acquaintance with the mechanical properties of the materials which the engineer must use. Mathematics, physics, chemistry, and mechanics are the physical sciences which most directly serve the engineer and he must be sufficiently versed in these to be able to use them reliably in his plans. Other sciences—biology, geology, and economics—also have a bearing on some of his work. Engineering is sometimes called *applied science,* but this term is unsatisfactory because there are other applied sciences and, furthermore, it includes many features of investigative science.

As an *art,* engineering is based on the accumulated experience of the past masters. The general procedure, the kinds of working tools best suited to a purpose, the capacities of tradesmen and their rates of working, the relative advantages of laborsaving machinery, and the proper organization of the working force are all matters primarily of experience.

As a *business,* engineering involves the selling of one's professional services advantageously. This aspect is particularly important in the work of the engineer engaged in private or consulting practice. He must be on the alert to learn where his services might be needed, and he must have a faculty for convincing industrial managers, boards of directors, city councils, and others that his services are adequate to their needs, without too blatantly proclaiming his own merits.

An engineer may practice his profession in either one of two ways, *viz.,* (1) as an employee of a corporation, such as a railroad, a public utility, an industry, a city or other public body, which has sufficient engineering work to do to warrant maintaining its own regularly organized engineering staff; or (2) as an engineer, or the employee of an engineer, engaged in open private practice, commonly called a *consulting engineer,* who undertakes to perform engineering services for anyone who may retain him.

In the first type of work, the engineer receives a regular salary and devotes all of his time to one employer, working coöperatively with the other engineers on the staff. In the second group, an engineer in private practice may charge for his services a per diem (per day) rate, or he may charge a retainer fee plus a per diem rate, or he may charge on the basis of the cost of the work, say 5 per cent of the cost, where both design and inspection of work are required of him.

In either case, the professional service rendered consists of advice concerning plans, procedures, or the status of existing works. When an engineer becomes an executive, as so frequently happens, his function is to direct the operations of others, either near or remote from the technical activities.

In the early years of his practical life, an engineer may expect to act as an assistant to more experienced engineers, performing sub-professional duties and working under direction. The work that he will do in this capacity will include making surveys and other measurements, drafting, computing, testing, clerical work, and inspection. So much of the ultimate practice of engineering is the result of experience that such assistant positions afford a natural vestibule through which to enter the more definitely professional phases of engineering. This period corresponds to an internship for a physician, but fortunately in engineering there are elementary duties that may be done satisfactorily by the beginner while he learns the more complicated features of the work, and, hence, the young engineer has the ability to earn a salary from even his first employment. . . .

THE YOUNG ENGINEER AND HIS ENGLISH

BY ROBERT I. REES *

When I accepted [an] invitation to talk to this group on the subject "The Young Engineer and His English," I resolved that I must obtain substantial supporting evidence for any opinions I might express to you. Generalization from a few striking instances is too frequent and too easy in dealing with such a topic. Even sharp criticism of teaching methods and their results often rests on no more secure a foundation. Precise measurements may be impossible but it is not impossible to obtain fairly objective judgments from a representative group of individuals who are in intimate contact with the problems this subject implies.

There is, of course, some evidence of this character already available. The investigation of engineering education conducted by this Society a few years ago obtained the opinions of over 500 members of engineering faculties and several thousand graduates in engineering, concerning the importance of training in English. In brief, over 95 per cent of the faculty members considered English composition to be of primary importance as a fundamental element in all engineering curricula. English speech was thought of primary importance by 75 per cent, and English literature was so considered by 45 per cent of these men. Two-thirds of them, moreover, thought that courses of purely cultural value should be *required* in engineering curricula and half of them recommended literature as an especially valuable element in their cultural content. Although the graduates ranked cultural subjects last in importance after those of a scientific, technical, and economic character, over 60 per cent of that group thought them indispensable or of considerable value. One-quarter of these men believed that more attention should be given to English in college. A similar proportion were continuing their study of it after graduation.

These data conclusively support the general opinion that English training is of major importance to the young engineer, and at least suggest that more emphasis should be placed upon it in the engineer-

* *Collected Papers of the Session on English*, Pittsburgh, The Society for the Promotion of Engineering Education [since 1946, The American Society for Engineering Education], March, 1933, pp. 42–53. ("Selected Papers of the Summer School for Engineering Teachers," Bulletin No. 20.) The author was Assistant Vice President, American Telephone and Telegraph Company, Personnel Relations Department. Two middle sections of the address are omitted in this reprint.

ing curricula. They do not indicate whether the engineering graduate
has been handicapped in his work by inadequate training in English
and, if so, how that training might be strengthened. Further evidence
on these and similar points seemed most desirable, and it is this which
I have attempted to secure. In doing so, I have drawn upon three
groups of men: (1) about 400 engineering graduates less than five
years out of college, now employed in the several Bell System Companies; (2) about 90 supervisors of such men, who come into intimate contact with their work; (3) a few Deans of graduate schools
in which both engineering and other college graduates are enrolled in
some numbers. In the case of the first two groups, rather formal questionnaires were submitted, permitting tabulation of the replies, but
individual comments were also invited. From the Deans, only general
statements were requested.

Care was taken to have the graduates replying to these questionnaires representative of all such men in our organizations, rather than
selected men of above average ability. We believe, however, that
there is some evidence which indicates that they are above the average of their college classes. In the case of the supervisors, however, we
endeavored to select men likely to be especially discriminating and
thoughtful in their replies.

THE POINT OF VIEW OF THE RECENT GRADUATE

The specific results of the questionnaire to recent graduates were
as follows:

QUESTION 1: Please enumerate the definite uses which you have in
your work for written or spoken English, indicating about
what proportion of your working time is spent in those
particular activities.

ANSWER: About 25 per cent of the working time of these men is
spent in preparing letters, memoranda, reports, and other
written material. Slightly over 20 per cent of their time is
spent in contacts with the public or with their supervisors
and other employees of the Company. Naturally, these
proportions vary in individual cases, but on the whole, it is
evident that in the Bell System, young engineering graduates spend nearly half their time in work which requires
the use of written or spoken English.

QUESTION 2: Has the preparation of letters, memoranda, and written
reports been more difficult for you than other phases of
your work?

ANSWER: Nearly 40 per cent of these men replied in the affirmative, and slightly over 60 per cent replied in the negative to this question. That two-fifths of them should find their written work more difficult than other parts of it is hardly surprising. I am not certain we should not find similar results even among a group of teachers of English.

QUESTION 3: Have your supervisors found it necessary to revise, not the facts or reasoning of these letters and reports, but the way in which your thought was expressed? If so, has this occurred (*a*) frequently, (*b*) occasionally, (*c*) seldom?

ANSWER: About 10 per cent of the men stated that frequent correction of their written material was necessary; somewhat over 50 per cent stated that it occurred occasionally; and rather less than 40 per cent said that it occurred but seldom. On the whole, this seems encouraging, as we may judge that only a relatively small proportion have serious difficulty with their written reports. In some cases too, corrections by supervisors may be arbitrary or based on formal rules; in any event, certain of the graduates feel that this is true.

QUESTION 4: Do you find it difficult to express your ideas orally in individual conferences with your supervisor or in group conferences?

ANSWER: Thirty per cent of the men replying answered in the affirmative and 70 per cent in the negative. The number of men who find this sort of expression difficult is rather less than in the case of written work. My feeling is that this percentage may be more disturbing than in the former case.

QUESTION 5: Do you feel that college graduates in Arts and Science or Business Administration are able to express themselves more easily and effectively than you are (*a*) in writing? (*b*) orally?

ANSWER: In the case of both writing and speaking, slightly less than half the men felt inferior to the Arts and Science or Business Administration graduates, with slightly more than half feeling no such deficiency. Many of the men, too, stated that this was probably due to the types of men who undertook the different curricula, rather than to the content of their college courses.

QUESTION 6: Would you favor more emphasis on English in the engineering curriculum? If more emphasis is to be given to English, do you believe that more time should be devoted to definite instruction in (*a*) composition? (*b*) speaking? (*c*) literature?

ANSWER: Ninety per cent of the men answered the first part of this question in the affirmative. Something over 80 per cent favored more emphasis on composition, and a slightly larger proportion favored more emphasis on speaking. Only 25 per cent, however, felt that more time should be devoted to literature.

There is a clear demarcation here. Evidently the engineering graduate believes in pursuing the thing which he is after directly, and is skeptical of the incidental values which literature might bring him. For my own part, I am not sure that range of vocabulary and quality of style can be gained without more contact with great literature. If I should be correct in this, a distinct challenge is presented to the teacher of literature in engineering schools to arouse his students to an appreciation of its worth.

QUESTION 7: To what extent do you feel that effective results could also be obtained by stressing better writing and speaking in classes other than English?

ANSWER: About 13 per cent of the men replying felt that no, or very little, value could be gained in this way. Half of them expected some value from it, and the remainder expected a good deal of value. It is interesting to compare these results with the decidedly frequent suggestion from the supervisors that this method of attack would be decidedly worthwhile.

QUESTION 8: Do you believe that the quality of instruction you received in English at college was as high as that received in your technical subjects?

ANSWER: Slightly more than half of the men answered "yes" to this question, but nearly half felt that they obtained better instruction in their technical subjects. Here again, the question of major interest on the part of men pursuing engineering courses comes into play. Many of them, with less interest in the subject of English, may feel that the caliber of the instruction in it is not high.

QUESTION 9: Was there any tendency at your institution to regard English courses as of minor importance (*a*) on the part of the students? (*b*) on the part of the faculty?

ANSWER: Nearly 90 per cent of the men agreed that the students considered English courses of little importance, but less than 30 per cent felt that the faculty had shared this opinion.

QUESTION 10: Please describe your own attitude toward its importance when you entered college, during your senior year, and at present.

ANSWER: The answers to this question throw a good deal of light on the replies to the preceding one. A large majority of the men said that English seemed of little importance during the freshman year; that by senior year its importance had become apparent; and that they now feel it was very important indeed, in fact approaches their technical work in importance.

QUESTION 11: Please give any general comments you may have concerning training in English for engineering students, which have not been covered in the preceding questions.

ANSWER: A large proportion of the men desire that more emphasis be placed on the importance of English by faculty, alumni, and business men with whom students come in contact, in order that they may recognize, during their college course, the need for devoting more attention to it. The implication is that these men feel they have missed something which they could have gained if they had only had a somewhat different point of view during their college course. In fact, some of these men felt that English should be taught during the entire four years and that, if necessary to accomplish this, the engineering course should be lengthened. Many different opinions were expressed concerning changes in the methods of teaching English to engineers. One suggestion was that English should be taught by instructors directly connected with the engineering department, who would then have more understanding of the interests of engineering students. On the contrary, another man suggested that the examinations in engineering subjects should be corrected both by engineering professors and English professors, for errors in expression. Some men feel that the trouble has been in the English preparation obtained in high school. Others favor special courses in public speaking. One man believed that the cultural side of English should be stressed in order to develop the habit of wide reading. Another man suggested that a course in English should be given in the senior rather than in the freshman year, while still another man felt that the training in English could best be obtained through courses pursued after graduation. A wholesome warning against over-emphasis on the importance of English was voiced by one man who agreed that it was important, but secondary in value to "accuracy and truthfulness."

In general, the replies of the young engineering graduates in the Bell Telephone Company of Canada paralleled those of the men in the

United States very closely. Somewhat higher percentages of the Canadians, however, were skeptical of the quality of the English instruction there, and believed that it was considered of minor importance by both faculty and students. Their supervisors, on the other hand, were quite as well satisfied with their use of English as those in the United States.

. . , ...

SUMMARY

To sum up the points of view of these three groups of men, it is evident that a substantial part of the engineer's time is spent in work requiring written or oral expression and that a large majority of the younger engineers believe more emphasis should have been placed on English during their college days. In the case of a substantial minority, work involving writing or speaking was more difficult for them than their other work and, in a similar proportion of the cases, the results were not satisfactory to their supervisors. Half of the graduates and two-thirds of the supervisors believe that Arts and Science graduates, and to a somewhat smaller degree, graduates in Business Administration, excel engineers in the use of English.

The most frequent suggestions for improvement are (1) a greater emphasis on the value of English that its importance may be recognized by the undergraduate; (2) scrutiny of engineering and other reports for errors of expression and lack of clarity; (3) additional English courses, especially in public speaking.

These results, on the whole, hardly warrant despair on the part of the teachers of English in engineering colleges. When the difficulty of their task is appreciated it seems they have done astonishingly well with it. There are, at least, two unique inherent difficulties which they face. In the first place, the engineering student is the sort of man who expresses himself far more naturally in concrete and mathematical symbols than in words. In the second, his courses other than English give him very little opportunity to write or speak as compared with the students in other curricula who write in all and speak in many of them. These distinctions amply explain the differences in their facility.

But something substantial remains to be done. One thing obviously is a somewhat different attitude toward English in the whole engineering faculty and effective reflection of that attitude in the student body. I feel that the data presented here fully justify you in urging this most vigorously. Beyond that, if I were president or dean of an engineering college, I should feel warranted in asking why the following requirements in English were not the minimum necessary in its curriculum, fully realizing that excellent reasons might be given to the contrary.

(1) A freshman course definitely pointed to correct, clear writing and speaking, through frequent compositions, class discussions, and a certain amount of reading, with an inflexible standard of performance.

(2) The reading outside of class during sophomore and junior years, of ten to twelve great books, with written or oral examinations to make certain that they had been more than superficially covered.

(3) A substantial seminar course in senior year, where written and oral reports of some length and complexity are presented and discussed for organization of thought, choice of language, and style.

In addition, I should urgently request every member of the faculty to scrutinize papers in all courses, from time to time, especially where the nature of the material makes it appropriate, from the point of view of correct and clear English. It is probably true that such a procedure would not be practical in the case of all student reports.

These suggestions require an adequate staff, a problem which, as I am not president or dean of an engineering college, I shall leave to those who are, but urgently commend to their attention.

SURVEYING IN THE ROMAN PERIOD

BY WILLIAM BARCLAY PARSONS *

When the engineering works of the Roman and the Renaissance periods are considered, one is impressed by the fact that the long, straight roads and the carefully adjusted aqueducts of the former epoch and the extensive canal systems of the latter required surveyor's instruments of considerable precision to lay out their alignments and fix even gradients. So before examining the instruments and the surveying methods of the engineers of the Renaissance [the projected chapter on that subject was left unwritten at the death of the author], let us briefly investigate those employed by their Roman predecessors when the construction era of ancient Rome was at its height. This will show what information and precedents were available and enable us to estimate the progress made in the later period.

The best accounts of the early instruments are those in the writings of Hero, Archimedes, Aristotle and Vitruvius. On the invention of the printing press all their works except one were printed and so were made easily available to engineers. This exception is a work by Hero, *On the Dioptra*, which survives in manuscript. It is singular that this work was not printed, because it is the best and most detailed of the early descriptions of surveying that survived the ravages of time until they could be put in type.

There are three copies of the manuscript, one in the Bibliothèque Nationale at Paris, one at Strasbourg, and the third, a fragment only, at Vienna. All three are in Greek. The oldest appears to be the one at Strasbourg, of which the Paris manuscript is probably a copy. They are without date, but the Paris copy was made perhaps not earlier than the seventeenth century. In 1858 A. J. H. Vincent translated the Paris copy, after comparing it with the Strasbourg manuscript in order to eliminate errors in transcribing, and published the original text and his translation in French with scholarly notes ("Le traité de la dioptre d'Héron d'Alexandrie," *Notices et extraits des manuscrits de la Bibliothèque Impériale*, Vol. XIX, 1858). A previous translation had been made by Venturi in 1814, but the work of Vincent is more accurate.

Hero's treatise is a remarkable document not only for the light it

* From *Engineers and Engineering in the Renaissance*, Baltimore, The Williams & Wilkins Company, 1939. Part II, Chapter VII. General Parsons was a leading military and civil engineer, as well as a historian of engineering.

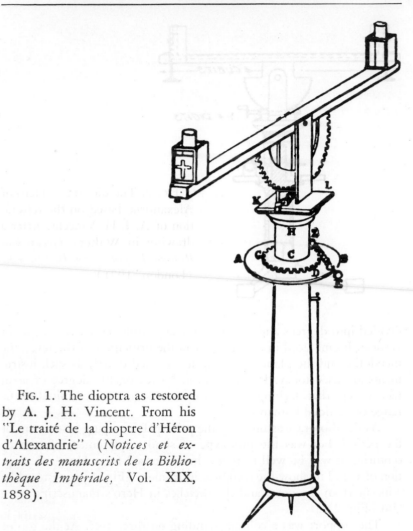

FIG. 1. The dioptra as restored by A. J. H. Vincent. From his "Le traité de la dioptre d'Héron d'Alexandrie" (*Notices et extraits des manuscrits de la Bibliothèque Impériale,* Vol. XIX, 1858).

throws on surveying methods in use two thousand years ago, but because many of his recommendations are followed today.

The word *dioptra* was applied by the Greeks to any instrument through which or over which one could sight. As shown by Hero, the dioptra had several applications. Although it consisted primarily of a water level revolving horizontally on a tripod, it could be converted into an alignment instrument, as the arm had vertical as well as horizontal movement, or the arm could be made to turn on a disk

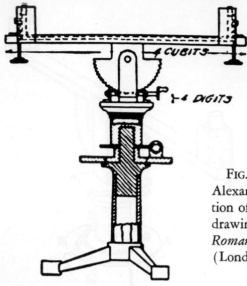

FIG. 2. The dioptra of Hero of
Alexandria, based on the restora-
tion of A. J. H. Vincent. After a
drawing in Walters' *Greek and
Roman Engineering Instruments*
(London, 1921).

divided into degrees and thus measure any angle, either horizontal or
vertical. It embraced in one instrument the principles of the level, the
theodolite and the plane table, and it was used exactly as such instruments are used today. It also furnished a reasonable degree of accuracy, except that, lacking the telescope, all sights were limited to the
range of unaided human vision.

As the dioptra was not only the principal surveying instrument of
the period, but was the prototype of similar instruments for many
centuries, it will be well to repeat in condensed form Hero's description of it and to show the complete instrument [Fig. 1] as restored by
Vincent from the notes and the sketches in Hero's manuscript. (See
also [Fig. 2].)

The support was a column standing on three feet. At the top of
the column was fixed a horizontal copper plate, *AB.* To this was
attached a vertical copper tube, *HC,* which was free to turn about the
axis of the column and the plate. Forming part with the tube was a
geared wheel, *DG,* the teeth of which meshed into a worm, *EZ,* whose
supports were fixed to the plate, *AB.* On the capital of *HC,* which
Hero said was of Doric design, was a second plate, *KL,* to which
were attached two vertical supports. These supports carried an arm
hinged centrally on a single pin, but beneath the arm and controlling
its motion in a vertical plane was a vertical semicircular geared

wheel whose teeth, like those of the horizontal wheel, meshed into a worm. On the top of the arm, which was about six feet long, a longitudinal trough was cut with a cylindrical or quadrangular cross-section, to hold a copper tube. At the ends of the tube and at right angles to it were two short vertical copper tubes. On the top of these were two tubes of glass of the same diameter as the copper tubes and sealed to them by wax or other mastic, the several tubes forming a connected whole.

Surrounding the glass tubes were hollow boxes in the end faces of which were small copper disks sliding in grooves along their vertical edges, close to the sides of the glass tubes. In the middle of the disks were slits through which one could look. Projecting from the lower edge of the disks were pins which passed through the main arm and which were cut with a worm thread engaging a screw collar in the arm. By turning these pins, the disks with their peep slits would be raised or lowered and then held in place.

To insure a vertical setting, a plumb-bob hung at one side of the main column. The axis of the column was vertical when the cord of the plumb-bob just touched the center of a stud attached to the side of the column near the base.

Hero's dioptra contained all the fundamental elements of a good surveying instrument. It could be set vertically and had motions in both horizontal and vertical planes. The worm gears permitted close setting and locked the instrument fast. The water surfaces in the upright arms of the bent tube gave two surfaces in the upright glass tubes that marked the horizontal. The sliding disks could be fixed accurately by the screw adjustments to bring the horizontal slits at the level of the water, where they became peep sights through which to project a horizontal plane in any direction.

Hero appreciated the fact that geared wheels and worms gave a slow movement. In order to bring either geared wheel quickly to its approximate desired position, he described a slot slightly wider than the thickness of the engaging wheels, cut lengthwise in the thread of the worms. By turning the worm until the wheel was unlocked, the latter could be revolved freely, and when it was in approximate position, a slight turn of the worm reëngaged it, as the mechanism was fixed to make and hold close adjustment.

For giving alignment and the turning of angles, the dioptra was serviceable. With possible motion in two planes at right angles to each other, all the operations of alignment could be completed, the vertical slit in the copper disks giving sights through which to set

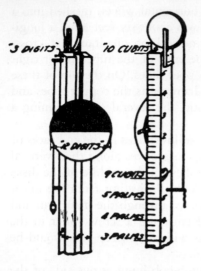

FIG. 3. The leveling staff of Hero of Alexandria, as restored by A. J. H. Vincent. After a drawing in Walter's *Greek and Roman Engineering Instruments* (London, 1921).

stakes or rods. If the level tube was filled and the peep sights adjusted to it, then it is evident that, by means of the vertical semicircle supporting the arm, vertical angles above and below a horizontal plane could be readily measured. For laying out horizontal angles with considerable accuracy or to use the dioptra as a plane table, Hero removed the level arm and established in its place a horizontal plate, on which the arm could be moved either freely as the alidade on a plane table or pivoted at the center. A circle concentric with the pivot was described on the plate and divided into degrees. By revolving the arm and sighting through the vertical slits, not only the simple right angle in a horizontal plane, but, by inclining the plate from the horizontal, any angle in any plane could be read at once.

To measure distances accurately, Hero said that the measuring cord must be "well stretched and tested and one that cannot in any manner either lengthen or shrink." In another work he showed that this could be accomplished by stretching and restretching the measuring cord between two posts, or by leaving it suspended vertically with a weight attached until it would lengthen no more and then coating it with a mixture of wax and resin to protect it against a change in length through absorption of moisture from the atmosphere.

To read elevations, Hero described a level rod [Fig. 3], the counterpart of its modern descendant, in the following words:

"Two pieces of wood are dressed true to be each 10 cubits [18 feet] long, 5 digits [3¾ inches] wide and 3 digits [2¼ inches] thick. A dovetailed groove is cut the whole length of the broad side, the narrow side of the dovetail being on the exterior. In this groove a tenon runs freely without coming out. On the tenon is fixed a circular disk ten or twelve digits [7½ to 9 inches] in diameter, which is divided by a straight line, perpendicular to the length of the rod, into two semicircles, one of which is colored white, the other black. To the tenon is attached a cord which passes over a pulley on top of the rod and goes down the other side opposite to that of the disk.

"Now, if the rod be held in a vertical position and the cord is pulled from behind, the disk is made to rise; if, on the contrary, the cord be loosened, the disk will descend by virtue of its own weight, especially if precaution has been taken to nail a plate of lead on the back, for this will naturally render it more mobile. Consequently, having drawn the cord to raise the disk, it can be stopped and held at any desired part of the rod. The length of the rod, beginning from the bottom, should be divided into cubits, palms and digits. Then at these points draw lines on the side of the staff to the right of the disk marking the graduated divisions of the length. The disk carries a pointer on the back in line with the diameter, to which reference has been made, which points to the scale marked on the rod.

"The rod must be held in a vertical position exactly perpendicular to the ground. On the plane side opposite to that on which the divisions are marked, a peg about three digits [2¼ inches] long is fixed, at the end of which is a vertical hole through which a string passes carrying a weight. Near the bottom of the rod is another peg of a length equal to the distance of the hole from the staff on the top peg, and on the end of this is marked a vertical straight line. When the plumb-line coincides with this line it will show that the staff is exactly vertical."

From this description it is apparent that the leveling rod of the Roman engineer, as he used it to lay out his aqueducts, did not differ in principle from that used in similar work today. There is no essential change except that the cord controlling the target is replaced by a metal spring and binding screw. To run levels, he used backsights and foresights and entered them in a field record exactly as is done now.

In his treatise Hero gave full descriptions of various surveying operations, including projecting a line into the opposite side of a hill in order to bore a tunnel and tracing mining operations on the surface of the ground so as to sink a shaft to an existing subsurface gallery. While the dioptra was the most highly developed surveying in-

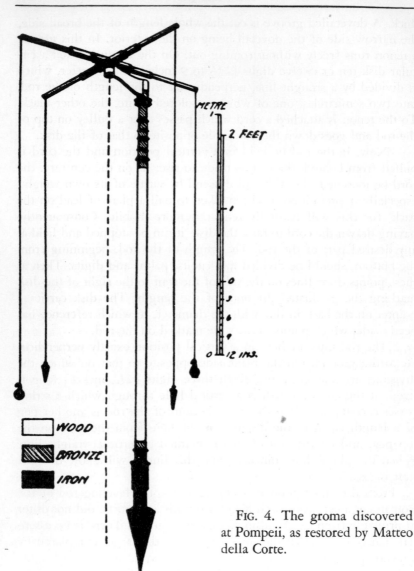

METRE

2 FEET

WOOD
BRONZE
IRON

FIG. 4. The groma discovered at Pompeii, as restored by Matteo della Corte.

strument in use during the time of the Roman Empire, there were at least two others frequently used. One was the "star," or "groma," whence the Latin word *gromaticus* (surveyor), by which lines were projected and the other the "chorobates," or level. As no clearly accurate description of the groma had come down, writers during the

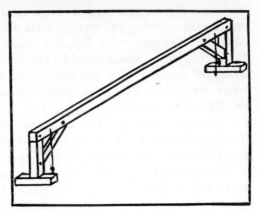

FIG. 5. The choro-
bates, as restored by
A. J. H. Vincent. After
a drawing in Stone's
*Roman Surveying Instru-
ments* (Seattle, 1928).

Middle Ages differed as to its exact form. Hero referred to it as less accurate than the dioptra, stating that the plumb-lines, being affected by air currents, could not be depended upon for accurate sighting, but he gave no details. Fortunately this deficiency in description was overcome when the metal parts of a groma were found in the excavations at Pompeii. They consist of an iron cross-piece with four arms, four bronze socket pieces, two thin bronze strips and an iron shoe, and are described (pp. 303–19, Volume XXVIII [1922], of the Accademia Nazionale dei Lincei) by Signor Matteo della Corte, who after studying the remains reconstructed the instrument pictorially [Fig. 4].

The groma was operated by setting the staff vertically, when one pair of cords gave the "cardo" (a line north-south) and the other pair a line at right angles called "decumanus." Such an instrument would quickly give lines at right angles by sighting on the hanging cords and so would be useful in setting out rectangular buildings. It would not measure, except by approximation, angles other than those of 90° and thus was obviously inferior to the dioptra, although it possessed the advantages of lightness and, therefore, of greater facility in handling.

The other instrument, the chorobates, was described in detail by Vitruvius (first century A.D.) in his *Ten Books on Architecture*. From his account, the chorobates was little more than a magnified builder's level, being a straight piece of wood 20 feet long, supported on legs, with two plumb-bobs near the ends [Fig. 5]. When the plumb-bobs hung so that the supporting cords coincided with certain marks on cross-pieces connecting the legs, the straight edge was level.

If the wind prevented the bobs from coming to rest, there was a second means to bring the straight edge level. On top of the straight edge a groove was cut 4 feet, $8\frac{1}{4}$ inches long, $\frac{3}{4}$ inch wide, and $1\frac{1}{8}$ inches deep, which could be filled with water and thus indicate when the straight edge was horizontal. Vitruvius realized that the water surface would not be, strictly speaking, level, as is shown by the following quotation:

"Perhaps some reader of the works of Archimedes will say that there can be no true level by means of water because he holds that water has not a level surface but is of spherical form having its centre at the centre of the earth. Whether water is plane or spherical it necessarily follows that when the straight edge is level it will support the water evenly at its extremity on the right and left. Although the water must have a swelling and curvature at the centre, yet the extremities must be on a level with each other."

This surprising piece of refined accuracy in reasoning on the curvature of the earth indicates correct understanding of the fundamentals of physical science.

A chorobates would establish levels for house foundations sufficiently close to satisfy the demands of Vitruvius, who was primarily an architect, and this would account for his preferring it to the dioptra. But compared with the latter it was very cumbersome, lacked sighting arrangement in both vertical and horizontal planes, not to mention the convenience of the dioptra for giving lines as well as levels. As a scientific instrument of precision the chorobates was distinctly inferior.

From the above descriptions, it is evident that Roman engineers at the beginning of the Christian era had at their command instruments by which they could readily perform all operations of surface and subsurface surveying and had fully developed field methods for their use. These instruments, while subject to improvements in details, embodied all the fundamental principles that such instruments should possess.

Thus the art of surveying stood at the beginning of the Renaissance, as little or no improvements had been made in the later Roman period.

SELECTIONS FROM BACON

BY FRANCIS BACON (1561–1626)

[The Author's Motives *]

. . . Being convinced, by a careful observation, that the human understanding perplexes itself, or makes not a sober and advantageous use of the real helps within its reach, whence manifold ignorance and inconveniences arise, he was determined to employ his utmost endeavors toward restoring or cultivating a just and legitimate familiarity between the mind and things.

But as the mind, hastily and without choice, imbibes and treasures up the first notices of things, whence all the rest proceed, errors must forever prevail, and remain uncorrected by either the natural powers of the understanding or the assistance of logic; for the original notions being vitiated, confused, and inconsiderately taken from things, and the secondary ones formed no less rashly, human knowledge itself, the thing employed in all our researches, is not well put together or justly formed, but resembles a magnificent structure that has no foundation.

And while men agree to admire and magnify the false powers of the mind, and neglect or destroy those that might be rendered true, there is no other course left but with better assistance to begin the work anew, and raise or rebuild the sciences, arts, and all human knowledge from a firm and solid basis.

This may at first seem an infinite scheme, unequal to human abilities, yet it will be found more sound and judicious than the course hitherto pursued, as tending to some issue; whereas all hitherto done with regard to the sciences is vertiginous, or in the way of perpetual rotation.

Nor is he ignorant that he stands alone in an experiment almost too bold and astonishing to obtain credit, yet he thought it not right to desert either the cause or himself, but to enter boldly on the way and explore the only path which is pervious to the human mind. For it is wiser to engage in an undertaking that admits of some termination, than to involve oneself in perpetual exertion and anxiety about what is interminable. The ways of contemplation, indeed, nearly correspond to two roads in nature, one of which, steep and rugged at the commencement, terminates in a plain; the other, at first view smooth and easy, leads only to huge rocks and precipices.

* From Proemium of *Instauratio Magna* (*The Great Renewal*).

Uncertain, however, whether these reflections would occur to another, and observing that he had never met any person disposed to apply his mind to similar thoughts, he determined to publish whatsoever he found time to perfect. Nor is this the haste of ambition, but anxiety that if he should die there might remain behind him some outline and determination of the matter his mind had embraced, as well as some mark of his sincere and earnest affection to promote the happiness of mankind. . . .

[Liberal Education *]

. . . I express my surprise that among so many illustrious colleges in Europe, all the foundations are engrossed by the professions, none being left for the free cultivation of the arts and sciences. Though men judge well who assert that learning should be referred to action, yet by reposing too confidently in this opinion, they are apt to fall into the error of the ancient fable, which represented the members of the body at war with the stomach, because it alone, of all parts of the frame, seemed to rest, and absorb all the nourishment. For if any man esteem philosophy and every study of a general character to be idle, he plainly forgets that on their proficiency the state of every other learning depends, and that they supply strength and force to its various branches. I mainly attribute the lame progress of knowledge hitherto to the neglect or the incidental study of the general sciences. For if you want a tree to produce more than its usual burden of fruit, it is not anything you can do to the branches that will effect this object, but the excitation of the earth about its roots and increasing the fertility of the soil; nor must it be overlooked that this restriction of foundations and endowments to professional learning has not only dwarfed the growth of the sciences, but been prejudicial to states and governments themselves. For since there is no collegiate course so free as to allow those who are inclined to devote themselves to history, modern languages, civil policy, and general literature, princes find a dearth of able men to manage their affairs and efficiently conduct the business of the commonwealth.

Since the founders of colleges plant, and those who endow them water, we are naturally led to speak in this place of the mean salaries apportioned to public lectureships, whether in the sciences or the arts. For such offices being instituted not for an ephemeral purpose, but for the constant transmission and extension of learning, it is of the

* From *De Augmentis Scientiarum* (*The Advancement of Learning*), Book II, Chapter I.

utmost importance that the men selected to fill them be learned and gifted. But it is idle to expect that the ablest scholars will employ their whole energy and time in such functions unless the reward be answerable to that competency which may be expected from the practice of a profession. The sciences will flourish only on the condition of David's military law—that those who remain with the baggage shall have equal part with those who descend to the fight; otherwise the baggage will be neglected. Lecturers being in like manner guardians of the literary stores whence those who are engaged in active service draw, it is but just that their labors should be equally recompensed . . .

[Experimentation *]

. . . here we may properly observe that those sciences which depend too much upon fancy and faith, as this degenerate magic, alchemy, and astrology, have their means and their theory more monstrous than their end and action. The conversion of quicksilver into gold is hard to conceive, though it may much more probably be effected by a man acquainted with the nature of gravity, color, malleability, fixedness, volatility, the principles of metals and menstruums, than by one who is ignorant of these natures, by the bare projection of a few grains of the elixir. The same may be understood of the prolongation of youth or retarding of old age, which may more rationally be expected by dietary regimen, bathings, anointing, and proper medicines, directed by an accurate knowledge of the human frame, the nature of arefaction, sustentation, assimilation, and the reciprocal action of the mind upon the body, than by a few drops or scruples of some precious liquor or quintessence. But men are so headstrong and notional, as not only to promise themselves things impossible, but also hope to obtain the most difficult ends without labor or exertion.

This practical doctrine of nature requires two appendages of very great consequence. The first is that an inventory be made of the stock of mankind, containing their whole possessions and fortunes, whether proceeding from nature or art, with the addition also of things formerly known, but now lost; so that he who goes upon new discoveries may have a knowledge of what has already been done. This inventory will be the more artificial and useful, if it also contains things of every kind, which, according to common opinion, are impossible; as likewise such as seemed next to impossible, yet have

* From *De Augmentis*, Book III, Chapter V.

been effected, the one to whet the human invention, and the other to direct it, so that from these optatives and potentials actives may the more readily be deduced.

The second thing is that a calendar be made of such experiments as are most extensively useful, and that lead to the discovery of others. For example, the experiment of artificial freezing, by means of ice and bay salt, is of infinite extent, and discovers a secret method of condensation of great service to mankind; fire is ready at hand for rarefaction, but the means of condensation are wanted. And it would greatly shorten the way to discoveries, to have a particular catalogue of these leading experiments.

[The Doctrine of "Idols," or Delusive Appearances *]

. . . we observe that idols are the deepest fallacies of the human mind; for they do not deceive in particulars, as the rest, by clouding and ensnaring the judgment; but from a corrupt predisposition, or bad complexion of the mind, which distorts and infects all the anticipations of the understanding. For the mind, darkened by its covering, the body, is far from being a flat, equal, and clear mirror that receives and reflects the rays without mixture; but rather a magical glass, full of superstitions and apparitions. Idols are imposed upon the understanding, either: (1) by the general nature of mankind; (2) by the nature of each particular man; or (3) by words, or communicative nature. The first kind we call idols of the tribe; the second kind, idols of the cave; and the third kind, idols of the market. There is also a fourth kind, which we call: (4) idols of the theater, being superinduced by false theories, or philosophies, and the perverted laws of demonstration. This last kind we are not at present concerned with, as it may be rejected and laid aside; but the others seize the mind strongly, and cannot be totally eradicated. Therefore no art of analytics can be expected here, but the doctrine of the confutation of idols is the primary doctrine of idols. Nor, indeed, can the doctrine of idols be reduced to an art, but can only be employed by means of a certain contemplative prudence to prevent them.

For the idols of the tribe, it is observable that the nature of the understanding is more affected with affirmatives and actives than with negatives and privatives, though in justness it should be equally affected with them both; but if things fall out right, or keep their course, the mind receives a stronger impression of this than of a much greater number of failures, or contrary events, which is the

* From *De Augmentis*, Book V, Chapter IV.

root of all superstition and credulity. Hence Diagoras, being shown in Neptune's temple many votive pictures of such as had escaped shipwreck, and thereupon asked by his guide if he did not now acknowledge the divine power, answered wisely: "But first show me where those are painted that were shipwrecked, after having thus paid their vows." And the case is the same, in the similar superstitions of astrological predictions, dreams, omens, etc. Again, the mind, being of itself an equal and uniform substance, presupposes a greater unanimity and uniformity in the nature of things than there really is, as may be observed in astronomical mathematicians, who, rejecting spiral lines, assert that the heavenly bodies move in perfect circles; whence our thoughts are continually drawing parallels, and supposing relations in many things that are truly different and singular. Hence the chemists have fantastically imagined their four principles corresponding to the heavens, air, earth, and water; dreaming that the series of existences formed a kind of square battalion, and that each element contained species of beings corresponding to each other, and possessing, as it were, parallel properties. And again, men make themselves, as it were, the mirror and rule of nature. It is incredible what a number of idols have been introduced into philosophy by the reduction of natural operations to a correspondence with human actions: that is, by imagining nature acts as man does, which is not much better than the heresy of the anthropomorphites, that sprung up in the cells and solitude of ignorant monks; or the opinion of Epicurus, who attributed a human figure to the gods. Velleius the Epicurean need not, therefore, have asked why God should have adorned the heavens with stars and lights, as master of the works. For, if the grand architect had acted a human part, he would have ranged the stars into some beautiful and elegant order, as we see in the vaulted roofs of palaces; whereas we scarce find among such an infinite multitude of stars any figure either square, triangular, or rectilinear; so great a difference is there between the spirit of man and the spirit of the universe.

The idols of the cave have their origin from the peculiar nature, both of mind and body, in each person; as also from education, custom, and the accidents of particular persons. It is a beautiful emblem, that of Plato's cave; for, to drop the exquisite subtlety of the parable, if anyone should be educated from his infancy in a dark cave till he were of full age, and should then of a sudden be brought into broad daylight, and behold this apparatus of the heavens and of things, no doubt but many strange and absurd fancies would arise in his mind;

and, though men live indeed in the view of the heavens, yet our minds are confined in the caverns of our bodies; whence of necessity we receive infinite images of errors and falsehoods, if the mind does but seldom, and only for a short continuance, leave its den, and not constantly dwell in the contemplation of nature, as it were, in the open daylight. And with this emblem of Plato's cave agrees the saying of Heraclitus: viz., that men seek the sciences in their own narrow worlds, and not in the wide one.

But the idols of the market give the greatest disturbance, and, from a tacit agreement among mankind, with regard to the imposition of words and names, insinuate themselves into the understanding: for words are generally given according to vulgar conception, and divide things by such differences as the common people are capable of; but when a more acute understanding, or a more careful observation, would distinguish things better, words murmur against it. The remedy of this lies in definitions; but these themselves are in many respects irremediable, as consisting of words: for words generate words, however men may imagine they have a command over words, and can easily say they will speak with the vulgar and think with the wise. Terms of art also, which prevail only among the skillful, may seem to remedy the mischief, and definitions premised to arts in the prudent mathematical manner, to correct the wrong acceptation of words; yet all this is insufficient to prevent the seducing incantation of names in numerous respects, their doing violence to the understanding, and recoiling upon it, whence they proceeded. . . .

[The "Idols of the Theater" *]

Lastly, there are idols which have crept into men's minds from the various dogmas of peculiar systems of philosophy, and also from the perverted rules of demonstration, and these we denominate idols of the theater: for we regard all the systems of philosophy hitherto received or imagined, as so many plays brought out and performed, creating fictitious and theatrical worlds. Nor do we speak only of the present systems, or of the philosophy and sects of the ancients, since numerous other plays of a similar nature can be still composed and made to agree with each other, the causes of the most opposite errors being generally the same. Nor, again, do we allude merely to general systems, but also to many elements and axioms of sciences which have become inveterate by tradition, implicit credence, and neglect. . . .

* From *Novum Organum* (*The New Instrument*), Book I, Aphorisms 44 and 62.

The idols of the theater, or of theories, are numerous, and may, and perhaps will, be still more so. For unless men's minds had been now occupied for many ages in religious and theological considerations, and civil governments (especially monarchies) had been averse to novelties of that nature even in theory (so that men must apply to them with some risk and injury to their own fortunes, and not only without reward, but subject to contumely and envy), there is no doubt that many other sects of philosophers and theorists would have been introduced, like those which formerly flourished in such diversified abundance among the Greeks. For as many imaginary theories of the heavens can be deduced from the phenomena of the sky, so it is even more easy to found many dogmas upon the phenomena of philosophy—and the plot of this our theater resembles those of the poetical, where the plots which are invented for the stage are more consistent, elegant, and pleasurable than those taken from real history.

In general, men take for the groundwork of their philosophy either too much from a few topics, or too little from many; in either case their philosophy is founded on too narrow a basis of experiment and natural history, and decides on too scanty grounds. For the theoretic philosopher seizes various common circumstances by experiment, without reducing them to certainty or examining and frequently considering them, and relies for the rest upon meditation and the activity of his wit.

There are other philosophers who have diligently and accurately attended to a few experiments, and have thence presumed to deduce and invent systems of philosophy, forming everything to conformity with them.

A third set, from their faith and religious veneration, introduce theology and traditions; the absurdity of some among them having proceeded so far as to seek and derive the sciences from spirits and genii.

There are, therefore, three sources of error and three species of false philosophy: the sophistic, empiric, and superstitious.

Of Studies *

Studies serve for delight, for ornament, and for ability. Their chief use for delight is in privateness and retiring; for ornament, is in discourse; and for ability, is in the judgment and disposition of business. For expert men can execute, and perhaps judge of particulars, one by one; but the general counsels, and the plots and marshal-

* From *Essays, or Counsels*, Essay 50.

ing of affairs, come best from those that are learned. To spend too much time in studies is sloth; to use them too much for ornament is affectation; to make judgment wholly by their rules is the humor of a scholar. They perfect nature, and are perfected by experience: for natural abilities are like natural plants, that need pruning by study; and studies themselves do give forth directions too much at large, except they be bounded in by experience. Crafty men contemn studies; simple men admire them; and wise men use them: for they teach not their own use; but that is a wisdom without them and above them, won by observation. Read not to contradict and confute, nor to believe and take for granted, nor to find talk and discourse; but to weigh and consider. Some books are to be tasted, others to be swallowed, and some few to be chewed and digested: that is, some books are to be read only in parts; others to be read, but not curiously; and some few to be read wholly, and with diligence and attention. Some books also may be read by deputy, and extracts made of them by others; but that would be only in the less important arguments, and the meaner sort of books; else, distilled books are like common distilled waters, flashy things. Reading maketh a full man; conference, a ready man; and writing, an exact man. And, therefore, if a man write little, he had need have a great memory; if he confer little, he had need have a present wit; and if he read little, he had need have much cunning, to seem to know that he doth not. Histories make men wise; poets, witty; the mathematics, subtile; natural philosophy, deep; moral, grave; logic and rhetoric, able to contend. . . . So every defect of the mind may have a special receipt.

THE INSUFFICIENCY OF APPLIED SCIENCE

BY THOMAS HENRY HUXLEY (1825–1895) *

. . . I often wish that this phrase, "applied science," had never been invented. For it suggests that there is a sort of scientific knowledge of direct practical use, which can be studied apart from another sort of scientific knowledge, which is of no practical utility, and which is termed "pure science." But there is no more complete fallacy than this. What people call applied science is nothing but the application of pure science to particular classes of problems. It consists of deductions from those general principles, established by reasoning and observation, which constitute pure science. No one can safely make these deductions until he has a firm grasp of the principles; and he can obtain that grasp only by personal experience of the operations of observation and of reasoning on which they are founded.

Almost all the processes employed in the arts and manufactures fall within the range either of physics or of chemistry. In order to improve them, one must thoroughly understand them; and no one has a chance of really understanding them unless he has obtained that mastery of principles and that habit of dealing with facts, which is given by long-continued and well-directed purely scientific training in the physical and the chemical laboratory. . . .

And, as to the desirableness of a wider culture than that yielded by science alone, it is to be recollected that the improvement of manufacturing processes is only one of the conditions which contribute to the prosperity of industry. Industry is a means and not an end; and mankind work only to get something which they want. What that something is depends partly on their innate, and partly on their acquired, desires.

If the wealth resulting from prosperous industry is to be spent upon the gratification of unworthy desires, if the increasing perfection of manufacturing processes is to be accompanied by an increasing debasement of those who carry them on, I do not see the good of industry and prosperity.

Now it is perfectly true that men's views of what is desirable depend upon their characters, and that the innate proclivities to

* From "Science and Culture" (an address delivered in 1880), in *Science and Culture and Other Essays*, 1881.

READINGS

which we give that name are not touched by any amount of instruction. But it does not follow that even mere intellectual education may not, to an indefinite extent, modify the practical manifestation of the characters of men in their actions, by supplying them with motives unknown to the ignorant. A pleasure-loving character will have pleasure of some sort; but, if you give him the choice, he may prefer pleasures which do not degrade him to those which do. And this choice is offered to every man who possesses in literary or artistic culture a never-failing source of pleasures which are neither withered by age, nor staled by custom, nor embittered in the recollection by the pangs of self-reproach. . . .

THE COLLAPSE OF A SUSPENSION BRIDGE *

. . . *Behavior of Bridge November 7, 1940:* It is possible to get a fairly accurate account of the failure from the statements of eye witnesses and from photographs and motion pictures taken during the collapse.

Early on the morning of November 7, 1940, the bridge developed vertical wave motions of a character previously experienced and of sufficient amplitude to attract special attention. The southerly wind, with a velocity recorded at forty-two miles per hour, was striking the bridge at a quartering angle. The undulations had continued for several hours prior to 9:30 A.M., at which time the main span was vibrating in eight or more segments, with a frequency of 36 cycles per minute and a double amplitude of about three feet. The bridge floor did not twist at this time, indicating that the cables were vibrating in phase with one another as they always had done.

Shortly after 10:00 A.M., the motion changed so that the main span vibrated in two segments with a node at mid-span, with a frequency of 14 cycles per minute. Then the cables began vibrating out of phase with one another resulting in a twisting or warping motion of the roadway, one side going down as the other side came up. A little later, the frequency changed from 14 to 12 cycles per minute. Photographs and motion pictures show a tilting of the deck amounting to more than 30 degrees each way from the horizontal. The double amplitude of the waves probably attained a maximum of 28 feet.

There was little lateral movement of the bridge even when the wave motion was most violent, the maximum value at mid-span probably being of the order of two feet.

Some observers reported that the motion was more violent in the west than in the east half. There was little movement in the side spans.

* From *The Failure of the Suspension Bridge over Tacoma Narrows,* Report to the Narrows Bridge Loss Committee (Paul Carew, Chairman) on the Damage Produced by the Failure, by Board of Consulting Engineers (Clifford E. Paine, Chairman), Seattle, Washington, June 2, 1941; photographed and lithoprinted in Section C of *The Failure of the Tacoma Narrows Bridge: a Reprint of Original Reports* ("Bulletin of the Agricultural and Mechanical College of Texas," Fourth Series, Vol. XV, No. 1), College Station, Texas Engineering Experiment Station, 1944, Bulletin No. 78. From Part A (*INTRODUCTION*), Section II (*General Description of Failure*), of the report, pp. 23–28; printed by permission of Mr. Carew.
The suspension bridge over Puget Sound which collapsed on November 7, 1940, about four months after it had been opened to traffic, had a central span of 2800 feet and east and west side spans of 1100 feet each.

Two cars were on the main span when the tilting started, a truck delivering material to the west end of the bridge, and a passenger car. Unable to control the truck on the pitching roadway, the driver and a companion left it just before it turned over, and, suffering from fright and bruises, had to be helped off the bridge and taken to a hospital. The passenger car was headed west near the east quarter point of the main span when the first twisting motion started. The driver reported that as he was driving along the north curb the opposite side of the roadway seemed to drop suddenly and his car headed for the south curb. The tilting then reversed and the car pitched back toward the north curb and struck it violently. He got out of the car, was thrown to the pavement, and skidded completely across the roadway to the south curb, along which he crawled until he reached the east side span.

The main span began to break up just before 11:00 A.M. A panel of floor adjacent to an expansion joint just east of mid-span dropped out. This was followed shortly by the dropping of a section of floor about 600 ft. long, leaving an open gap extending from a point about 300 ft. west of mid-span to within 500 ft. of the west tower. The north stiffening girder of this section tore loose by breaking suspenders progressively from east to west, turned completely upside down as its entire weight swung onto the south cable and its floorbeams successively tore loose from the south stiffening girder. The latter then tore loose. As its suspenders broke, they were snapped high into the air. Other portions of the main span broke loose and dropped into the Sound during the next ten minutes leaving, finally, 250 ft. of main span floor on the east side and 150 ft. of main span floor on the west side. As the weight dropped off the cables in the main span, their sag there was reduced, the tower tops were pulled shoreward, and the cable sag in the side spans increased. The behavior of the east side span is well recorded by motion pictures. They show that the sagging of the side span was accompanied by some vertical wave motion combined with a slight twisting and lateral movement. The magnitude of the dynamic effect upon the deflection of the side span is indicated in the pictures by the amount the falling side span sagged beyond the position it assumed when it came to rest. During this period, the south girder of the east side span struck and broke the top rail of a parapet wall beneath it, 132 ft. out from the east abutment. At the same time the north girder barely touched the same rail, leaving on it only the marks of a rivet head.

The parts that remained suspended from the main span cables

when the structure came to rest after the failure are as follows: 250 ft. of floor adjacent to the east tower, an additional 250 ft. of twisted stiffening girder suspended from the north cable, a length of stiffening girder with some floorbeams attached dangling from the south cable 250 ft. out from the east tower, 150 ft. of floor adjacent to the west tower, 200 ft. of stiffening girder with some floorbeams attached dangling from the north cable 150 ft. out from the west tower, and some broken suspenders distributed along both cables throughout the intervening space. All of the floor structure of the two side spans remained suspended from the cables.

The cables, fixed to the tower tops, assumed the curve required for equilibrium, thus increasing the sag of the side span cables from 36.2 ft. to about 75 ft. This pulled the tops of both towers shoreward, and the displacement from the vertical was then 12.4 ft. for the east tower and 12.7 ft. for the west tower. The maximum shoreward movement of the tower tops during the collapse was 16 or 17 feet. . . .

PHYSICS IN THE CONTEMPORARY WORLD

BY J. ROBERT OPPENHEIMER *

. . . .

Responsibility of Scientists

The great testimony of history shows how often . . . the development of science has emerged in response to technological, and even economic needs, and how in the economy of social effort, science, even of the most abstract and recondite kind, pays for itself again and again in providing the basis for radically new technological developments. In fact, most people, when they think of science as a good thing, when they think of it as worthy of encouragement, when they are willing to see their governments spend substance upon it, when they greatly do honor to men who in science have attained some eminence, have in mind that the conditions of their life have been altered by just such technology, of which they may be reluctant to be deprived.

The debt of science to technology is just as great. Even the most abstract researches owe their very existence to things that have taken place quite outside of science, and with the primary purpose of altering and improving the conditions of man's life. As long as there is a healthy physics, this mutual fructification will surely continue. Out of its work there will come in the future, as so often in the past, and with an apparently chaotic unpredictability, things which will improve man's health, ease his labor, and divert and edify him. There will come things which, properly handled, will shorten his working day and take away the most burdensome part of his effort, which will enable him to communicate, to travel, and to have a wider choice both in the general question of how he is to spend his life, and in the specific question of how he is to spend an hour of his leisure. There is no need to belabor this point, nor its obverse—that out of science there will come, as there has in this last war, a host of instruments of destruction which will facilitate that labor, even as they have facilitated all others.

But no scientist, no matter how aware he may be of these fruits of his science, cultivates his work, or refrains from it, because of arguments such as these. No scientist can hope to evaluate what his

---

* Arthur Dehon Little Memorial Lecture, reprinted in part from *The Technology Review*, February, 1948, edited at the Massachusetts Institute of Technology. The author is Chairman of the General Advisory Committee of the U.S. Atomic Energy Commission and Director of the Institute for Advanced Study.

studies, his researches, his experiments may in the end produce for his fellow men, except in one respect: if they are sound, they will produce knowledge. And this deep complementarity between what may be conceived to be the social justification of science, and what is for the individual his compelling motive in its pursuit, makes us look for other answers to the question of the relation of science to society.

One of these is that the scientist should assume responsibility for the fruits of his work. I would not argue against this, but it must be clear to all of us how very modest such assumption of responsibility can be, how very ineffective it has been in the past, how necessarily ineffective it will surely be in the future. In fact, it appears little more than an exhortation to the man of learning to be properly uncomfortable; and, in the worst instances, is used as a sort of screen to justify the most casual, unscholarly and, in the last analysis, corrupt intrusion of scientists into other realms of which they have neither experience nor knowledge, nor the patience to obtain it.

The true responsibility of a scientist, as we all know, is to the integrity and vigor of his science. And because most scientists, like all men of learning, tend in part also to be teachers, they have a responsibility for the communication of the truths they have found. This is at least a collective if not an individual responsibility. That we should see in this any insurance that the fruits of science will be used for man's benefit, or denied to man when they make for his distress or destruction, would be a tragic naïveté.

There is another side of the coin. This is the question of whether there are elements in the way of life of the scientist which need not be restricted to the professional, and which have hope in them for bringing dignity and courage and serenity to other men. Science is not all of the life of reason; it is a part of it. As such, what can it mean to man?

Perhaps it would be well to emphasize that I am talking neither of wisdom, nor of an elite of scientists, but precisely of the kind of work and thought, of action and discipline, that makes up the everyday professional life of the scientist. It is not of any general insight into human affairs that I am talking. It is not the kind of thing we recognize in our greatest statesmen, after long service devoted to practical affairs and to the public interest. It is something very much more homely and robust than that. It has in it the kind of beauty that is inseparable from craftsmanship and form, but that has in it also the vigor which we rightly associate with the simple ordered lives of artisans or of farmers, that we rightly associate with lives to which limitations of scope, and traditional ways, have given robustness and structure.

The Discipline of Science

Even less would it be right to interpret the question of what there is in the ways of science which may be of general value to mankind in terms of the creation of an elite. The study of physics, and I think my colleagues in the other sciences will let me speak for them too, does not make philosopher-kings. It has not, until now, made kings. It almost never makes fit philosophers—or so rarely that they must be counted as exceptions. If the professional pursuit of science makes good scientists, if it makes men with a certain serenity in their lives, who yield perhaps a little more slowly than others to the natural corruptions of their time, it is doing a great deal, and all that we may rightly ask of it. For if Plato believed that in the study of geometry, a man might prepare himself for wisdom and responsibility in the world of men, it was precisely because he thought so hopefully that the understanding of men could be patterned after the understanding of geometry. If we believe that today, it is in a much more recondite sense, and a much more cautious one.

When then is the point? For one thing it is to describe some of the features of the professional life of the scientist, which make of it one of the great phenomena of the contemporary world. Here again, I would like to speak of physics; but I have enough friends in the other sciences to know how close their experience is to ours. And I know too that despite profound differences in method and technique, differences which surely are an appropriate reflection of the difference in the areas of the world under study, what I would say of physics will seem familiar to workers in other disparate fields, such as mathematics, or biology.

What are some of these points? There is, in the first instance, a total lack of authoritarianism, which is hard to comprehend or to admit unless one has lived with it. This is accomplished by one of the most exacting of intellectual disciplines. In physics the worker learns the possibility of error very early. He learns that there are ways to correct his mistakes; he learns the futility of trying to conceal them. For it is not a field in which error awaits death and subsequent generations for verdict: the next issue of the journals will take care of it. The refinement of techniques for the prompt discovery of error serves as well as any other as a hallmark of what we mean by science.

In any case, it is an area of collective effort, in which there is a clear and well-defined community whose canons of taste and order simplify the life of the practitioner. It is a field in which the technique of experiment has given an almost perfect harmony to the balance between thought and action. In it we learn so frequently that we could almost become accustomed to it, how vast is the novelty of the world, and how much even the physical world transcends in delicacy and in balance the limits of man's prior imaginings. We learn that views may be useful and inspiriting although they are not complete. We come to have a great caution in all assertions of totality, of finality or absoluteness.

In this field quite ordinary men, using what are in the last analysis only the tools which are generally available in our society, manage to unfold for themselves and all others who wish to learn, the rich story of one aspect of the physical world, and of man's experience. We learn to throw away those instruments of action and those modes of description which are not appropriate to the reality we are trying to discern, and in this most painful discipline, find ourselves modest before the world. . . .

THE PLACE OF ENGINEERING
IN THE POST-WAR WORLD

BY FRANCIS DONALDSON *

. . . To begin with, what is engineering? No dictionary has given a really good definition; so, many of the engineering societies have tried to define it, without agreement or pronounced success. A composite result of their efforts might be phrased as follows: "Engineering—the scientific application of the forces of nature to the materials of nature for the benefit of mankind."

Well, this sounds fine, and the first part of the definition is a reasonable approximation. The last part, however, is only an expression of an ethical wish and not of reality. It could better say "to further the purposes of mankind" or "for the benefit of the fellow that hires the engineer." The feats of military engineering demand no less intelligence and present as many absorbing problems to the engineer as the most beneficent projects of peace time. The engineer, as an engineer, is no better or worse than any other human worker, and whether or not the end toward which he works is beneficial depends upon the vision and the imagination of the promoter of the underlying idea.

The engineer in applying natural forces to natural materials has in reality two functions quite different in character and in their effect on human life. The first and older of these is to do or create by the use of machinery what otherwise could not be done or created at all. The second is to create with *little* human labor what otherwise would require *much* human labor. While these two functions often intermingle or overlap, it is well to remember their essential difference.

The first function is made possible by the application of mechanical power in a concentration that cannot be obtained by hitching more and more men or horses to the windlass. For instance, a horse or a man, if you consider each as a heat engine, weighs about half a ton per horsepower, whereas a modern airplane motor weighs about a pound and a quarter. A standard transport plane requires about 2,500 horsepower to fly it, and it is obviously impossible to put 2,500 horses aboard—it would crowd the passengers. . . .

The second category of engineering accomplishment—making things with little labor—began with the so-called industrial revolu-

---

* From a leading article published in *The Villager*, XVII (May, 1945), 9–15. Mr. Donaldson (M.E., Lehigh University, 1901) is a specialist in subaqueous tunnels.

tion and is exemplified by modern mass production. Mass production started in England in the early eighteen hundreds when steam power was applied to the spinning jenny and the Arkwright loom, and since then has spread, at first slowly and then with increasing acceleration, to take in everything that human beings want in quantity. No end is in sight. Through the preceding ages mankind's wants were supplied by hand labor and hand tools in quantities insufficient to afford a decent standard of living. Now, overnight so to speak, they can be produced in such quantities that many of the people who want them have nothing to offer in exchange. Before the war, markets were glutted, and our advanced living standard began to recede.

To enumerate the reduction in the man hours of labor that machine production has effected in shoes and ships, and sealing wax— and even cabbages—would bore you even if I had taken the trouble to look up some statistics, which I have not. I just wish to make clear the distinction between the two categories of engineering function, and it is this: The first, the creation by the use of power and machinery of things that otherwise could not be produced, increases human activity, and the demand for labor; the second category—mass production—may increase or may decrease both.

No doubt this statement will be challenged by some economists. Business economists accept as facts of general application the theses that the reduced cost of producing any given product in quantity makes possible a correspondingly reduced price, which in turn stimulates the market, and that the workers displaced by the initial installation of machinery are re-employed at better wages by the enlargement of industry as a whole. The trouble is that the economists do not think far enough ahead in time. For these statements apply only to the earlier part of the history of an industry. It is further a fact that the improvements in technology of production, particularly under competitive conditions, are made continuously, whereas the resulting reductions in price cannot or certainly do not increase the market proportionately. The productive man hours required by the industry eventually tend to decrease. Thus we have seen shorter working hours and feather-bedding in an attempt to spread the work, more nonproductive employees in industry, higher overhead and bigger government payrolls, C.C.C.'s and W.P.A.'s, large unemployment, and finally war.

. . . Can the inventor think up enough new human wants to take up the slack of technological unemployment? I, for one, am entirely sure he cannot and base my belief not only on observation but on the dictum that man lives not by bread alone. I deny that the material wants of mankind are insatiable, and I know for certain that there is no limit to the improvement of technology in production. . . .

Since the dawn of history public works have been used by governments as a last resort to make work in times of unemployment. It is said that the Egyptian Kings built the pyramids for this reason and it is certainly why F.D.R. built the Fort Peck and Grand Coulee Dams. In fact, the favorite wisecrack in Spokane, Washington, when I was there was that Grand Coulee was "three times as big as the Great Pyramid and three times as useless." The war changed this idea.

Another favorite slogan of the times was "you can't spend your way out of a depression." Literally this isn't true, for when the war came we did just that very quickly. The question really is whether a nation can afford to spend its way out of a depression, and the answer depends on what the money is spent for. Economically we can't afford war, or battle monuments, or monumental buildings to house new bureaus or bureaucrats, or uncoördinated boondoggled projects, but we can and must afford projects which add to our natural wealth. After all, isn't this what spending by private industry is supposed to do?

A deplorable amount of Federal spending throughout our history has been in the pyramid class. I remember once when bidding on a lock and dam on the Big Sandy River, I looked up figures on the locks previously built. The interest charge on the money which had been spent came to something over a hundred dollars for every ton of freight hauled. According to an analysis made, I admit, by the railroads but which I believe to be quite accurate, the New York State Barge Canal is also a lemon, its transportation cost being three times that of the New York Central Railroad which follows the same route.

In spite of its detractors, the Grand Coulee project would have helped to develop the Northwest and would have justified itself eventually. With the outbreak of the war, however, the installation of its electrical equipment became an urgent necessity, and units destined for other sites were actually borrowed and temporarily set. At present the West power plant is producing over a million electrical horsepower, serves as the balance wheel of the Northwestern power pool, and has made possible the vast expansion of the region's war industry.

Another great dam, built at the same time as Grand Coulee, the Fort Peck Dam across the upper Missouri, is actually twelve times as big as Grand Coulee, but since it is built of fine sand pumped into place and stretches across the wide valley like a low flat mountain, it is not so spectacular. It, too, cost a lot of money but by itself and without further development of the watershed has little economic value.

Good reasons may be set forth against spending public funds in peace time for projects like those I have been describing. But here are some that it would be hard to criticize:

New York City's Catskill and Delaware Aqueducts, which together will provide the city and its environs with over a billion gallons of pure water a day, flowing ceaselessly through a hundred and eighty-five miles of tunnels and sixty miles of covered conduit built in open cut.

Los Angeles Metropolitan Aqueduct, a 250-mile stretch of tunnel and conduit carrying over a half billion gallons of Colorado River water a day to thirsty farms and citrus groves in the semi-arid region around the city of Los Angeles.

The Boulder Dam, whose power makes that aqueduct and much of Southern California's industrial development possible.

The tunnels beneath the Hudson and the East River, enabling people to escape from Brooklyn and New Jersey and get to New York.

I could go on indefinitely.

Much public work has been projected for execution after the war. The program of the Bureau of Reclamation includes nearly three billion dollars' worth of dams and irrigation canals; the Army Engineer Corps proposes over three billion in harbor development and river improvements for navigation and flood control. Both programs include the construction of hydroelectric plants to utilize the available power. To these must be added a third of a billion for other Federal work, seven billion for state and municipal projects, and a billion for private jobs, making a total of fourteen and a half billion reported to date.

This sounds like a lot of money. But unfortunately, much of it is not yet authorized, and at this date plans have been drawn or are in progress for less than one third of the total. But even the whole amount is far from big enough, since . . . it does not begin to make up the deficit in normal construction, now almost at a standstill for three years. We are already fifteen or twenty billion behind.

Yes, we must plan for more, much more, and I should like to suggest some things we ought to do.

First on the list, to my mind, is waste and sewage disposal. All over our country we have dumped filth and factory wastes into the streams, killing the fish, polluting the banks, often fringing them with slums. Does anybody want to swim in the Hudson or the Schuylkill? To correct this condition everywhere would cost many billion dollars of invested capital; the interest on this would be paid in better health, in enhanced property values, in lessened cost of water treatment for domestic and industrial use. No one who remembers the Bronx Valley before the sewer was built could think this a questionable investment. But this kind of improvement is hard to put across; vested interests stand in the way; and, as a politician once said to me, "There are no votes in sewage." The fourteen billion of projected work includes less than a billion for sewers and disposal in the entire U.S.A.

Next consider soil conservation and reforestation. Take a look at the gutted hillsides of the South, the overgrazed or overcultivated prairies of the dust bowl, the cut out and burned timberlands of the North and Northwest and see how far we have gone towards making a China of our country. Much of this land can be reclaimed, but the doing of it will require much labor and the laborers must be paid. Can any American doubt that this will be a wise investment?

Much of the work that I have talked about should be and will be planned, financed, and performed by districts, counties, municipalities, states. The more done locally the better. But when desirable projects transcend state lines the Federal Government must take over.

We must indeed make far greater plans. There is a growing belief in the world that to permit large-scale unemployment is the greatest offense of which an industrial civilization can be guilty. I believe that another great depression will cost us not only our property but our American form of government and our liberty.

We must build and we must build usefully. To avoid the waste due to uncoördination, we must coördinate—to put it brutally, we must become a planned society as regards many of our natural resources. Private industry cannot do this kind of planning; experience tells us that the states are not going to do nearly enough of it, much as we wish they would; so practically the job devolves upon the Federal Government as surely as did the conduct of the war.

What kind of plans can we have that do not involve centralization, more bureaucracy, and their attendant evils? Fortunately, we have one working example to talk about old enough to have shown results. I refer, of course, to the T.V.A. There is too little space to describe this great project in detail—many of you have been to see it or have read Mr. Lilienthal's book—but briefly its purpose is to utilize most effectively within the watershed of the Tennessee River its supply of water, the substance upon which the growth of civilization depends.

The Authority's offices are not in Washington, but in Knoxville, the heart of the region, and its officers are thus "close to the grass roots," as Mr. Lilienthal likes to repeat. Its twenty-one great dams are regulated to prevent floods, to provide navigable channels, and to generate two million electrical horsepower.

But more than this, the Authority assists and encourages the inhabitants of the region to conserve their land, its soil and its forests. By providing cheap power at points where the communities can pick it up and distribute it, by providing fertilizer free to farmers who agree to conduct their farms as demonstrations of modern agricultural practice, by establishing models of quick refrigeration and dehydration plants, by practicing and encouraging reforestation and erosion control, the Authority is making the Tennessee Valley a better place to live in.

Has it paid? Mr. Lilienthal claims that it has, based on sales of electric power alone. But whether or not you accept his figures on this item, even the original opponents of the project agree that the living standards of the region have advanced; population, payrolls, and tax returns have increased far beyond normal growth; and private industry, especially small business, has boomed. What more can we ask?

Let us go ahead. Let us tackle the Columbia Valley, the Red River Valley and a lot more, and even tough ones like the Colorado and the Missouri, the Big Muddy. The engineer can lick the silt; he can eventually lick the climate.

Yes, the engineer can do almost anything you tell him to do. He can make the old world over into a better place for his children and yours to grow and to live in, or he can fill it with gadgets and gadgets to make gadgets until the robots take over and evict the human race. Make your choice.

CITY ZONING

by L. B. Ryon *

. . . The control of private property for the protection of the citizenry is known as zoning. After the major street plan, zoning is probably the next most important factor in city planning. Zoning, in a word, divides the city into three major types of districts, residential, business, industrial. If the city planner were planning for a new city which was to be built, he could say, "Here we will locate the business district, beyond the business district and along any navigable water and along railroad rights-of-way we will locate our industrial sections, here we will locate our apartment and family residence districts, and there we will have our single family residence districts. These areas we will devote to parks, fire and police stations"—and so on for all of the various appurtenances that go to make a modern urban community, and plan so that the whole could be expanded to make a great city. Few planners have such an opportunity, one exception being Major L'Enfant, who was retained by George Washington when the infant United States decided to build our nation's capital. Those who have marveled at its magnificent system of streets, boulevards, parks, and general layout can realize what may be accomplished if the planner has vision and the opportunity to begin before a city is actually built.

In most instances cities have grown to a considerable size before they have thought of planning as such. Certainly many have been in existence a long time before zoning was heard of, for it began in New York City as lately as 1916. Zoning is an attempt to remold a city into an ideal pattern such as would be obtained if it were remade and to avoid the mistakes of the first making. Its basis is the welfare of the majority of the people of the city and accords with our democratic form of government, the well-being and will of the majority of the people of the United States.

The "predominating uses of property" map . . . shows the predominant uses to which the people of a given section of the city devote their land. If the land is used mostly for business, that land should be zoned for business. If it is used predominantly for resi-

* From "Planning of Cities," *The Rice Institute Pamphlet*, XXX (October, 1943), 262–267. Professor Lewis Babcock Ryon, Chairman of the Department of Civil Engineering at the Rice Institute, was City Planning Engineer of Houston from 1924 to 1930 and Secretary of the City Planning Commission of Houston from 1927 to 1930.

dences, it should be zoned for residences. Similarly for all of the use classifications. For each section of the city the predominant uses map shows what the land is mostly used for, in many instances 90 or 95 per cent of it being devoted to a specific use. A tentative zone map may readily be prepared setting aside each part of the city for the specific purpose it is being mainly used for at the time of the survey. Zoning then attempts by law to continue those uses, to safeguard the homes and investments of the great majority of the people in their use of their land.

It has been found by experience that people prize their homes above other interests. They want them protected as homes. That this is so is proven by the widespread use of contract restrictions of residence property for residence uses for a definite period of years. When the contract restrictions expire and various businesses and light industries begin to creep in, the land begins to decrease in value for residence purposes. . . . Zoning replaces the expired contract restrictions with new restrictions if the residents of the area want them, and the zoning restrictions do not expire at the end of a given period of years. They remain in effect until changed, after due process of law, by the expressed will of a majority of owners of property in the affected area. When carefully drawn zone ordinances have been put in effect, citizens do not want them voided.

The procedure to establish zoning is simple. The tentative use zones prepared by the city planner are taken to the people of the city and explained and discussed in detail. This taking to the people is accomplished by dividing the city into small, convenient sections, establishing a central meeting place, and inviting the people of a given section to meet at a certain, convenient time in the stipulated meeting place. At the meeting the proposed "zone uses" for the area are gone over in detail and all residents present are invited to offer criticisms and suggestions for changes. Such suggestions are studied, and if there are revisions another meeting is held. This procedure is continued until a substantial majority of the property owners and residents of each area are satisfied with the zone uses proposed.

A zone ordinance is then drawn, and the ordinance and maps are presented to the city council or other governing body of the municipality. It is the duty of the governing body to hold final public hearings on the proposed ordinance before finally enacting it.

It might be well to describe zones in greater detail. As previously stated, there are three use classifications: residential, business, industrial. Residence uses are subdivided into single family and multi-family use districts. Multi-family districts may be either duplex or apartment districts. Single family districts primarily are home owner districts. Property in multi-family districts is primarily rent property. Single family residences are permitted in multi-family or rent property districts but multi-family residences are not permitted in single family sections. It is not to be inferred that owners of property in single family districts may not rent their houses if they so choose. New stores or industries may not be established in any kind of residence district. Local business centers are convenient and desirable and are provided, but industries are not placed in residence sections. Property in business zones may be used for residences or business, but industries are excluded. There are two types of industrial sections, light and heavy, the distinction being based on size of machinery, or use, or size of plant. Property in industrial zones may be used for residences, business, or industries. Thus one may build a house in a residential, commercial, or industrial section if he chooses, but he will not have stores and factories in the neighborhood if he builds in a zoned residence district.

Zoning is not retroactive. Uses and structures existing lawfully in a zone at the time of passage of the zone ordinance may remain in that zone even though they do not conform to the use zone provisions. An industry in a business section or residence section or any established business in a residence section is not required to move. It simply remains as a nonconforming use. It may not expand. It may not be rebuilt if destroyed by fire or damaged severely. No person is prevented by zoning from a reasonable use of his property. Any person who feels himself aggrieved has the right to seek redress in the courts. Courts have upheld the provisions of zone ordinances in a great number of test cases.

When the term "zoning" is used most people think of "use zoning." In addition there is height and area zoning, which stipulates the areas required in front, side, and back yards, and permitted heights of buildings. By requiring side and back yards in residence districts, each structure is assured its fair share of the light and air of the neighborhood. The requirement of front yards is similar to building lines in residence districts having private deed restrictions. Use, height, and area zoning gives the owner of land in unrestricted residential sections what deed restrictions give the owner of property in newer subdivisions. Few people in unzoned cities would spend their money for property in unrestricted subdivisions. Zoning protects the property of the unrestricted district. Many cities have experienced new construction and re-construction in older unrestricted districts after the adoption of zone ordinances. Confident new construction results. Owners of older properties feel warranted in maintaining them and the process of decay is halted.

It is well to add that much property is held for sale as business property in growing cities after deed restrictions have expired. Since only about 1.5 per cent of the street frontage of property in the entire city can be supported by business of the city, it is manifestly impossible for all areas of cities to become business or potential business property merely because the deed restrictions on the residence property have expired. The land is not needed for business; few residents will venture to construct new residences on the land; so there is nothing for the property to do but age, and thus decay, unless zoning is resorted to when restrictions expire.

If cities, and utility companies serving the people of the cities, know rather definitely what the land in the urban territory will be used for, and the probable density of population in the residence sections, and know the extent of the business and industrial sections, then both city and utility companies know what facilities to provide and a marked economy in utility costs results in the city. The required size of water and sewer mains, of telephone and light cables, and of gas mains, may be anticipated. The probable numbers of lanes of traffic to be provided on the major streets also may be anticipated much more accurately.

So zoning ties into city planning very definitely and plays a stellar rôle. It is no wonder that some fifteen thousand cities in this country have zoning, and that there are only three cities in the United States having a population over two hundred thousand that do not have zoning. No major city, once zoned, has invalidated its zoning ordinance. It is inevitable that mistakes are made in zoning cities, but these mistakes are correctible and the ordinances prescribe the orderly fashion to be followed in correction of these errors.

Finally it may be said that city planning attempts no miracles, but is an effort intelligently to preserve the good points of the community and to improve the weaknesses; that it is a continuing process requiring constant vigilance and much hard and painstaking care, unselfish work, vision, and constant effort to build a more useful, convenient, and pleasant city in which to dwell, so that posterity may approve the thought expressed in the words of John Ruskin:

". . . when we build, let us think that we build for ever. Let it not be for present delight, nor for present use alone; let it be such work as our descendants will thank us for, and let us think, as we lay stone on stone, that a time is to come when those stones will be held sacred because our hands have touched them, and that men will say as they look upon the labour and wrought substance of them, 'See! this our fathers did for us.' "

SOURCES OF POWER

BY LIONEL S. MARKS *

. . . The possible sources of power are the gravitational pull of the moon, the internal energy of the earth, and solar energy.

The gravitational pull of the moon produces the tides, and it is possible to obtain useful work from the tides in a few specially favored localities. Such power always entails great first cost and, as it is discontinuous, it requires arrangements for the storage of power if the power demand is continuous. There are very few places where tidal power can be utilized economically. . . . The estimate by Jeffries [1] of the tidal drag on the earth is 1.4×10^9 kw., which is not much more than the total power that could be developed by all the automobiles of the United States operating at full load.

The internal energy of the earth is utilizable in those places where high-pressure steam emerges continuously, but it is of such infrequent occurrence as to be of no real importance. No hopeful practical suggestions have been made for more general utilization of the internal energy of the earth.

· · ·

Solar energy is the only important source of power. It is the cause of winds, of rain, and of plant growth. The solar energy of earlier ages is stored in coal, petroleum, and natural gas. Solar energy of recent times is stored in vegetable and animal matter and in water above sea level.

Certain energy sources are immediately available for doing work, as in water wheels or windmills. In such cases it is in general conceivable that all the available energy should be converted into work. Actually, there are losses from friction or other causes, but these may be reduced indefinitely as progress is made in the mechanic arts; efficiencies of 90 per cent are usual in such cases. Heat is not available energy, and some form of heat engine is necessary for its transformation into work. The efficiency of this process in actual engines is less than 40 per cent.

The value of an energy source for power generation depends in addition on certain other characteristics. The energy may be concen-

* From *Science in Progress* (Third Series), ed. George A. Baitsell, New Haven, Yale University Press, 1942. From Ch. VI, "Recent Developments in Power Generation." The author is Professor Emeritus of Mechanical Engineering, Harvard University.
[1] JEFFRIES, HAROLD. The earth, 2d ed., p. 277. Cambridge Univ. Press, 1929.

trated as in a high waterfall, or diffuse as in a slow-moving stream; it may be continuous as in a waterfall, or intermittent as with sunlight or wind; it may be storable as with water in reservoirs, or not storable as with the wind. These and other characteristics of sources of energy have a controlling influence on their value for doing the daily work of the world.

Wind Power. An estimate of the order of magnitude of the energy of the winds can be made in various ways. The global wind power is probably of the order of magnitude of about 10^{12} kw. This is equivalent to several hundred times the heat of combustion of all the coal mined during the year, but is only about 1 per cent of the solar energy reaching the earth's surface.

The winds of the world are not in general usable, since they extend to heights of many miles and are present over large areas of the seas and in the polar areas. In addition, they are usually variable, intermittent, and of low intensity. Nevertheless, they have been most valuable in the past for the generation of small amounts of power, for purposes such as grinding corn and pumping water, which do not demand continuity of service. The old-fashioned Dutch-type windmill with four sails, each 24 ft. long and 6 ft. wide, develops less than 5 hp. in a 20-mile wind.

For the continuity necessary for modern industrial uses, wind power must be tied in with some steady source of power, such as a steam plant or a water-power plant with limited storage, so that the power which it generates may save fuel or water. For satisfactory operation, such a windmill must be located at the top of a hill, on a site of fairly constant winds of good velocity. The first plant of this type . . . is now being put into operation in Vermont on a mountain summit, 2,000 ft. above sea level. The unit is a two-bladed propeller-type windmill [2] of 1,000 kw. capacity with an over-all diameter of 175 ft. and with blades 16 ft. in maximum width. The blades are designed in accordance with modern aerodynamic theory and have a variable pitch (as in airplane propellers), controlled by governor action so as to maintain a constant speed of 30 rpm. for wind speeds from 15 to 70 mph. Above 70 mph. the blades come to a feathering position and the mill ceases to rotate. It develops full power with a wind velocity of 30 mph. or more. Adequate winds for driving this unit blow about 60 per cent of the time. Full power should be obtainable about 50 per cent of the time.

Water Power. Of the solar energy arriving at the earth's crust

[2] The Smith-Putnam wind turbine. Various authors. *Mech. Eng.*, *63*, 473, 1941.

about one-half is used in evaporation; 100,000 cubic miles of water are evaporated by it every year. Of this amount about two-thirds is evaporated from the oceans, and more than half of it falls there as rain. The volume falling on land surfaces is about 45,000 cubic miles per year, of which about one-fifth reaches the rivers. If this water were available at an average elevation of 50 ft. above sea level, it could yield an output of 5×10^{12} kw. The actual world water power appears to be about 7×10^7 kw.; the economically feasible water power is probably not more than 10 times this quantity, or about 10^9 kw.

The development of a water-power plant usually demands high initial expenditures but the operating costs are low. At those localities in the United States where the first costs are low enough to make water power competitive with steam power, such plants have generally been built by private enterprise. The recent large developments by the Federal Government at Tennessee Valley, Bonneville, and Grand Coulee have had to rely for their economic justification on their incidental values for irrigation, flood control, navigation, and the like. Under these circumstances, it is impossible to allocate costs satisfactorily to the various services. Moreover, the design and operation should be different for the various services. Flood control is best obtained by empty reservoirs, but power requires full reservoirs. Power can be obtained most economically with high dams, but navigation and irrigation can often be best served by a sequence of low dams. In some cases power is charged only with the cost of the power plant, while the much greater costs of the dams, reservoirs, etc., are charged to the other purposes. This has resulted in much confused thinking about the cost of hydraulic power.

In earlier times water power was used principally for grinding grain and for pumping water to higher levels. It had to be used where it occurred, since the means for power transmission were not available; the only source of continuous power away from a water wheel until the eighteenth century was animal power.

The water power of the United States is about one-third of the total central-station power, and it is used chiefly for the generation of electrical energy. The efficiency of this conversion at rated load is very high. The turbine itself may have an efficiency of 93 per cent or over, and the electric generator may have an efficiency of over 96 per cent. The product of these two may be over 90 per cent. These efficiencies are obtainable with the best installations with all types of turbines at rated load, but with partial loads or with varying hydraulic

head, the efficiency may be considerably lower. In the comparatively
recent Kaplan turbine, . . . which is of the propeller type, adapted
to heads of not more than 70 ft., a high efficiency is maintained
through a wide range of operating conditions by making the propeller
blades rotatable about their axes so that their pitch can be modified.[3]
This is standard practice in airplane propellers and, as stated above,
is used in the new type of windmill. The largest turbines of this type
built in this country are the 66,000 hp. units at Bonneville Dam,
which have an outside diameter of the runner of 23 ft. 4 in., a hub
diameter of 10 ft., run at 75 rpm., and operate with an average head
of about 54 ft. The runner is essentially similar to a ship's propeller,
to an airplane propeller, and to the windmill already [described].
The Bonneville Dam runners have each 5 blades. The total weight
of the rotating parts is over 1,000 tons; their support by practically
frictionless bearings is one of the triumphs of modern mechanical
science.

The largest water wheel in this country is of the Francis reaction
type and has over 108,000 hp. capacity. . . .

Solar Energy. The solar energy [4] arriving at the outside of the
earth's atmosphere on a plane normal to the sun's rays is about 1.1 kw.
per sq. yd.; of this only about 43 per cent, or $\frac{1}{2}$ kw. per sq. yd.,
reaches the earth's surface. The total solar energy arriving at the
earth's surface is at the rate of 7.5×10^{13} kw. To give some meaning
to this astronomical figure, it may be compared with the heat of combustion of all the petroleum which has been deposited in the earth's
crust. A liberal estimate, making large allowance for future discoveries, indicates that the volume of this petroleum is certainly less than
one trillion barrels. The heat of combustion of this quantity of petroleum is about equal to the solar energy arriving at the earth's crust in
half a day. A similar estimate of the coal in the earth's crust indicates
that its heat of combustion is equivalent to the solar energy arriving at
the earth's surface in less than six months.

Nearly all of the incident solar energy is converted to low-tem-
perature heat and is of small value for power generation. An exceedingly minute fraction is converted into the available energy of winds
and of water as a result of the uncontrolled convection of heated air
currents, of evaporation, and of condensation. A very small but, to
us, all-important fraction of the solar energy is caught by photosyn-

[3] GALBRAITH, C. C. The Kaplan turbine. *Eng. News-Record, 118,* 765, 1937.
[4] BAUR and PHILLIPS. *Gerlands Beiträge zur Geophysik, 42,* 232, 1934; also
45, 1935, and *47,* 1936.

thetic processes in growing plants and is there stored as the heat of combustion of the plant. Under certain circumstances plant material has become coal or petroleum and as such has been stored for long periods. Usually, unless the plant material is harvested and utilized by human agency, it oxidizes rapidly and becomes carbon dioxide and water again.

Solar Motors. It is possible to receive the sun's rays on properly shaped and controlled reflecting surfaces, to concentrate these rays on a steam boiler or equivalent device, to generate steam with them, and to use this steam in some form of steam engine. A number of such "solar engines" have been built and installed in localities, such as Egypt and Arizona, where there is maximum sunshine. Solar engines can deliver available energy only during the sunshine hours and then only in an amount which varies with the sun's position; they cover a large area for the amount of power delivered and have a first cost per unit of power which is usually prohibitive. While functioning they may convert into useful work as much as 3 per cent of the solar energy falling on the area which the reflectors occupy. If the demand for power is continuous, there must be added some device for storing power, and such devices are costly and inefficient. There are not many places in which a solar engine could be economically justified.

Photosynthesis. The photosynthetic process is actually the most efficient natural starting point for converting solar energy into work. Under favorable circumstances [5] it is possible to store as heat of combustion of plants as much as 1.5 per cent of the solar energy which falls during the growing months on a planted area. This is the performance obtained in the growth of corn during the three summer months in a Midwest area. In the tropics, with proper selection of plants, this performance might be repeated two or three times per year. This would make it possible to store about 1 per cent of the total annual solar energy falling on such areas. With large-scale operation, about 25 per cent of the heat of combustion of plants could be converted into work, giving an over-all efficiency of conversion from solar energy to useful work of about one-fourth of 1 per cent. This may seem small, but amounts to a continuous supply of work at the rate of 5 kw. per acre in certain tropical areas. . . .

[5] TRANSEAU, E. N. *Ohio Jour. of Sci.*, 26, 1, 1926.

A SUMMARY OF WHAT TO DO

BY GEORGE A. STETSON *

My formula for writing a technical paper is . . . summarized as follows:

1. Become thoroughly familiar with the subject and assemble all the material at your disposal. Don't neglect the literature.

2. Decide upon the purpose and scope of the paper as affected by the occasion and the audience. Visualize the persons to be addressed, their familiarity with the subject matter, their education, interests, prejudices, etc. Determine the limitations of time, space, illustrative material, etc., and get from those who ask you to prepare the paper or who intend to publish it any special instructions that may be helpful to you.

3. List the major items to be covered and choose the material to be used.

4. Get a good title, not too long, not too general, but precise and significant.

5. Let the reader know at once what you propose to write about and of any major conclusions that can be effectively divulged.

6. Get his interest at the start and keep it.

7. Have him constantly in mind while you write and don't "write down" to him.

8. Choose some logical order of presentation and stick to it, building on the reader's knowledge and interest.

9. Be careful in the choice of words and in the use of examples and analogies. Avoid pedantry and unusual terminology; explain unfamiliar words if they must be used. Use standard symbols and abbreviations.

10. Be brief, but clear and coherent. Save the reader's time and publication expense.

11. Leave out irrelevant details and qualifying phrases that are obviously unessential. Let curves, sketches, illustrations, and tables tell as many of the tiresome details as possible. Don't interrupt a well-planned story with substantiating material and mathematical demon-

---

* Conclusion of "The Art of Technical Writing," *Collected Papers of the Session on English*, Pittsburgh, The Society for the Promotion of Engineering Education [since 1946, The American Society for Engineering Education], March, 1933, pp. 60–61. ("Selected Papers of the Summer School for Engineering Teachers," Bulletin No. 20.) The author is Editor, The American Society of Mechanical Engineers.

strations that can be relegated to appendices for the use of those particularly interested in them. Don't quote at length when you can refer to the original.

12. Give the reader a good bibliography but don't annoy him with too many footnotes. Provide a good summary and a brief synopsis.

13. When the paper is written, check it over to see if it is properly proportioned. Pay particular attention to first and concluding paragraphs. Check all references, figures, computations, mathematics, numerals, drawings, and other details.

14. Lay the paper aside and read it over several days later to make sure it is complete, well-proportioned, logical, and coherent.

15. Be properly humble about your paternity. Welcome rather than resent suggestions for improving your paper and give the editor as much credit for knowing his job as you would like to have him give you for knowing yours.

INDEX

Recommendation report, 267
Recommendations—in report, 285
Redundancy, 36, 67, 271. (*See also*
Tautology.)
REES, ROBERT I., "The Young Engineer and His English," 397
Reference—in letter, 205; in speech, 361
Reference books (*see* Library tools)
Reference figures—with footnotes, 249
Reference words—for transition, 148, 351
Regional accent, 59. (*See also* Provincialisms.)
Register of National Bibliography, 239
Relative pronoun, 16
Relevance, 183, 271
Repetition, 36, 49, 148, 351. (*See also* Redundancy *and* Tautology.)
Reply to inquiries (specimen letters), 211
Report writing (Chapter X)—characteristics, 265, 269; classification, 266; definition of report, 265; formal report, definition of: 273; formal report, make-up of: abstract, 278, appendices, 287, cover, 289, body, 282, letter of transmittal or foreword, 274, table of contents, 276, miscellaneous elements, 289, title page, 274; letter report, 273; mechanics and fundamentals, 268, 269; memorandum report, 273; specimens, 298; types of student reports, 290; utility and range, 265, 272, 290
Request for technical information (specimen letter), 210
Research, library (*see* Documentation; Library investigation, report on; *and* Library tools)
Research report, 267

Restrictive and nonrestrictive modifiers, 81, 84, 92
Restrictive word of degree, position of, 37
Results, conclusions, and recommendations—in report, 285
Return address—of envelope, 193
Review, 49
Revision, 112, 204
Roget's Thesaurus, 63
Round-table conference, 368
RYON, L. B., "City Zoning," 436

Sales letter (specimen), 226
Salutation—in letter, 93, 194
Scientific classification, 152
Scientific principle (specimen letter), 211
Semicolon, 88
Semiformal group discussion, 368
Semiparenthetical elements, 81, 92
Sentence fragment (*see* Period fault)
Sentence outline—for exposition (*see* Analytical sentence outline); for description, 158, 159
Sequence of tenses, 26
shall, will and *should, would,* 21
Short forms, 65, 108
sic, 246
Sign of the infinitive (*to*), 24
Sign writing, 126, 156, 284
Signature—of letter, 197
Simple and hierarchical classifications, 152
Sincerity, 181
Single-spacing and double-spacing —in letter, 188, 195; in other compositions, 112
Slang, 65, 100
so, such, and *too,* 41, 42
some and *somewhat,* 32
sort, kind, class, type, 13, 71
SONNENSCHEIN, W. S., *The Best Books,* 238

ALPHABETICAL GUIDE TO HANDBOOK OF FUNDAMENTALS

(For use with Chapters II, III, IV, and V)